MAKING CONNECTIONS: Foundations for Algebra
Course 2, Version 3.0

Managing Editors / Authors

Leslie Dietiker (Both Texts)
Michigan State University
East Lansing, MI

Evra Baldinger (Course 1)
Phillip and Sala Burton Academic High School
San Francisco, CA

Barbara Shreve (Course 2)
San Lorenzo High School
San Lorenzo, CA

Contributing Authors

Elizabeth Baker
Zane Middle School
Eureka, CA

Tara Bianchi
American Canyon Middle School
American Canyon, CA

Bev Brockhoff
Glen Edwards Middle School
Lincoln, CA

Mark Coté
Beaver Lake Middle School
Issaquah, WA

Suzanne Cisco Cox
Turner Middle School
Berthoud, CO

Kathleen Davies
Rincon Valley Middle School
Santa Rosa, CA

Josea Eggink
El Colegio Charter School
Minneapolis, MN

William Funkhouser
Zane Middle School
Eureka, CA

Brian Hoey
CPM Educational Program
Sacramento, CA

Janet Hollister
La Cumbre Jr. High School
Santa Barbara, CA

Carol Jancsi
CPM Mentor Teacher
Cardiff by the Sea, CA

Rakesh Khanna
Hotmath, Inc.
Berkeley, CA

Judy Kysh, Ph.D.
San Francisco State University
San Francisco, CA

Bruce Melhorn
Whatcom Middle School
Bellingham, WA

Chris Mikles
Post Falls Middle School
Post Falls, ID

Misty Nikula
Whatcom Day Academy
Bellingham, WA

Bob Petersen
CPM Educational Program
Sacramento, CA

Tom Sallee, Ph.D.
Department of Mathematics
University of California, Davis

Lorna Thomas Vázquez
Math Consultant
Neillsville, WI

Stephanie Whitney
Illinois Institute of Technology
Chicago, IL

Program Directors

Leslie Dietiker
Michigan State University
East Lansing, MI

Brian Hoey
CPM Educational Program
Sacramento, CA

Judy Kysh, Ph.D.
Departments of Education and Mathematics
San Francisco State University, CA

Tom Sallee, Ph.D.
Department of Mathematics
University of California, Davis

Puzzle Investigator Problems

Ethan Baldinger
Sonoma State University
Rohnert Park, CA

Susan Baskin
Math Consultant
Oakland, CA

Leslie Dietiker
Michigan State University
East Lansing, MI

Parent Guide

Brian Hoey
Sacramento, CA

Bob Petersen
Sacramento, CA

Extra Practice Materials

Bob Petersen
Sacramento, CA

Based on the Skill Builder materials created for Foundations for Algebra (2003), created by:

Heidi Ackley
Bev Brockhoff
Scott Coyner
Brian Hoey
Robert Petersen
Kristie Sallee

Steve Ackley
Ellen Cafferata
Sara Effenbeck
Judy Kysh
Edwin Reed
Tom Sallee

Elizabeth Baker
Elizabeth Coyner
William Funkhouser
Kris Petersen
Stacy Rocklein
Howard Webb

Assessment Manager

Karen Wootten
Director of Assessment
Odenton, MD

Assessment Assistants

Elizabeth Baker
Zane Middle School
Eureka, CA

William Funkhouser
Zane Middle School
Eureka, CA

Illustration

Jonathan Weast
Sacramento, CA

Cover Art

Kevin Coffey
San Francisco, CA

Technical Managers

Sarah Maile
Sacramento, CA

Aubrie Maze
Sebastopol, CA

Technical Assistants

Robert Ainsworth
Jason Cho
Matthew Donahue
Jerry Luo
Atlanta Parrott
Rachel Smith

Bethany Armstrong
Hannah Coyner
Bethany Firch
Eli Marable
Anna Poehlmann
Alex Yu

Rebecca Bobell
Carmen de la Cruz
Michael Li
James McCardle
John Ramos

1 2 3 4 5 6   16 15 14 13 12 11 10   Version 3.0

Printed in the United States of America   ISBN-13: 978-1-60328-038-9

A Note to Students:

Welcome to a new year of math! In this course, you will learn to use new models and methods to think about problems as well as solve them. You will be developing powerful mathematical tools and learning new ways of thinking about and investigating situations. You will be making connections, discovering relationships, figuring out what strategies can be used to solve problems, and explaining your thinking. Learning to think in these ways and communicate about your thinking is useful in mathematical contexts, other subjects in school, and situations outside the classroom. The mathematics you have learned in the past will be valuable for learning in this course, and will prepare you for future courses.

In meeting the challenges of this course, you will not be learning alone. You will cooperate with other students as a member of a study team. Being a part of a team means speaking up and interacting with other people. You will explain your ideas, listen to what others have to say, and ask questions if there is something you do not understand. In this course, a single problem can often be solved several ways. You will see problems in different ways than your teammates do. Each of you has something to contribute while you work on the lessons in this course.

Together, your team will complete problems and activities that will help you discover mathematical ideas and develop solution methods. Your teacher will support you as you work, but will not take away your opportunity to think and investigate for yourself. Each topic will be revisited many times and will connect to other topics. If something is not clear to you the first time you work on it, you will have more chances to build your understanding as the course continues.

Learning math this way has an advantage: as long as you actively participate, make sure everyone in your study team is involved, and ask good questions, you will find yourself understanding mathematics at a deeper level than ever before. By the end of this course, you will have a powerful set of mathematical tools to use to solve new problems. With your teammates you will meet mathematical challenges you would not have known how to approach before.

In addition to the support provided by your teacher and your study team, CPM has also created online resources to help you, including help with homework, a parent guide, and extra practice. You will find these resources and more at www.cpm.org.

We wish you well and are confident that you will enjoy this next year of learning!

Sincerely,

The CPM Team

Making Connections: Foundations for Algebra
Course 2
Student Edition
Version 3.0

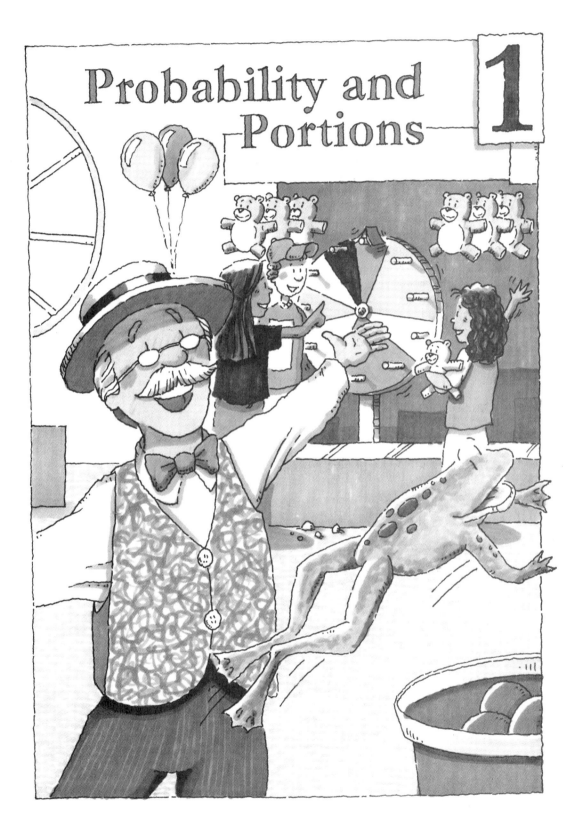

Probability and Portions

1

CHAPTER 1

Welcome to math class! This chapter will introduce you to many of the big ideas that you will explore and the ways that you will work during this course. You will apply your current mathematical knowledge to solve problems, some of which you will solve again later in the course using new tools.

This chapter will also introduce you to the five Ways of Thinking that are threaded throughout this course. They are **generalizing** (finding ways to describe all members of a group), **reasoning and justifying** (explaining, verifying, and communicating your ideas), **reversing your thinking** (creating and solving problems "backwards and forward"), **choosing a strategy** (deciding what the most useful tools are for solving a problem), and **visualizing** (creating and using visual representations).

Guiding Questions

Think about these questions throughout this chapter:

How can I represent this?

How can I organize my work?

How can the number be rewritten?

Are the numbers equal?

Later in the chapter, you will focus on finding **probability**, a way of measuring the chance that something will happen. You will also look carefully at relationships between fractions, decimals, and percents to rewrite numbers in different forms and to compare them to each other.

In this chapter, you will learn new ways to:

➤ Find out how likely it is that a specific event will occur.

➤ Calculate the probabilities of two separate events to decide which is more likely to happen.

➤ Rewrite numbers in different forms in order to compare them.

➤ Determine whether a fraction can be rewritten as a repeating decimal.

Chapter Outline

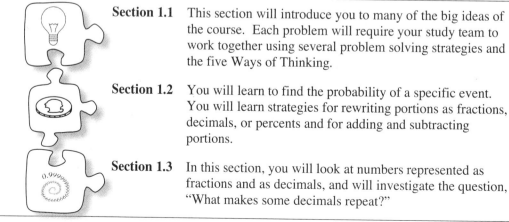

Section 1.1 This section will introduce you to many of the big ideas of the course. Each problem will require your study team to work together using several problem solving strategies and the five Ways of Thinking.

Section 1.2 You will learn to find the probability of a specific event. You will learn strategies for rewriting portions as fractions, decimals, or percents and for adding and subtracting portions.

Section 1.3 In this section, you will look at numbers represented as fractions and as decimals, and will investigate the question, "What makes some decimals repeat?"

1.1.1 What do they have in common?

Finding Shared and Unique Characteristics

Have you ever tried to learn how to play a new game just by watching others play it? Chances are you were watching for patterns in the game such as what each player did to earn points or what actions earned penalties. If you were watching a game of soccer, you might figure out that kicking the ball into the goal earned the team a point. You might also notice that the goalie is the only player allowed to use his or her hands on the field. Describing those patterns could help you describe some of the rules of the game. This type of observation is also called **generalizing**. When you make an observation about what a set of objects or actions have in common, like the actions that will *always* allow you to score a point, you are making a **generalization**.

Today you will be working in a team with the goal of making **generalizations** about characteristics of various sets of objects. As you work, keep the following questions in mind:

What do the items have in common?

What makes the items different?

What are other characteristics that could describe the groups or sets?

1-1. MATH STARS

What do you have in common with your teammates? What makes you unique? Today you will work with your teammates to discover some characteristics that you share and some that make each person in your team different.

Your task: Get a copy of the Lesson 1.1.1A Resource Page and scissors. Fold the resource page along the dotted lines and then cut along the solid lines. Unfold the cutout and glue it onto a piece of paper. Write each team member's name on a star.

- As a team, brainstorm something that all of you have in common that the rest of the class does not already know.

- List your team's common attribute on the paper in the center of the four stars.

- Find ways that each person in the team is unique from the others (things that are true about that person only), and write those things on the individual's star.

To help you work together today, each team member has a specific job, assigned by your first name (or by your last name if two individuals have the same first name).

Team Roles

Resource Manager: If your first name comes first alphabetically:

- Make sure your team has a Lesson 1.1.1A Resource Page, scissors, a glue stick, and colored paper.

- Ask the teacher when the *entire* team has a question. *"No one has an idea? Should I ask the teacher?"*

- Make sure your team cleans up by delegating tasks. You could say, *"I will put away the _____ while you _____ ."*

Facilitator: If your first name comes second alphabetically:

- Start the team's discussion of similarities and differences by asking, *"What might we have in common?"*

- Keep everyone discussing each part together by asking questions such as,
  "Does anyone have ideas for what makes us each unique (different)?" and *"What else might we have in common?"*

Recorder/Reporter: If your first name comes third alphabetically:

- When your team is called on, share your team's ideas and **reasons** with the class.

- Help the team agree on an idea: *"Do we agree that this would not be obvious to the rest of the class?"*

Task Manager: If your first name comes fourth alphabetically:

- Remind the team to stay on task and not to talk to students in other teams. You can suggest, *"Let's move on to the next part of the problem."*

  Listen for **reasons** and ask your teammates to **justify** their thinking. *"Why do you think that?"* or *"Would this be obvious to the rest of the class?"*

1-2.   WHAT DO THEY HAVE IN COMMON?

In mathematics it is sometimes useful to make **general** statements about sets of objects. In this problem you will be given a set of cards with mathematical objects on them. With your team:

- Determine what each set has in common.

- Record what is written on the cards on your paper.

- Add two new examples that would belong in the set on your paper.

- Describe in words what it is they have in common.

When you are finished with a set of cards, call the teacher to your team. Explain your **generalization** to the teacher and get another set of cards.

1-3.   **Mathography:** A mathography is a lot like your life history, except that it is focused on the mathematics in your life.

a.   Write a letter about yourself to your teacher. The letter will help your teacher get to know you as an individual. The letter should talk about these three general topics: you, you as a student, and you as a math student.

Remember to use complete sentences and make sure that it is neat enough to be read easily. Start the letter with "Dear...." Make sure you sign your letter. This assignment should take 15 to 20 minutes to complete. Parts (b), (c), and (d) have suggestions for what to write about each of the three topics.

b.   **You:** Introduce yourself using the name you like to be called. Describe your hobbies, talents, and interests. State your goals or dreams. What are you proud of? What else would you like to share?

Problem continues on next page. →

1-3.   Problem continued from previous page.

    c. **You as a Student:** State the importance of school in your life. Describe yourself as a student. What kinds of classroom activities do you do best? What kinds of activities do you find frustrating? Explain which subject(s) is/are your favorites. Tell why you like it (them). How often do you finish in-class assignments? How faithfully do you do your homework?

    d. **You as a Math Student:** Describe your most memorable moment in math and explain why you remember it. State your favorite math topic. Name your least favorite. Explain how you feel about math this year.

1-4.   Decide what the shapes below have in common. Write your answer in a complete sentence. Then draw two more shapes that belong to the same set.

1-5.   According to the diagrams below, how long is each unknown piece?

a.

b.

1.1.2 How does it change?

Perimeter and Area Relationships

Many ancient cities were constructed inside great walls in order to protect and defend the city. The city of Carcassonne, France, still exists and has a double wall around it. The length of the inner wall around the city measures about 1245 meters and the land inside the walls is approximately 105,400 square meters.

When measuring shapes it is sometimes important to look at the space the shape covers, while other times it can be important to look at the length of the boundary around a shape. In this lesson you will be using toothpicks and tiles to measure attributes of various shapes, and to complete a challenge with your team. For example, when describing the shape above there are several things you could say, including, *"There are 11 tiles,"* *"It takes 14 toothpicks to surround the shape,"* or *"It takes three more toothpicks to surround the figure than tiles to fill it."*

1-6. TOOTHPICKS AND TILES

Cruz, Sophia, and Savanna are using toothpicks and tiles to describe the attributes of the shapes below. Cruz made a pattern and gave the girls the number of tiles, and Sophia and Savanna each tried to be the first to see who could call out how many toothpicks, or units of length, were on the outside.

a. Cruz made the tile pattern shown at right and said, "There are six tiles." Savanna quickly said, "There are ten toothpicks." Copy the tile pattern on your paper and show where Savanna counted the 10 toothpicks. **Justify** your answer with words, numbers, or pictures.

b. Cruz put down the pattern as shown at right, but he ran out of toothpicks. How would you describe this shape using toothpicks and tiles?

c. Get a set of tiles from your teacher and work with your team to:

   • Make a pattern so that there are four more toothpicks than tiles.

   • Draw your tile pattern on your paper

   • Label the number of toothpicks and tiles on your drawing.

   Is there more than one answer?

1-7.   When you are working with your team to solve "Toothpicks and Tiles" puzzles, as well as other problems in this course, it will be important to work effectively with other people. Effective math conversations are a valuable part of the learning process throughout this course. Choose a member of your team to read aloud these Collaborative Learning Expectations:

COLLABORATIVE LEARNING EXPECTATIONS

Working with other students allows you to develop new ways of thinking about mathematics, helps you learn to communicate about math, and helps you understand ideas better by having to explain your thinking to others. The following expectations will help you get the most out of working together.

T	Together, work to answer questions.
E	Explain and give **reasons**.
A	Ask questions and share ideas.
M	Members of your team are your first resource.
S	Smarter together than apart.

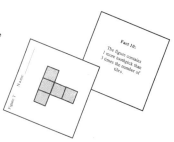

1-8.   TEAM CHALLENGE: TOOTHPICKS AND TILES

Today you and your team members will work together to participate in the "Toothpicks and Tiles" challenge. You each will have one card that shows a tile shape and there will be a fifth card to share as a team. Any extra cards should go in the center of your workspace so that everyone can see them.

Your task: As a team, do the following:

- Each team member should write his or her name on one of the shape cards.

- Place any extra shape cards and all of the fact cards face up in the middle of the table so that everyone can see them.

- Work together to match each tile shape with one fact statement so that each fact has *only one* shape and each shape has *only one* fact.

- If you want to change the shape that matches a fact card, you *must* convince the person whose name is on the card of the shape you want to change. He or she is the only person who can touch that shape card.

- Once everyone in your team is convinced that each fact is paired with one shape, call your teacher over. Be prepared to **justify** your choices!

Making Connections: Course 2

1-9. Does changing the number of toothpicks always change the number of tiles? Think about this question as you look at the following tile shape.

    a. Write a fact statement that includes information about the number of tiles and toothpicks that would describe the tile shape at right.

    b. How can you add a tile to the shape in part (a) but not change the number of toothpicks? **Justify** your response.

1-10. The **perimeter** of a design is the length of the boundary around the outside of the design (the toothpicks). The number of squares needed to fill the design (the tiles) is called the **area**.

    a. Use these words to write a fact statement with your team describing the toothpicks and tiles in the tile pattern at right.

    b. For your fact statement in part (a), build and draw a different shape that could also be described by the fact. Label the figure with the area (tiles) and perimeter (toothpicks).

Perimeter and Area

The **perimeter** of a shape is the total length of the boundary (around the shape) that encloses the interior (inside) region on a flat surface. In the game, "Toothpicks and Tiles," the number of tile side lengths (toothpicks) is the same as the **perimeter** of the shape. See the examples at right.

Perimeter = "toothpicks" = 20 units

Perimeter = $5 + 8 + 4 + 6 + = 23$ cm

The **area** is a measure of the number of square units needed to cover a region on a flat surface. In the game, the **area** is equal to the number of "tiles" in the shape.

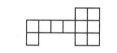

Area = "tiles" = 11 sq. units

A **rectangle** is a quadrilateral (four sides) with four right angles. The opposite sides are equal in length. Two sides that come together (meet) at a right angle are referred to as the length and width or base and height. The area of a rectangle is found by multiplying the lengths of the base and height.

Area = $5 \cdot 3 = 15$ square units

Making Connections: Course 2

1-11.   Janelle wants to challenge you to a "Toothpick and Tiles" game (described in problem 1-8). Using exactly four tiles, solve her challenges below. **Justify** your answers with pictures and labels.

   a.   Find a tile pattern where the number of toothpicks is exactly double the number of tiles.

   b.   Find a tile pattern where the number of toothpicks is more than double the number of tiles.

1-12.   In this lesson, you looked at the number of tiles and number of toothpicks used to form shapes made of square tiles as you played the "Toothpick and Tiles" game. The math words that also describe the number of tiles and toothpicks are *area* and *perimeter*. Read the Math Notes box for this lesson to review how area and perimeter are related to tiles and toothpicks, then answer the questions below.

   a.   Find the area and perimeter of the figure at right.

   b.   Find the area and perimeter of the rectangle below right.

   c.   Now design your own shape with 5 square tiles. Record the perimeter and the area.

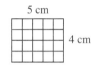

1-13.   How long is the unknown piece?

1-14.   Copy the number line below onto your paper. Place a point on the number line and label the point for each of the following numbers: −4, 3, 0.5, −3.5, 0, 1, −2, 5.

1.1.3 What is my number?

Finding Unknowns

Today you will think about how to find a mystery number based on information given to you as part of a game. You will practice mental math computations and investigate ways to represent the situation as you try to solve the problem. When you solve these puzzles, you might need to **reverse your thinking**. **Reversing** is an important way of thinking mathematically. It means solving problems both backwards and forwards. As you work with your team, ask the following questions:

How can I represent it?

What is the best approach for this problem?

Have I found all of the answers?

1-15. GUESS MY NUMBER

Today you will play the "Guess My Number" game. You will need a pencil and a piece of paper. Your teacher has thought of a number and will tell you some information about it. Your task is to figure out what your teacher's number is. (You can use your paper if it helps.) Then explain why you think it is the mystery number.

Game #1: *When I triple my number and add five, I get eleven. What is my number?*

Game #2: *When I add two to my number and then multiply it by five, I get thirty. What is my number?*

Game #3: *When I take half of my number and add two, I get twenty-four. What is my number?*

Game #4: *When I double my number and add eight I get my number plus twelve. What is my number?*

Game #5: *When I double my number, add four, and then subtract my number and subtract three, I get my number plus one. What is my number?*

1-16. Make up your own Guess My Number games with your team and be ready to share them with the class. Make at least one game that has only one answer and one that works for all numbers. Can you create a game that works for no numbers?

METHODS AND MEANINGS

Mean

MATH NOTES

To understand a set of data, you often need to be able to describe the approximate "center" of that data. One way to do this is to find the **mean** of the data set, which is also called the **arithmetic average**.

To find the mean of a set of data, add the values of the data elements (numbers) and then divide by the number of items of data. The mean is a useful way to describe the data when the set of data does not contain **outliers**, that is, numbers that are much smaller or much larger than most of the other data in the set.

Suppose the following data set represents the number of home runs hit by the best seven players on a major league baseball team:

$$16, 26, 21, 9, 13, 15, \text{ and } 9.$$

The mean is $\frac{16+26+21+9+13+15+9}{7} = \frac{109}{7} \approx 15.57$.

This number shows that a typical player among the best seven home run hitters on the team hits about 15 or 16 home runs each season.

1-17. Thu wants to play "Guess My Number." She states, "*When I triple my number and add 5, I get 26. What is my number?*" What is her number? Show how you know.

1-18. One of the subjects that you will study in this course is how to describe a set of data. One of the ways that you may have seen before is finding an **average** (also called a **mean**). Review what an average is, as well as how to find it, in the Math Notes box for this lesson. Then find the average (mean) for each set of data below.

a. Jane's quiz scores: 82, 64, 73, 91, 85

b. The number of cats your teammates have as pets: 0, 1, 3, 2

c. The number of minutes Pam talked on the phone: 35, 40, 12, 16, 25, 10

1-19.   Find the perimeter of each polygon below. Note that the markings on part (e)
         show that all sides are the same length. Show your work.

a.   8 cm

b.   5 cm

c.

d.   6 mm

e.

f.

1-20.   For each shape drawn in problem 1-19, choose one of the labels below that best
         describes that shape. Be as specific as you can. Look in the glossary of this
         book for more information if you do not remember what one of the words
         describes.

right triangle	scalene triangle	obtuse triangle
isosceles triangle	rhombus	rectangle
square	trapezoid	hexagon

1-21.   Use the bar graph at right to answer the following
         questions.

a.   How many people attended the fair on Tuesday?

b.   Which day had the largest attendance?

c.   What was the total attendance for the week?

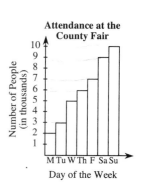

1.1.4 How can I organize information?

Representing Data

Perhaps the most famous frog jumping contest takes place each May in Calaveras County, California. For more than 80 years, contestants have been entering large bullfrogs that measure at least 4 inches long in a contest to see which frog can move the farthest in three hops. Each year people travel from around the country (and sometimes the world) to see the frogs jump. Scientists have come to the fair to study the frogs.

In this lesson, you will ask questions and analyze data about some of the frogs in the contest. As you work, you will need to **choose a strategy** for organizing the information that will show patterns. As a team, you will need to share ideas about how to represent the data and work together to describe it as completely as you can.

1-22. JUMPING FROG JUBILEE

When it is time to compete in the Jumping Frog Jubilee, the frog is put on a starting pad. The frog hops three times, and then the distance is measured from the center of the starting pad to the end of the third hop to get the official jump length.

The chart below shows data about the 8th place frogs in 2008 and 2009. Your teacher will show you a chart of data with the best eight frogs from each of those years. *Before* you look at the rest of the data, think about what else you could learn about the frogs and their jumps from the numerical data.

a. With your team, brainstorm questions that you could use the numbers (data) to answer. For example, you might ask, *"What was the longest jump?"* Use the bullet points below to help your team come up with as many questions as you can (at least four).

Frog name	Jump length (inches)	Year
Dr. Frog	185.25	2009
Delbert Sr.	216.5	2008

- What could the numbers tell us about all of the frogs as a group?

- What could the numbers tell us about the frogs in just 2008 or just 2009?

- What could we ask to compare frogs from 2008 to frogs from 2009?

- What could we ask to compare individual frogs?

Problem continues on next page. →

1-22.   *Problem continued from previous page.*

    b.   As a class, discuss the different questions each study team wrote. Then, look over the data from the contest found on the Lesson 1.1.4A Resource Page. Decide which questions you can answer using the data and which you cannot.

    c.   With your team, choose two of the class questions to answer.

        •   Choose one that requires using all of the numbers to answer the question.

        •   Choose one that can be answered using just some of the data.

        Think carefully about how to organize the data in order to find the answer. Write your conclusions in complete sentences.

1-23.   Different ways of presenting data can tell you different things. For example, some of your questions might have been easy to answer with an organized table of data. However, other questions can be easier to answer if the data is arranged in a different way, such as in the **histogram** below.

    a.   Look carefully at the graph. Use it to try to answer the questions below. If you cannot answer a question, explain why not.

        •   Between which two numbers on the graph were most of the jump lengths?

        •   What was the median jump length?

        •   What was the mean (average) jump length?

    b.   What other statements can you make for this graph?

1-24.   In the book, *If You Hopped Like a Frog*, written by David M. Schwartz and illustrated by James Warhola, the author shares that when he was a child, he wondered how far he could hop if he hopped like a frog. In his letter to the reader at the front of his book, he wrote, "I imagined soaring through the air with grace and ease, landing gently on my big, springy legs. How far could I hop?"

a.   Obviously, people and frogs are different sizes and have different jumping abilities. But imagine if you had the hopping muscles of a bullfrog but were still the same size you are now: how far could you hop? With your team:

   - Estimate how far *you* might be able to jump if you were a giant frog. (Think about how the information from problem 1-22 could help you.)

   - **Justify** your estimate.

   - Use pictures and/or words to help explain your thinking.

b.   The book assumes that a 3-inch frog can jump about 60 inches in one hop. Does this estimate seem **reasonable** when looking at the data from problem 1-22? Why or why not?

1-25.   **Additional Challenge:** With your team, take measurements to predict how far you could jump if you were a bullfrog competing in the contest. Discuss what extra information you will need to make your prediction and how you will get it. Use words and/or pictures with labels to explain your process.

METHODS AND MEANINGS

MATH NOTES

Median and Mode

The mean is a useful way to find the center when data values are close together or are evenly spaced. Two other tools, **median** and **mode**, locate the approximate "center" of a set of data in different ways.

The **median** is the middle number in a set of data <u>arranged numerically</u>. If there are an even number of values, the median is the mean of the two middle numbers. The median is more accurate than the mean as a way to find the center when there are outliers in the data set.

The **mode** is the value in the data set that occurs more often than any other value. Data sets may have more than one mode, and some do not have any mode. The mode is useful when the data are not numeric, such as showing a "most popular" choice.

Example: Suppose the following data set represents the number of home runs hit by the best seven players on a major league baseball team:

16, 26, 21, 9, 13, 15, and 9.

The median is 15, since, when arranged in order (9, 9, 13, 15, 16, 21, 26), the middle number is 15.

The mode is 9, since it occurs twice and no other number appears more than once.

Mean, median, and mode are called **measures of central tendency** because they each describe the "center" of a set of data, but in different ways.

1-26.   In the Math Notes box for this lesson, read and review the information about median and mode. Use that information to decide what the median and mode are for Andy's test scores: 76, 84, 93, 67, 82, 87, and 76.

Making Connections: Course 2

1-27.   Copy the number patterns below and write the next four numbers in the sequence. Assume the pattern continues as shown. Describe the pattern in words.

a.   2, 7, 12, 17, 22, ___, ___, ___, ___

b.   1, 4, 9, 16, 25, ___, ___, ___, ___

c.   1, 1, 2, 3, 5, 8, ___, ___, ___, ___

1-28.   Audrey made the histogram at right to show her recent bowling scores.

a.   How many games did she play in total?

b.   Between what two values did most of her scores fall?

c.   What portion of her scores fell between 130 and 140?

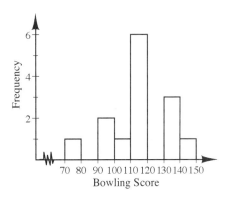

1-29.   The graph at right shows how far Ben is from home during a typical school day. Use the graph to answer the questions. Write your answers in complete sentences.

a.   What was Ben doing between 7:00 a.m. and 8:00 a.m.?

b.   What do you think Ben was doing between 9 a.m. and 2:30 p.m.?

c.   What time did Ben leave to return to his starting point?

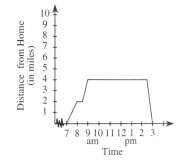

1-30.   As you can tell from the examples of the number lines below, not all number lines change by one unit from mark to mark. Copy these number lines onto your paper and fill in the missing numbers.

a.

b.

c.

d.

1.1.5 How can I rewrite it?

Investigating Number Patterns

In the past, you may have looked at number patterns to answer questions or to find the next part of a sequence, but have you ever considered the beauty of mathematics in those patterns? Today you are going to investigate number patterns and learn about equivalent ways to write the same number. As a team, you will share your **reasoning** and work to **justify** that two representations are the same. **Reasoning and justifying** is a way of thinking that you will use often in this course. When you are **reasoning and justifying**, you will focus on what makes a statement convincing or how you can explain your ideas. As you look at patterns today, ask your team:

What can we predict about the next number in the pattern?

How can we **justify** our answer?

1-31. Use a calculator to calculate the value of each expression below.

a. $1 \cdot 8 + 1$

b. $12 \cdot 8 + 2$

c. $123 \cdot 8 + 3$

d. $1234 \cdot 8 + 4$

e. What patterns do you see? Discuss them with your team. Be sure that when your team agrees on something, it is recorded on each person's paper.

f. Use patterns you found to *predict* the next three expressions and their solutions. Do not calculate the answers yet. Instead, what do you think they will be?

g. Use your calculator to check the solution for each expression you wrote in part (f). Were your predictions correct? If not, look at the pattern again and figure out how it is changing.

Making Connections: Course 2

1-32.   Sometimes patterns are not created with addition and
         multiplication, but with the numbers themselves. For
         example, when the fractions in the sequence below are
         changed to decimals, an interesting pattern develops.

$$\tfrac{1}{9}, \tfrac{2}{9}, \tfrac{3}{9}, \text{ and } \tfrac{4}{9}$$

   a.   Use your calculator to change each of the fractions
         above to a decimal. Write each fraction and its
         equivalent decimal on your paper.

   b.   Decimals like 0.3333... and the others you found in part (a) are called
         repeating decimals because the digits continue infinitely. Instead of using
         "..." to show that the numbers repeat, mathematicians write a bar over the
         digits that repeat, like this: $0.\overline{3}$. It is standard to write the repeating digits
         just once. For example, $0.2222... = 0.\overline{2}$.

         List the next five fractions in the sequence $\tfrac{1}{9}, \tfrac{2}{9}, \tfrac{3}{9},$ and $\tfrac{4}{9}$. Predict how
         they will look rewritten as decimals.

   c.   Find the decimal equivalents of the five fractions you wrote in part (b)
         using your calculator. Do they match your predictions? Are there any that
         are different?

1-33.   Are 0.999..., $0.\overline{9}$, and 1 equal? How do
         you know? Discuss this with the class
         and **justify** your response. Help others
         understand what you mean as you
         explain your thinking. A visual
         demonstration is available at
         www.cpm.org/students/technology.

1-34.   Decimal numbers that have only a finite number of digits such as 2.173 and
         0.04 are called **terminating decimals**. Some fractions can be written as
         terminating decimals, such as the examples below.

$$\tfrac{1}{2} = 0.5 \qquad \tfrac{3}{4} = 0.75$$

         Do the decimal equivalents of the numbers below terminate or repeat? Be ready
         to **justify** your answer.

   a.   0.125   b. $0.\overline{6}$ c. $\tfrac{5}{6}$

   d.   4   e. $\tfrac{2}{5}$ f. -0.33

1-35.   Representing numbers in multiple ways can help to show what those numbers mean. In problem 1-32, you saw that the fraction $\frac{9}{9}$ (or 1) can be represented as the decimal $0.\overline{9}$, and it can also be represented geometrically with a diagram. Portions can also be represented in words, such as "nine-ninths," and as **percents**, which are portions of 100. The diagram at right is called the "Portions Web."

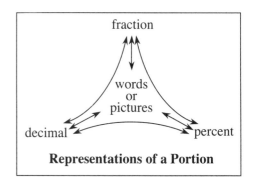

Representations of a Portion

Draw each of the portions webs below on your paper and complete them for the given fractions. In each part, determine if the decimal representation is terminating or repeating.

a. $\frac{2}{3}$

b. $\frac{5}{4}$

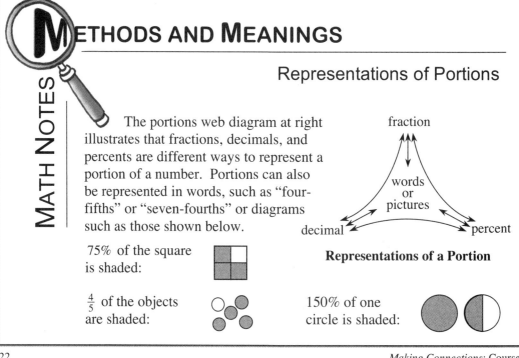

METHODS AND MEANINGS

Representations of Portions

MATH NOTES

The portions web diagram at right illustrates that fractions, decimals, and percents are different ways to represent a portion of a number. Portions can also be represented in words, such as "four-fifths" or "seven-fourths" or diagrams such as those shown below.

75% of the square is shaded:

$\frac{4}{5}$ of the objects are shaded:

Representations of a Portion

150% of one circle is shaded:

1-36.   Copy the rows of equations below and write what you *predict* will be the next
        five rows in the sequence, if the numbers continue to change in the same way.

$$1 \cdot 9 + 2 = 11$$

$$12 \cdot 9 + 3 = 111$$

$$123 \cdot 9 + 4 = 1111$$

$$1234 \cdot 9 + 5 = 11111$$

   a.   What patterns do you see? Write your answer in complete sentences.

   b.   Use a calculator to discover if your predictions were
        correct. If they were not correct, look at the pattern
        again and figure out how it is changing.

1-37.   Look at the representations shown in the Math Notes box for "Representations
        of Portions." Copy the diagrams below and write a fraction and a percent for
        the shaded portion of each one.

   a.   b.   c.

1-38.   Represent each of these fractions with a diagram and with words.

   a. $\frac{2}{3}$ b. $1\frac{1}{8}$ c. $\frac{6}{9}$

1-39.   Jack has four tiles and wants to find out how many different shapes he can make
        with them.

   a.   Sketch all of the arrangements that Jack could make with his tiles so that
        all of the tiles touch at least one other tile completely along a side.
        Assume that no tiles can overlap. How many arrangements are there?

   b.   For each diagram that you drew in part (a), find the area (the "tiles") and
        the perimeter (the "toothpicks"). What do you notice?

1-40.   Find the mean, median, and mode for the lengths of the jumping frogs' bodies
        shown below (the lengths are in centimeters).

        20.3, 12.5, 7.6, 13.9, 9.2, 21.7, 7.6, 17.5, 15.6, 14.1

1.2.1 How likely is it?

Exploring Probability

Every day we have to make decisions, many of them based on what we think will lead to the best result for each situation. You may pick a certain time to call your friend because she is more likely to answer. You might decide to do extra chores to improve the chance that you will be allowed to go to the movies this weekend. If you are deciding whether to enter a raffle, you may weigh the cost of the ticket against the chances that you would have of winning the prize. When you base decisions on your instincts about what will happen, you are using your sense of how likely an outcome will be. In this section, you will learn about ways to analyze the **probability** of an outcome using mathematics.

1-41.   Make a number line on your paper. Place the letter (a, b, c, ...) from each statement below in a position on the line that corresponds to the probability (that is, likelihood) of the event happening. Part (a) is done as an example.

a. It will rain today. (The weather station states there is a 50% chance of rain.)

b. A space alien will walk into class now.

c. You will learn something new in math class this week.

d. Someday, a member of your class will be elected president of the United States.

e. You will eat some vegetables for dinner today.

1-42.   THE GIANT SPIN

At a carnival, the most popular game is the Giant Spin, where players spin a giant wheel divided into 24 sections that are labeled with the numbers $-2, -1, 0, 1, 3$. The number that the spinner lands on determines whether a player will win a prize. The winning number and the prize change every day. Get a copy of the Lesson 1.2.1 Resource Page and look at the Giant Spin spinner.

Problem continues on next page. →

Making Connections: Course 2

1-42. *Problem continued from previous page.*

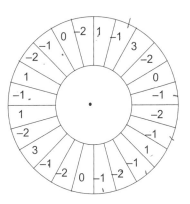

a. Based on a quick look at the wheel, can you predict on which number the spinner will land most often? Where will it land least often?

b. On Mondays, a player will win a stuffed animal if the spinner lands on a "0" space and a free ride on the roller coaster if it lands on a "1" space. Work with your team to find the **probability** of winning each kind of prize.

- Read the Math Notes box about probability at the end of this lesson.

- Use that information and the spinner to find the probability that the spinner lands on "1," written $P(1)$, and then the probability that it lands on "0," or $P(0)$.

- Determine the probability that a player will not win a prize.

c. On Tuesdays, the rules change. Players win if they do *not* spin −1. Find $P(\text{not} -1)$ and explain how it is related to $P(-1)$.

d. On Wednesdays, a player will win a gift certificate if she spins −1 or 3. During this time, what is the probability of winning, $P(-1 \text{ or } 3)$?

e. The carnival owner wants to set up the wheel so that on Fridays, players have a 50% chance of winning. Work with your team to find the number (or numbers) the owner could choose as the winning spin. Is there more than one choice the owner could make? Be prepared to share your **reasoning** with the class.

1-43. If you played the Giant Spin 50 times, about how many times do you think the spinner would land on either a −1 or 1? Discuss this as a team, then write down a prediction.

a. Use the Lesson 1.2.1 Resource Page and a bobby pin to make the Giant Spin spinner. Work with your team to spin the wheel 50 times. Record the outcome of each spin.

- How many times did your team spin a 1?

- How many times did your team spin a −1?

b. How did your results compare to your predictions? If they were different, why do you think that happened? Explain your **reasoning**.

1-44.   Lila is making a spinner game for her cousins to play. She has divided it into 8 equal sections, and has labeled each one with a symbol. When the spinner lands on a flower (✿), her cousins will win a prize.

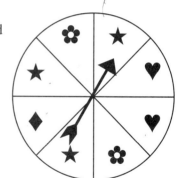

   a.   What is P(★)?

   b.   What is P(not ♦)?

   c.   What is P(✿)?

   d.   If Lila's cousins spin 100 times, about how many times would you expect them to spin a heart (♥)?

1-45.   **Additional Challenge:** Lila's sister wants to increase the chances that her cousins will spin a flower when they play Lila's game. *"I wonder how I should change the spinner to help people spin the flower (✿)?"* she asked. Analyze each of her ideas below.

   a.   What will happen to the chances of spinning a flower if Lila's sister changes all of the heart (♥) spaces to flowers (✿)? Find P(✿) for this new spinner.

   b.   What would happen to the chance of spinning a flower (✿) if the number of spaces with each symbol is doubled, so that there are 16 equal spaces on the wheel? How does this answer compare to the probability of spinning a flower that you found in problem 1-44?

   c.   What would happen to the chances of spinning a flower (✿) if Lila's sister makes a new wheel, and doubles only the number of flower spaces? (Assume all the spaces on the new wheel are still equal to each other in size.) Find P(✿) for this new wheel.

   d.   Look at your answers for parts (a) through (c). Answer each question below and explain your **reasoning**.

   •   Which changes to the wheel changed the probability of landing on a flower (✿) space, and which did not?

   •   How would you change the original spinner if you wanted to increase a player's chances of spinning a heart (♥)?

METHODS AND **M**EANINGS

Probability

The **probability** of an event is the likelihood or chance that the event will occur. An **event** is the desired outcome (sometimes called favorable outcome) from among all possible outcomes. If all outcomes are equally likely, we can calculate the probability of an event, written **P(event)**, as:

$$P(\text{event}) = \frac{\text{number of outcomes in the event}}{\text{total number of possible outcomes}}.$$

For a standard number cube like the ones shown here, P(2) means the probability of rolling a 2 (the event). To calculate the probability, first figure out how many possible outcomes there are. Since there are six faces on the number cube, the number of possible outcomes is 6. Of the six faces, only one of the faces has a 2 on it. Thus, to find the probability of rolling a 2, you would write:

$$P(2) = \frac{\text{number of ways to roll 2}}{\text{number of possible outcomes}} = \frac{1}{6} \text{ or } 0.1\overline{6} \text{ or approximately } 16.7\%.$$

Probabilities may be written as fractions, decimals, or percents. An event that is guaranteed to happen has a probability of 1, or 100%. An event that has no chance of happening has a probability of 0, or 0%. Events that "might happen" have probabilities between 0 and 1 or 0% and 100%. In general, the more likely an event is to happen, the greater its probability.

Examples:

The probability of pulling a king out of a standard deck of cards, P(king), is $\frac{4}{52} = \frac{1}{13}$, since there are 4 kings and 52 cards.

The probability of getting tails when you flip a coin, P(tails), is $\frac{1}{2}$.

The probability of landing on a number less than 5 on a spinner with nine equal regions numbered 1 to 9, P(less than five), is $\frac{4}{9}$.

1-46.   Copy the number line below and place the following probabilities on it:

a.   A $\frac{1}{4}$ chance that you will be the team member who gets supplies tomorrow.

b.   A 25% chance of snow tomorrow.

c.   A 0.8 probability of eating vegetables with dinner.

d.   P(blue marble) $= \frac{5}{8}$.

e.   A 0.01 probability that it will be 85° on Saturday.

1-47.   A standard deck of playing cards has four suits (symbols) in two colors: diamonds and hearts are red; clubs and spades are black. Each suit has 13 cards: an ace, the numbers two through ten, a jack, a queen, and a king.

a.   What is P(black)?   b.   What is P(ace)?   c.   What is P(club)?

d.   If you drew a card from the deck and then replaced it, and repeated this 100 times, about how many times would you expect to draw a face card (king, queen, or jack)?

1-48.   FRACTIONS AND PERCENTS

Marianna represented several percents as portions of 100 in the pictures below.

i.   *ii.*   *iii.*

a.   Write the percent represented in each picture.

b.   Write the portion represented in each picture as a fraction in at least two different ways.

1-49.   Simplify the expressions in parts (a) through (f). Then answer the questions in part (g) using complete sentences.

a. $13 \cdot 1$

b. $1 \cdot 5.5$

c. $6 \cdot \frac{1}{2}$

d. $12 \cdot 2$

e. $4 \cdot \frac{3}{3}$

f. $14 \cdot \frac{1}{7}$

g.   Use these examples to answer the following questions:

- What happens when you multiply a number by one?

- What happens when you multiply a positive number by a positive number less than one?

- What happens when you multiply a positive number by a number greater than one?

1.2.2 How accurately can I predict it?

Comparing Experimental and Theoretical Probabilities

Sometimes an event is guaranteed to happen (for example, rolling a number less than 7 with a standard number cube), so it is called a **certainty**. Other times, an event is an **impossibility** (for example, rolling a 10 with a standard number cube), and so it has 0 (or no) chance of happening. For an event that will happen sometimes, you saw in Lesson 1.2.1 how math can help to predict how often it will happen. In life, however, results are often less exact than we might expect. In this lesson, you will explore the difference between mathematical predictions and real-world outcomes.

1-50.   COIN FLIP EXPERIMENT

When a coin is flipped, there are two possible outcomes: heads or tails. A fair coin is one where heads and tails are equally likely outcomes of a flip.

a.   What is the probability that you will flip heads when you flip a fair coin?

b.   If you flip the same coin 30 times, how many times do you think you should flip heads? Write a prediction.

Problem continues on next page $\rightarrow$

Chapter 1: Probability and Portions

1-50.   *Problem continued from previous page.*

   c.   What will really happen? To find out, your teacher will assign you and a
        partner a number of flips and give you a Lesson 1.2.2 Resource Page to
        match that number of flips. With your partner, flip a coin and:

        •   Record the outcome (heads, H, or tails, T) on the chart.

        •   Keep flipping until you have data for each row of the chart (or charts)
            on your resource page.

        How many times did you flip heads? Was the result what you expected?

   d.   Your prediction in part (a) is called a **theoretical probability** because it is
        calculated based on analyzing the possible outcomes in the situation (heads
        and tails) and the desired outcome (heads). The results you got in part (c),
        written as a probability, are called an **experimental probability**. It is
        called experimental because it is based on data you collected in your
        experiment.

        Write the experimental probability for your coin flipping results from part
        (c) and record your probability with the results from other pairs of students
        as directed by your teacher.

1-51.   People often make statements about probability when they talk about future
         events. For example, weather forecasters often describe "the chance of rain
         tomorrow" as they announce their forecasts. Another example is the likelihood
         that you will be allowed to go to the mall this weekend. For each of the
         problems below, decide whether the situation is describing a theoretical or
         experimental probability. Be prepared to explain your **reasoning**.

   a.   The probability I can come to your house is 100% because the last twelve
        times I asked my dad if I could, he said yes.

   b.   The likelihood of rolling a 4 on a standard number cube is $\frac{1}{6}$ because there
        is only one side with a 4 and there are six sides.

   c.   The probability of winning the state lottery is said to be $\frac{1}{1000000}$ because
        only one combination of one million possible combinations will be
        selected.

   d.   Based on my last 60 times batting in softball, I have a $\frac{4}{5}$ chance of striking
        out.

   e.   There is a 0% probability that it will snow today in Fiji because snow has
        never been recorded there.

1-52.   Look at the class results for the Coin Flip Experiment (problem 1-50).

   a.   Did all teams get the same experimental probability?

   b.   Which team flipped the highest proportion of heads? How can you
        compare the different results?

1-53.   After 25 flips in the Coin Flip Experiment
         (problem 1-50), Lorraine and her partner
         recorded 14 heads ($\frac{14}{25}$ heads).

   a.   Is this more than, less than, or equal to
        50%, the theoretical probability of
        flipping heads? Talk with your partner
        about how you know.

   b.   Percentages are one way to compare different portions of the total. If you
        have not already done so, work with your partner to calculate what
        percentage of Lorraine's flips were heads. Be prepared to share your
        strategy for finding the percentage with the class.

1-54.   DaMarr wrote his experimental probability of flipping
         heads as the fraction $\frac{7}{20}$. He wants to rewrite $\frac{7}{20}$ as a
         percent. To do that, he knows he needs to rewrite it as a
         portion of 100. He started by drawing the picture at right
         to represent $\frac{7}{20}$:

   a.   As he looked at his picture, DaMarr realized that he
        could adjust his drawing to show 100 parts instead
        of 20. DaMarr then drew a new diagram below his
        original picture. How many of the 100 parts are
        shaded? Explain your **reasoning**.

   b.   Explain how DaMarr can use his new picture to
        write $\frac{7}{20}$ as a percent.

   c.   Use a similar **strategy** to rewrite $\frac{3}{10}$ as a
        percent. Show your steps.

New diagram

1-55.   Randy was playing "Double Heads" where he would flip two coins at a time. He recorded the number of times he flipped two heads at the same time. He flipped the coins 50 times and there were 20 times when both coins landed heads up, which he recorded as $\frac{20}{50}$.

Note: This stoplight icon will appear periodically throughout the text. Problems with this icon display common errors that can be made. Be sure not to make the same mistakes yourself!

a.   How does $\frac{20}{50}$ compare to 50%?

b.   Randy claims, "$\frac{20}{50}$ is equivalent to $\frac{70}{100}$ *because if I add 50 to the denominator to get 100 and add 50 to the numerator to get 70, the fraction becomes $\frac{70}{100}$.*" Explain to Randy why $\frac{20}{50}$ and $\frac{70}{100}$ are not equivalent portions.

1-56.   Three students invented a game in which they flip coins for a minute then determine who flipped the highest percentage of heads. After their first round, each of them thinks that they won the game. Below is what they reported:

- "I think I won," said Maria, "Of my flips $\frac{12}{25}$ were heads."

- Autymn said, "I flipped my coin 40 times and had a total of 18 heads. Since both of my numbers are larger than yours, I must have won."

- Kumar reported, "I recorded 44% of my flips as heads."

Help the students determine their percentage of heads. **Justify** your answer.

1-57.   Did your experimental probability of flipping heads in the Coin Flip Experiment (problem 1-50) exactly match the theoretical probability of 50%, or $\frac{1}{2}$? Was it close?

a.   Change the results from each team in problem 1-50 to percents using DaMarr's **strategy** from problem 1-54. Add your results to your paper and the class data.

b.   Which result was closest to 50%? Which result was the most surprising?

c.   Combine all of the results for the number of flips and the number of heads to get a total number of flips and a total number of heads for the class.

- What percent of the flips landed heads?

- How does the experimental probability for the class compare to your own results?

- How does it compare to the theoretical probability?

Making Connections: Course 2

METHODS AND MEANINGS

Probability: Vocabulary and Definitions

Outcome: Any possible or actual result or consequence of the action(s) considered, such as rolling a five on a standard number cube or getting heads when flipping a coin.

Event: A desired (or successful) outcome or group of desired (successful) outcomes from an experiment, such as rolling an even number on a standard number cube.

Sample Space: All the possible outcomes of a situation. For example, the sample space for flipping a coin is H and T; rolling a standard number cube has six possible outcomes: 1, 2, 3, 4, 5, and 6.

Theoretical Probability: A calculated probability based on the possible outcomes when each outcome has the same chance of occurring.

$$\text{Theoretical Probability} = \frac{\text{number of successful outcomes (events)}}{\text{total number of possible outcomes}}$$

By "successful" we usually mean desired or specified outcome (event), such as rolling a five on a standard number cube ($\frac{1}{6}$), pulling a king from a deck of cards ($\frac{4}{52} = \frac{1}{13}$), or flipping a coin and getting heads ($\frac{1}{2}$).

Experimental Probability: The probability based on data collected in experiments.

$$\text{Experimental Probability} = \frac{\text{number of successful outcomes in the experiment}}{\text{total number of outcomes in the experiment}}$$

Impossibility: An event that has a probability of zero; that is, an event that cannot occur, such as rolling a seven on a standard number cube.

Certainty: An event that has a probability of one or 100%; that is, an event that will definitely occur, such as rolling a number between one and six on a standard number cube.

1-58.   For each situation below, write the indicated probability.

a.   A coin is flipped 80 times. It lands "tails" 47 times. Based on this data, what is the experimental probability that the coin will land on heads?

b.   A bag contains purple and orange marbles. Samantha randomly takes out one marble, and then returns it to the bag. She does this 18 times, and 12 of those times an orange marble is pulled out. For her experiment, what is the probability that she will pull out a green marble?

c.   Sarina pulls a playing card from a standard deck and then replaces it. She does this 30 times, and 40% of the time it is hearts. Based on these results, what is the probability that she will *not* pull a heart out of the deck?

1-59.   Write four different fractions that are equal to 1. Use your calculator to check that you are correct.

1-60.   Elizabeth wants to challenge you to a "Toothpicks and Tiles" game. Using exactly 6 tiles, solve her challenges below. **Justify** your answers with pictures and labels.

a.   Find a pattern where the number of toothpicks is more than double the number of tiles.

b.   Find a pattern where the number of toothpicks is 4 more than the number of tiles.

1-61.   Kayla has a 14-foot rope. She cut it into three parts. Two of the pieces are the same length and the third piece is 2 feet long.

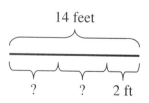

a.   Copy Kayla's diagram at right onto your paper.

b.   How long were each of the two equal pieces?

1-62.   Rewrite each fraction as a percent and each percent as a fraction. Show your thinking with pictures or labeled calculations.

a. $\frac{2}{5}$ b.   45%   c.   120%   d. $\frac{21}{40}$

1-63.   Locate the coordinates of the three highlighted points on the graph of the triangle below and write them as ordered pairs (x, y).

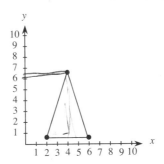

1-64.   Lulu is playing "Toothpicks and Tiles" from Lesson 1.1.2. She has arranged 10 tiles as shown at right. She wants to rearrange them so that the number of toothpicks is still equal. Draw one possible arrangement of the tiles.

1-65.   Find a pattern in each number sequence below. Then use your pattern to generate the next five numbers in the sequence. Explain the pattern.

a.   2, 5, 3, 6, 4, ___, ___, ___, ___, ___

b.   100, 99, 97, 94, 90, ___, ___, ___, ___, ___

1-66.   Alice said, "*I am thinking of a number. If you triple my number and subtract 11, you get my number plus 33. What's my number?*" Find Alice's number. Show how you know your answer is correct.

1.2.3 How can I represent it?

· ·

Rewriting Fractions

When probabilities and portions are expressed as fractions, they can sometimes be difficult to compare. For example, is a $\frac{2}{5}$ probability of winning a game greater than a $\frac{3}{7}$ probability?

Earlier, you used different ways to represent a portion to help figure out if $0.\overline{9}$ is equal to 1. In this lesson, you will develop **strategies** for rewriting fractions in different forms in order to compare different portions.

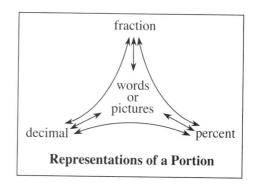

Representations of a Portion

1-67.   FRACTION TO PERCENT

Lila wants to rewrite $\frac{10}{25}$ as a percentage. She decided to represent $\frac{10}{25}$ first in a picture.

a.   How many sets of 25 will she need to make 100?

b.   How many sets of shaded squares will she need? How many shaded squares is that in total?

c.   Lila drew the picture below, and then wrote the equation to the right to represent her work with the shapes:

When Lila multiplies the number of shaded squares by 4 and the number of total squares by 4, did the amount of shading compared to the total squares change? Explain how you know.

1-68. Multiplying any number by one does not change the value of the number; this is called the **Identity Property of Multiplication**. When the numerator (top number) and denominator (bottom number) of a fraction are multiplied by the same number, some people like to say the fraction is multiplied by a **Giant One**. For example:

$$\frac{10}{25} \cdot \boxed{\frac{4}{4}} = \frac{40}{100}$$

a. Why is the fraction $\frac{4}{4}$ called a Giant One?

b. Use a Giant One to rewrite each fraction by multiplying each expression below.

   i. $\frac{9}{25} \cdot \boxed{\frac{6}{6}}$ ii. $\frac{6}{15} \cdot \boxed{\frac{3}{3}}$

c. What if you do not know which numbers to use in a Giant One? Copy and complete each problem below on your paper.

   i. $\frac{5}{7} \cdot \boxed{} = \frac{40}{}$ ii. $\frac{5}{7} \cdot \boxed{} = \frac{}{70}$

1-69. Use the Giant One to rewrite each fraction as a part of 100. Then write the equivalent percentage.

a. $\frac{3}{4} \cdot \boxed{} = \frac{}{100}$ b. $\frac{42}{200} \cdot \boxed{} = \frac{}{100}$ c. $\frac{7}{16} \cdot \boxed{} = \frac{}{100}$

d. How do you decide which number to use in the Giant One?

1-70. Deanna is trying to compare $\frac{3}{7}$ to $\frac{2}{5}$. She started by representing $\frac{3}{7}$ in a picture, then she divided the picture into five horizontal rows to rewrite the portion as $\frac{15}{35}$. Here is her work so far:

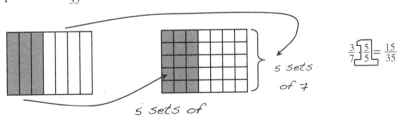

a. Rewrite $\frac{2}{5}$ as a portion of 35. Is $\frac{2}{5}$ bigger or smaller than $\frac{3}{7}$?

b. Why does rewriting the fractions make it easier to compare the two fractions?

c. Why did Deanna choose 35 for her new denominator? Could she have chosen a different number?

1-71.   FAMILIES OF FRACTIONS

Using a Giant One, any fraction can be rewritten as a different fraction that represents the same portion of a whole. Fractions that are equal but are written in different ways are called **equivalent fractions**.

Make three new fractions that are equivalent to each fraction below.

a. $\frac{7}{12}$ b. $\frac{3}{10}$ c. $\frac{9}{27}$

1-72.   Adele, Karla, and Lisa are reading the same book, and they have each read a different number of pages.

Adele has read $\frac{5}{8}$ of the book.

Karla has read $\frac{12}{16}$ of the book.

Lisa has read $\frac{13}{24}$ of the book.

Help them decide who has the most left to read.

a.   What denominator could they use to compare the portions they have read?

b.   Which girl has the largest part left to read? **Justify** your ideas.

c.   How many pages could the book have? Be ready to explain your answer.

1-73.   Which of the events below is most likely to happen? **Justify** your answer by rewriting the portion in a different form. In each case, show your thinking with pictures or labeled calculations.

a.   A $\frac{4}{5}$ chance of the teacher assigning homework today.

b.   A 78% chance of a thunderstorm tomorrow.

c.   A $\frac{7}{10}$ probability of picking a green marble.

1-74.   LEARNING LOG

In this course, you will often be asked to reflect on your
learning in a Learning Log. Writing about your
understanding will help you pull together ideas, develop
new ways to describe mathematical ideas, and recognize
gaps in your understanding. Your teacher will tell you
where your Learning Log entries should go.

For your first entry, think about which methods you have for comparing two
probabilities to decide which is greater. In your Learning Log, create an
example and explain two different **strategies** for comparing them. Title this
entry "Comparing Probabilities," and label it with today's date.

METHODS AND MEANINGS

Additive and Multiplicative Identities

If any number or expression is multiplied by the number "one,"
the number or expression does not change. The number "one" is called
the **multiplicative identity**. So, for any number x:

$$1 \cdot x = x \cdot 1 = x$$

One way the multiplicative identity is used is to
create equivalent fractions using a Giant One.

$$\frac{2}{3} \cdot \boxed{\frac{2}{2}} = \frac{4}{6}$$

By multiplying a fraction by a fraction equivalent to one, a new
equivalent fraction is created.

The number "zero" is the **additive identity** since adding zero does not
change the value or expression.

1-75.   In problem 1-67, Lila rewrote $\frac{10}{25}$ as $\frac{40}{100}$ and represented it with the picture at right. Tony thinks this fraction is also equal to $\frac{2}{5}$.

    a.   Is Tony correct? Use the picture or calculations to explain your **reasoning**. Write your answer in complete sentences.

    b.   How could Tony write an equivalent (equal) fraction using tenths? That is, what fraction in the form $\frac{?}{10}$ can represent the diagram above?

1-76.   Zaria wants you to solve this puzzle: *"I am thinking of a number. If you divide my number by two and subtract 4, you will get 2. What is my number?"* Show how you know your answer is correct.

1-77.   Marissa is drawing coins from a bag that contains 5 pennies, 4 nickels, 5 dimes, and 2 quarters.

    a.   What is the probability that she will draw a nickel?

    b.   If one penny, two dimes, and one quarter are added to the bag, what is the new probability that she will draw a nickel?

    c.   In which situation is it more likely that she will draw a nickel?

1-78.   Rewrite each fraction below as an equivalent fraction and as a percent.

    a. $\frac{5}{20}$ b. $\frac{9}{25}$ c. $\frac{9}{6}$

1-79.   Rewrite each expression as a single fraction.

    a. $\frac{3}{8}+\frac{1}{8}$ b. $\frac{4}{5}+\frac{3}{5}$ c. $\frac{6}{7}-\frac{2}{7}$

1.2.4 What if there are multiple outcomes?

Compound Probability and Fraction Addition

So far in this section, you have worked with probabilities where there is one specific outcome that is desired. Today you will investigate probabilities of **compound events**, that is, events with combinations of outcomes. Think about these questions as you work with your study team:

How is this probability related to the probability of a single event?

How can probabilities be combined?

Does this answer make sense?

1-80. A bag holds 40 marbles, and each marble is either yellow or green. If you reach into the bag and randomly pull out a marble, you have an 80% chance of pulling out a yellow marble.

a. How many of the marbles are green? Show how you know.

b. How could you add or remove marbles in the original bag to change the probability of drawing a green marble to 50%?

c. **Additional Challenge:** Design a new bag of marbles that contains at least 50 marbles that are yellow, green, or red. How many of each color should you put in the bag to create a 25% probability of drawing red? Is there more than one possible way?

1-81.   Thomas helps around the house by doing one chore after school. Each day Thomas and his aunt use the spinner at right to decide which chore he will do. Here is what Thomas knows:

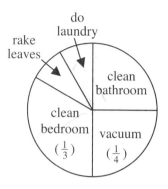

- The sections on the spinner for "rake leaves" and "do laundry" are the same size.

- The sections for "clean bathroom" and "vacuum" are equal in size and together make up half the spinner.

a.   What is the probability that Thomas will spin "do laundry"?

b.   Thomas hates to clean the bathroom. When he spins the spinner, what is the probability that it will not point to "clean bathroom"? Explain how you found this answer.

1-82.   Thomas' aunt hopes that he will spin "clean bedroom" or "rake leaves" today.

a.   What is P(clean bedroom)? What is P(rake leaves)?

b.   Spinning either chore would make Thomas' aunt happy. With your study team, discuss the questions below and record your team's answers. Be sure to **justify** your conclusions.

- What is the probability that he will spin either one of the chores?

- How can you write the two outcomes as a single probability?

1-83.   Ms. Nguyen lets her students borrow pens and pencils on days when they have a quiz. She has a paper bag with hundreds of wooden pencils, mechanical pencils, and blue pens in it.

Stuart forgot his pencil, and it is quiz day! Ms. Nguyen tells him that one out of every three students who reaches into the bag pulls out a wooden pencil. Two out of every five students pull out a mechanical pencil. The rest of the students pull out a blue pen.

a.   If Stuart reaches into the bag without looking, is it more likely that he will choose a wooden pencil or a mechanical pencil? **Justify** your thinking.

b.   How can you describe the probability that Stuart will pull out some kind of pencil by using the probabilities that you already know? Consider what you know about adding and subtracting fractions and see if you already have a **strategy** to write this probability as a single number.

Making Connections: Course 2

1-84. Felicia was trying to find the probability that she would pull a pencil out of Ms. Nguyen's bag from problem 1-83. *"I think I need to combine the probability that I will get a wooden pencil with the probability that I will get a mechanical pencil,"* she said. She set up this expression and drew a picture:

$\frac{1}{3} + \frac{2}{5}$

a. Felicia wondered if she could add the parts. Is the sum $\frac{3}{8}$? Why or why not?

b. Discuss with your team how Felicia could change the way she writes each fraction so that she can add them easily. Be ready to explain your **reasoning**. Then, find the sum.

1-85. Justin is working on a new problem: $\frac{1}{3} + \frac{1}{2}$. He drew the picture below to represent the problem:

a. Could you name Justin's sum as a single fraction? Would he be correct to name it $\frac{2}{3}$?

b. Kermit sees Justin's work, and says, *"You need to make all of the pieces the same size before you try to write the sum. You can use a Giant One to rewrite $\frac{1}{3}$ and $\frac{1}{2}$ each as sixths."* He writes:

$$\frac{1}{3} \cdot \boxed{} = \frac{}{6} \qquad \frac{1}{2} \cdot \boxed{} = \frac{}{6}$$

Finish Kermit's work to rewrite each fraction so that its denominator is six.

c. What is the sum of the new fractions? Fix Justin's picture or draw a new diagram to explain why your answer makes sense.

d. Discuss with your team why Kermit might have chosen to rewrite each fraction as sixths. Could he have used a different number? Be ready to share your thinking.

1-86.   Before we can write the sum of two fractions, they must be rewritten so that both wholes have an equal number of parts. In other words, they must be rewritten to have a **common denominator**. Three students were adding the fractions $\frac{1}{4} + \frac{5}{12}$ below, and they each found a different common denominator:

Lily: $\frac{1}{4} + \frac{5}{12}$ Armando: $\frac{1}{4} + \frac{5}{12}$ Josue: $\frac{1}{4} + \frac{5}{12}$

$\frac{12}{48} + \frac{20}{48}$ $\frac{3}{12} + \frac{5}{12}$ $\frac{6}{24} + \frac{10}{24}$

$\frac{32}{48}$ $\frac{8}{12}$ $\frac{16}{24}$

a.   Who is correct? Can any number be a common denominator? Explain your **reasoning**.

b.   Which of their common denominators is easiest to work with? Why?

c.   Find at least three different common denominators you could use to add $\frac{3}{10} + \frac{1}{5}$.

1-87.   Vu needs to add $\frac{3}{8} + \frac{5}{6}$. He knows that he can rewrite each fraction as a portion of 48 because 6 and 8 are each factors of 48 in his multiplication table. *"Is there a smaller number that could work as a common denominator?"* he wonders.

a.   Where can you look in the multiplication table to see if 6 and 8 are each factors of a number less than 48?

b.   Use the multiplication table on the Lesson 1.2.4 Resource Page to find other number(s) you could use as a common denominator to add $\frac{3}{8}$ and $\frac{5}{6}$.

c.   If Vu's next problem is to add $\frac{5}{4} + \frac{7}{10}$, use the multiplication table to find the smallest number you could use as a common denominator, called the **lowest common denominator**. Then, find the sum.

	1	2	3	4	5	6	7	8	9	10
1	1	2	3	4	5	6	7	8	9	10
2	2	4	6	8	10	12	14	16	18	20
3	3	6	9	12	15	18	21	24	27	30
4	4	8	12	16	20	24	28	32	36	40
5	5	10	15	20	25	30	35	40	45	50
6	6	12	18	24	30	36	42	48	54	60
7	7	14	21	28	35	42	49	56	63	70
8	8	16	24	32	40	48	56	64	72	80
9	9	18	27	36	45	54	63	72	81	90
10	10	20	30	40	50	60	70	80	90	100

1-88.   One study team is trying to find the sum $\frac{5}{6} + \frac{3}{4} + \frac{1}{5}$.

   a.   They first tried to use 24 as a common denominator. Why does 24 not work as a common denominator?

   b.   Find a common denominator for this problem and explain how you found it.

   c.   With your study team, describe how factors and multiples can help you to find a common denominator.

1-89.   With your team, find each sum. You may want to use the multiplication table to help you find common denominators.

   a. $\frac{1}{4} + \frac{3}{5}$ b. $\frac{2}{7} + \frac{2}{3}$ c. $\frac{5}{8} + \frac{1}{2}$ d. $\frac{2}{3} + \frac{1}{2} + \frac{1}{6}$

1-90.   THE POWER OF PRIME NUMBERS˙

   Additional Challenge: Prime numbers are numbers that have exactly two factors, namely, one and themselves. Said another way, prime numbers can only be divided evenly by themselves and one (except for 1, which is not prime). Every number that is not prime can be rewritten as a product of **prime factors**. For example, $20 = 2 \cdot 2 \cdot 5$ or $36 = 2 \cdot 2 \cdot 3 \cdot 3$. Prime factors can be used to build common denominators for fractions.

   a.   What are the prime factors of each denominator in the sum $\frac{5}{6} + \frac{3}{4} + \frac{1}{5}$ (from problem 1-88)?

   b.   What are the prime factors of the common denominator you found in part (b) of problem 1-88?

   c.   What do the lists of factors you made in parts (a) and (b) have in common?

   d.   How could the prime factors of each denominator in a pair of fractions help you find a common denominator for those fractions? Explain your thinking.

METHODS AND MEANINGS

Equivalent Fractions

Fractions that are equal, but written in different forms, are called **equivalent fractions**. Rewriting a fraction in an equivalent form is useful when you want to compare two fractions or when you want to combine portions that are divided into different size pieces.

A Giant One is a useful tool to create an equivalent fraction. To rewrite a fraction in a different form, multiply the original fraction by a fraction equivalent to 1. For example:

$$\frac{2}{3} \cdot \boxed{\frac{4}{4}} = \frac{2 \cdot 4}{3 \cdot 4} = \frac{8}{12}$$

A picture can also demonstrate that these two fractions are equivalent:

 =

1-91.   What is the probability of getting blue or green on a spinner that is $\frac{3}{10}$ green and $\frac{1}{5}$ blue? Show your work.

1-92.   The value of a decimal becomes clearer when the place value is spoken or written as the number it names. For example, 0.1 makes more sense if it is read as "one-tenth" rather than "zero point one."

   a.   Write the following numbers in words so that the place value can be identified.

   0.4   1.3   0.56   2.008

   b.   Now **reverse your thinking**. Write the decimals that go with the following words.

   thirty-five hundredths   three and two-tenths   six-hundredths

1-93.   For each part below, find a Giant One that will multiply the fraction on the left side of the equation to create the equivalent fraction on the right side of the equation. Then complete any other missing information.

a. $\frac{5}{6} \cdot \boxed{} = \frac{15}{}$

b. $\frac{}{3} \cdot \boxed{} = \frac{4}{6}$

c. $\frac{}{2} \cdot \boxed{} = \frac{8}{16}$

d. $\frac{}{4} \cdot \boxed{} = \frac{6}{24}$

1-94.   How many different rectangles can you draw with an area (number of "tiles") of 28? What is the perimeter (number of "toothpicks") of each one? Show your work.

1-95.   Fareed wants to add $\frac{1}{4} + \frac{5}{8}$.

a.   Add the fractions by using a Giant One to create a common denominator.

b.   How can factors help you find a common denominator?

1-96.   Marisa and Mario were visiting the carnival when they noticed a few number relationships. They made them into brainteasers for you.

a.   If three-tenths of the visitors were adults and there were 100 visitors, how many visitors were adults?

b.   Five-eighths of the prizes at the Giant Spin were dolls. If there were 64 prizes, how many prizes were not dolls?

1-97.   Order these numbers from least to greatest.

$\frac{1}{2} \quad 1.1 \quad \frac{5}{3} \quad 2 \quad 0 \quad 0.4 \quad -2 \quad \frac{7}{8}$

1-98.   Here are the lengths (in inches) of snakes in a reptile display at the zoo: 10, 31, 36, 36, 38, 42, 47, 48, 49, 52. Find the mean, median, and mode of the lengths.

1-99.   Find each sum.

a. $\frac{3}{5} + \frac{1}{3}$

b. $\frac{5}{7} + \frac{1}{2}$

c. $\frac{1}{6} + \frac{2}{8}$

1.2.5 What part is missing?

Subtracting Fractions

In this section, you have calculated probabilities for single events and combinations of events. You have also compared those probabilities to decide which outcomes are most likely. In this lesson, you will work with your study team to apply your knowledge of fractions to represent and calculate probabilities of a variety of events. As you work today, ask each other these questions to focus your discussion:

How can probabilities be combined?

How can the answer be rewritten in a different form?

1-100. Eustice is adding fractions. Here is her work:

$$\tfrac{1}{2} + \tfrac{2}{4} = \tfrac{3}{6}$$

a. How do you think Eustice got her answer? Does her answer make sense? Discuss Eustice's work with your team, and then explain your **reasoning** on your paper with diagrams and words.

b. Help Eustice find the correct answer.

1-101. Lindsay has a paper bag full of Fruiti Tutti Chews in three different fruit flavors. She says, *"If you reach into the bag, you have a $\tfrac{1}{3}$ chance of pulling out a Killer Kiwi. There is a $\tfrac{3}{5}$ chance that you will get Crazy Coconut."* If you reach into the bag:

a. What is P(coconut or kiwi)?

b. Does there have to be another flavor in the bag? How can you tell? If so, assuming that there is only one other flavor, what is the probability of getting that flavor?

c. How many candies might Lindsay have in the bag? Is there more than one possibility? Assume that all candies in the bag are whole candies.

Making Connections: Course 2

1-102. Lyle asked for a challenge problem, and his teacher gave him this one:

There is a $\frac{2}{7}$ chance of drawing a red marble out of a bag of marbles. If the probability of drawing a red or a blue marble is $\frac{2}{3}$, what is the probability of drawing a blue marble?

When Lyle's teammates saw the challenge he was working on, they each had a different idea for how he should start.

- Mayra suggested that he start by rewriting $\frac{2}{3}$ and $\frac{2}{7}$ so that they have a common denominator.

- Kenessa disagreed. *"You want to set up a subtraction problem,"* she said. She wrote the expression $\frac{2}{3} - \frac{2}{7}$ to show the number Lyle needs to find.

- Darren had a different idea. *"The probability that you would draw either red or blue is the same as the probability of drawing red added to the probability of drawing blue,"* he said. He wrote this expression:

$$\tfrac{2}{7} + ? = \tfrac{2}{3}$$

a. Which way would you suggest Lyle start working to find P(blue)?

- Discuss your ideas with your study team.

- Write a clear explanation of which method you recommend and why.

- Include your ideas about whether the other **strategies** will solve the problem and why you did not choose them.

b. What is the probability of drawing a blue marble? Explain your **reasoning**.

1-103. Louise is playing a game, but the spinner is incomplete. Each section of the spinner is labeled with the probability of spinning it. What fraction is missing?

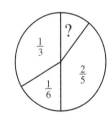

1-104. What math operations can you use to show your **reasoning** in problems 1-102 and 1-103? Discuss your **strategies** with your study team. Try to find more than one way to explain how you found each missing piece.

1-105. Charles found a spinner his teacher was making. He knew that if he put his problem-solving skills to use, he would be able to figure out the missing piece and finish the spinner for his teacher.

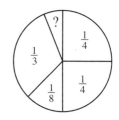

a. Write an expression for the problem Charles needs to solve. Is there more than one way to do this?

b. Find the solution.

1-106. Work with your study team to invent two new spinners with missing parts, like the spinners in problems 1-103 and 1-105. Then,

- Find the missing piece on your own paper.

- On a new sheet of paper, draw and label your spinner.

- Trade problems with another study team and find the missing parts of their spinners while they find yours.

1-107. LEARNING LOG

In your Learning Log, describe the process you use to add or subtract fractions when the fractions have different denominators. Create an example and show your solution with pictures and number expressions. Then, answer the questions:

- How do you rewrite the fractions to represent pieces that are the same size?

- How do you identify what common denominator to use?

Label this entry "Adding Fractions with Unlike Denominators," and include today's date.

MᴇTHODS AND MᴇANINGS

MATH NOTES

Scaling a Graph

The numbers on the axes of a graph show the **scaling** of the axes. The difference between consecutive markings tells the size of the **interval**. When you scale each axis you must use equal intervals to represent the data accurately. For example, an interval of 5 creates a scale numbered $-15, -10, -5, 0, 5, 10, 15$, etc. Unequal intervals distort the relationship in the data.

Notice on the graph at right that 80 marks the end of the *fourth* interval from zero. If you divide 80 years by 4 you can see the length of an interval on this graph is 20.

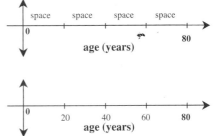

$$80 \div 4 = 20$$

The second graph at right has each interval labeled. We call labeling the graph "scaling the axis."

Review & Preview

1-108.　Rewrite each fraction in at least 2 different ways.

　　a.　$\frac{6}{9}$　　　　b.　$\frac{11}{12}$　　　　c.　$\frac{3}{8}$　　　　d.　$\frac{10}{7}$

1-109.　Jonathan measured two cups of flour into a bowl on the counter. Then he spilled part of it, and now there is only $\frac{3}{8}$ cup left. How much did he spill?

1-110. Mario is trying to explain to Marissa how to add fractions. He has written the work at right.

a. Why did Mario start by rewriting the fractions using a Giant One? Why did he choose 20 as his new denominator?

$\frac{1}{4} + \frac{2}{5}$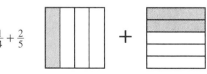

b. Finish the problem. Explain each step you would take, and why.

Step 1: $\frac{1}{4} \cdot \frac{5}{5} = \frac{5}{20}$ $\frac{2}{5} \cdot \frac{4}{4} = \frac{8}{20}$

1-111. Maggie is making a recipe that produces 18 muffins.

a. There are 12 people in Maggie's book club. If the muffins are divided evenly among each person, how much will each person get? Explain your thinking.

b. If Maggie wanted to divide the muffins evenly between the 36 students in her class, how much muffin would each person get? Explain your thinking.

1-112. Read the Math Notes box about scaling axes in this lesson. Then copy these incomplete axes on your paper and write the missing numbers on each one.

a.   b.   c.   d.

1.3.1 When do decimals repeat?

Fraction to Decimal Conversions

In Sections 1.1 and 1.2, you explored different representations of portions (parts) of wholes. You looked at portions represented as fractions and as decimals, and went back and forth between the representations. Some pieces look very similar when represented as fractions, but their decimal representations can appear different. Why does this happen? In this lesson, you will work with your team to determine what makes some decimals terminate (end) and some repeat.

1-113.   Compare the portions in each picture below:

Portion A: Portion B:

a.   Represent each portion as a fraction and as a decimal.

b.   The pictures and fractions for each representation are similar, but the decimals look very different. With your team, discuss how the two decimals look different and why they might look this way. Be ready to share your ideas.

1-114.   In Lesson 1.1.5 you rewrote fractions like $\frac{1}{9}$ as decimals by dividing on your calculator. Looking at how division works can help explain why fractions that look similar can look so different as decimals.

$$\frac{1}{9} = 1 \div 9 = 0.999... = 0.\overline{9}$$

Imagine that you have 13 cheese sticks that you need to divide evenly among 5 people. You can write this as 13 cheese sticks ÷ 5 people or $\frac{13}{5}$ or $5\overline{)13}$. The problem is represented with the pictures and symbols below.

13 cheese sticks

5 groups of 2 pieces

a.   Talk with your team about how this diagram represents beginning to divide 13 by 5, or $\frac{13}{5}$. Why are there five groups of two pieces?

b.   What does the 2 above the division symbol represent? What does the 10 represent?

c.   Where are the three leftover pieces shown in the symbols?

d.   To share the three leftover pieces between the 5 people, divide them up into tenths. Add a decimal point in the dividend to show that the three wholes are being rewritten as thirty tenths (3.0), as shown below:

3 pieces = $\frac{30}{10}$ pieces

How many tenths will each person get? Where is this written in the division problem?

e.   How much cheese will each person receive? Write your answer as a fraction and as a decimal.

Making Connections: Course 2

1-115.   Set up your own division problem to rewrite $\frac{3}{4}$ as a
          decimal *without a calculator* using the Lesson 1.3.1
          Resource Page. Show your work on the diagram and in
          symbols.

    a. Are there enough whole pieces (each bold line
        represents one piece) to put some in each of four
        groups? Explain.

    b. Divide each of the whole pieces into tenths and then divide these into four
        groups. How many tenths are left over?

    c. If you divide each tenth that is left over into 10 pieces again, what fraction
        of the original is each new piece? How many are there? You may need to
        visualize these pieces instead of drawing them.

    d. How many of these new smaller pieces will be in each of the four groups?
        How many will be left over?

    e. How can you tell that the decimal has terminated (ended)?

1-116.   To see why $\frac{2}{3}$ does not terminate, use the Lesson 1.3.1
          Resource Page to rewrite it as a decimal *without a
          calculator*.

    a. As you divide, what happens to the remainders?

    b. How is the process of dividing $\frac{2}{3}$ the same as dividing $\frac{3}{4}$, and how is it
        different? Why does one decimal terminate, but the other does not?

1-117. Katrina works at the Fraction Factory. Her job is to sort all of the customer orders into two groups: terminating decimals and repeating decimals.

a. Katrina's boss wants her to write $\frac{20}{33}$ as a decimal without using a calculator. Katrina's work so far is shown at right. What results did she get each time she subtracted?

b. Will the decimal for $\frac{20}{33}$ terminate or repeat? How do you know? How far should Katrina continue with her division to be sure?

$$
\begin{array}{r}
0.60 \\
33\overline{)20.000} \\
198\downarrow \\
\hline
20 \\
0 \\
\hline
200
\end{array}
$$

1-118. Represent $\frac{1}{7}$ as a decimal. When does it repeat? How do you know?

1-119. THE ROLE OF THE DENOMINATOR

Additional Challenge: Both $\frac{1}{3}$ and $\frac{2}{3}$ can be rewritten as repeating decimals ($0.\overline{3}$ and $0.\overline{6}$). Does the number in the denominator cause the fraction to repeat? For example, will every fraction with a denominator of 15 be equivalent to a repeating decimal? (Ignore fractions that are equal to whole numbers, like $\frac{15}{15} = 1$ or $\frac{45}{15} = 3$.)

a. With your team, try to find a fraction with 15 in the denominator that does not repeat (and is not equal to a whole number). Are you able to find one? More than one?

b. Why do some numbers with a denominator of 15 repeat and others do not? Discuss this with your team. Write down an idea, and test it.

METHODS AND MEANINGS

MATH NOTES

Fraction ⇔ Decimal ⇔ Percent

The **Portions Web** diagram at right illustrates that fractions, decimals, and percents are different ways to represent a portion of a number. Portions can also be represented in words, such as "four-fifths" or "twelve-fifteenths" or with diagrams.

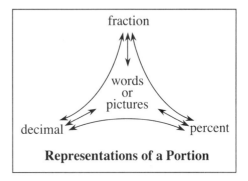

Representations of a Portion

The examples below show how to convert from one form to another.

Decimal to percent:
Multiply the decimal by 100.

$$(0.34)(100) = 34\%$$

Percent to decimal:
Divide the percent by 100.

$$78.6\% = 78.6 \div 100 = 0.786$$

Fraction to percent:
Set up an equivalent fraction using 100 as the denominator. The numerator is the percent.

$$\frac{4}{5} \cdot \frac{20}{20} = \frac{80}{100} = 80\%$$

Percent to Fraction:
Use 100 as the denominator. Use the digits in the percent as the numerator. Simplify as needed.

$$22\% = \frac{22}{100} \cdot \frac{1/2}{1/2} = \frac{11}{50}$$

Decimal to fraction:
Use the digits as the numerator. Use the decimal place value as the denominator. Simplify as needed.

Fraction to decimal:
Divide the numerator by the denominator.

1-120. How many tenths are in one whole? How many hundredths?

1-121. Convert the following fractions to decimals. Show your work.

a. $\frac{2}{5}$　　　　　　　b. $\frac{3}{8}$　　　　　　　c. $\frac{30}{20}$

1-122. Mario ordered a pizza for dinner. When it arrived, Mario quickly ate $\frac{1}{8}$ of the pizza. While Mario was getting napkins, his pet poodle ate $\frac{1}{3}$ of the pizza.

a. Draw a model of the pizza that shows the portion that has been eaten.

b. Write a numerical expression to show the fraction of the pizza that is left.

c. About what percent of the pizza is left?

1-123. Nicole has a machine that will produce a number from 1 through 50 when she pushes a button. If she pushes the button, what is:

a. P(multiple of 10)?　　　　　　　b. P(not 100)?

c. P(not a multiple of 4)?　　　　　　　d. P(one-digit number)?

1-124. Lyle and his study team are designing spinners.

a. If one-half of the sections on a spinner are green and there are 14 sections, how many are green?

b. If three-fourths of the sections on a different spinner have stripes and there are 24 sections, how many sections have stripes?

1-125. Copy the rows of equations at right onto your paper. If the numbers in the equations continue to change in the same way as the pattern shows, write the next five rows of equations in the sequence.

$$9 \cdot 9 + 7 = 88$$
$$98 \cdot 9 + 6 = 888$$
$$987 \cdot 9 + 5 = 8888$$
$$9876 \cdot 9 + 4 = 88888$$

1.3.2 How can I rewrite a decimal?

Rewriting Decimals as Fractions

In Lesson 1.3.1, you worked with different fractions and found ways to rewrite those fractions as repeating and terminating decimals. In this lesson, you will **reverse your thinking** and instead represent decimals as fractions.

As you work with your team today, ask each other these questions to focus your discussion:

How else can I describe the portion?

How many pieces are in the whole?

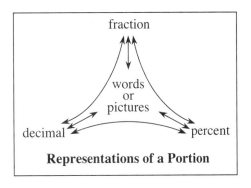

Representations of a Portion

1-126. Complete the portions web for each number below. An example for $\frac{2}{3}$ is shown at right.

a. $\frac{7}{10}$ b.   0.75

c. Three-fifths   d. $\frac{5}{8}$

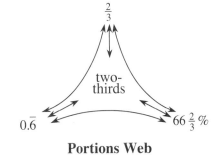

Portions Web

e. With your team, explain how you rewrote 0.75 as a fraction in part (b). Is there more than one way? Be as specific as possible.

1-127. Since 0.7 is described in words as "seven tenths," it is not a surprise that the equivalent fraction is $\frac{7}{10}$. Obtain a set of decimal cards from your teacher or use the list below to complete the following tasks:

- Use the names of fractions (like "twenty-three hundredths") to rewrite each terminating decimal as a fraction. First try to use what you know about place value to write the fraction.

- Check that the fraction is equal to the decimal with your calculator.

a.   0.19   b.   0.391   c.   0.001

d.   0.019   e.   0.3   f.   0.524

1-128.   Jerome works at the Fraction Factory in the department that changes decimals into fractions. He has just received an order to rewrite $0.\overline{73}$ as a fraction. He started to rewrite it as $\frac{73}{100}$, but he is not sure that he is correct. Is $\frac{73}{100}$ equal to $0.\overline{73}$? Be ready to **justify** your answer.

1-129.   Katrina is now responsible for finding the decimal equivalent for each of the numbers below. She thinks these fractions have something to do with the decimals and fractions in problem 1-127, but she is not sure.

Get a set of the fractions in parts (a) through (f) below on cards from your teacher, and use your calculator to change each fraction into a decimal. Add the decimal information to the card. Can you find a pattern?

a. $\frac{19}{99}$ b. $\frac{391}{999}$ c. $\frac{3}{9}$

d. $\frac{1}{999}$ e. $\frac{524}{999}$ f. $\frac{19}{999}$

g.   What connections do these fractions have with those you found in problem 1-127? Be ready to share your observations with the class.

h.   Use your pattern to predict the fraction equivalent for $0.\overline{24}$. Then test your guess with a calculator.

i.   Use your pattern to predict the decimal equivalent for $\frac{65}{99}$. Check your answer with your calculator.

1-130.   REWRITING REPEATING DECIMALS AS FRACTIONS

Jerome wants to figure out why his pattern from problem 1-129 works. He noticed that he could eliminate the repeating digits by subtracting, as he did in the work at right. This gave him an idea. *"What if I multiply by something before I subtract, so that I'm left with more than zero?"* he wondered. He wrote:

$$0.\overline{73} = 0.737373....$$
$$-0.\overline{73} = 0.737373....$$
$$0 = 0$$

$$10(0.\overline{73}) = 7.373737...$$
$$- (0.\overline{73}) = 0.737373...$$

"The repeating decimals do not make zero in this problem. But if I multiply by 100 instead, I think it will work!" He tried again:

$$100(0.\overline{73}) = 73.737373...$$
$$- 0.\overline{73} = 0.737373....$$
$$99(0.\overline{73}) = 73.0$$

a.   Discuss Jerome's work with your team. How did he get 99 sets of $0.\overline{73}$? What happened to the repeating decimals when he subtracted?

b.   *"I know that 99 sets of $0.\overline{73}$ are equal to 73 from my equation,"* Jerome said. *"So to find what just one set of $0.\overline{73}$ is equal to, I will need to divide 73 into 99 equal parts."* Represent Jerome's idea as a fraction.

c.   Use Jerome's **strategy** to rewrite $0.\overline{85}$ as a fraction. Be prepared to explain your **reasoning**.

1-131.   DESIGN A DECIMAL DEPARTMENT

Congratulations! Because of your new skills rewriting fractions and decimals, you have been put in charge of the Designer Decimals Department of the Fraction Factory. People write to your department and order their favorite fractions rewritten as beautiful decimals.

Recently, your department has received some strange orders. Review each order below and decide if you can complete it. If possible, find the new fraction or decimal. If not, write to the customer explaining why their order cannot be completed.

Order 1:   "Please send me $0.4\overline{3}$ written as a fraction."

Order 2:   "I'd like a terminating decimal to represent $\frac{44}{99}$."

Order 3:   "Could you send me 0.208 as two different fractions, one with 125 in the denominator and one with 3000 in the denominator?"

1-132.   **Additional Challenge:**
A strange order has arrived in the Designer Decimals Department, asking for a new kind of decimal to be written as a fraction. The order is reprinted at right. With your team, rewrite the decimal as an equivalent fraction or explain why you cannot.

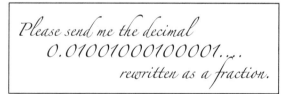

Please send me the decimal 0.01001000100001... rewritten as a fraction.

1-133.   Which of the following fractions are repeating decimals and which are terminating? Show how you made your decisions.

a. $\frac{2}{15}$ b. $\frac{11}{20}$ c. $\frac{17}{40}$ d. $\frac{1}{12}$

1-134.   Copy the Portions Webs below and fill in the missing parts.

a.

Portions Web

b.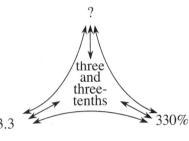

Portions Web

1-135.   Find the perimeter and area of the given shape.

1-136.   Copy the graphs below onto your paper. Then complete the scale by labeling the remaining tick marks.

a.

b.

c.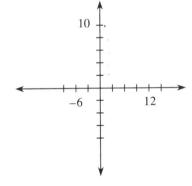

1-137.   About three out of every 25 Americans live in California. About three out of every 50 Americans live in New York, and about two out of every 25 Americans live in Texas.

a.   Which state has the largest population?

b.   Which state has the smallest population?

c.   About what percentage of Americans do *not* live in California, New York, or Texas?

Chapter 1 Closure What have I learned?

Reflection and Synthesis

The activities below offer you a chance to reflect about what you have learned during this chapter. As you work, look for concepts that you feel very comfortable with, ideas that you would like to learn more about, and topics you need more help with. Look for connections between ideas as well as connections with material you learned previously.

①   SUMMARIZING MY UNDERSTANDING

This section gives you an opportunity to show what you know about certain math topics or ideas.

Fraction, Decimal, Percent Pamphlet

You have been using fractions, decimals, and percents to write probabilities and portions, and to compare different numbers. You have seen that rewriting numbers in different forms can make it easier to compare them (for example, rewriting fractions with common denominators or percents can make it easier to decide which is greater). Now you will create a pamphlet explaining to others how fractions, decimals, and percents are related to each other and how to rewrite them in the other forms.

Set up the pamphlet: Follow your teacher's directions for folding a piece of paper to make a pamphlet. Your teacher may give you a Chapter 1 Closure GO Resource Page (pictured at right) to use. (GO is short for Graphic Organizer.)

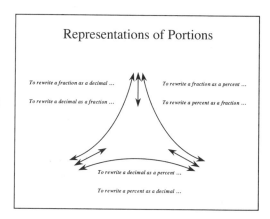

Examples to show what you know: Your teacher will help you choose one fraction, one decimal, and one percent for your explanations. Review how to rewrite numbers using your Toolkit, textbook and other classroom resources. Then, write each example number in each of the other representations. Use words, pictures, and color to show connections between the representations.

Explain your thinking: Write a **general** explanation for how to change from one representation to another.

                              Making Connections: Course 2

②   WHAT HAVE I LEARNED?

Working the problems in this section will help you to evaluate which types of problems you feel comfortable with and which ones you need more help with. This section will appear at the end of every chapter to help you check your understanding.

Solve each problem as completely as you can. The table at the end of this closure section has answers to these problems. It also tells you where you can find additional help and practice on problems like them.

CL 1-138. Make three new fractions that are equivalent to $\frac{6}{24}$. Show your work.

CL 1-139. Aiden is drawing coins from a bag containing 6 pennies, 3 nickels, 4 dimes, and 2 quarters. What is the probability that he will draw a penny?

CL 1-140. Tuan is playing a game, but the spinner is incomplete. If the numbers in the sections of the spinner represent the probabilities of spinning each section, help him figure out the fraction for the missing section of the spinner.

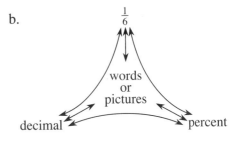

CL 1-141. Complete each portion web.

a.

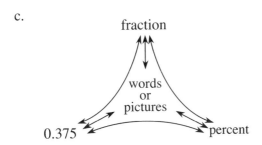

fraction

words or pictures

decimal   40%

b.

$\frac{1}{6}$

words or pictures

decimal   percent

c.

fraction

words or pictures

0.375   percent

CL 1-142. Add $\frac{1}{6} + \frac{1}{2}$. Show all of your steps.

CL 1-143. Find the perimeter and area of each figure below.

a.

b.

c.

15 cm

8 cm

d. Sketch at least one way to rearrange the tiles in part (a) so that the shape has a larger perimeter.

CL 1-144. Cheryl's parents and her older brother all have cell phones. Cheryl would like her own phone, so she surveyed her friends to see how many cell phones were in each of their homes. Here are her results: 3, 1, 7, 1, 1, 4, 2, 5, 3, 2, 6, 4, 1, 2, 3. Find the mean, median, and mode for the data. Can Cheryl use the results of her survey to convince her parents that she should have a cell phone?

CL 1-145. Kimberly is playing "Guess My Number." Her clue is, *"When I triple my number and subtract 7, I get 83."* Find Kimberly's number and explain how you know your answer is correct.

CL 1-146. For each of the problems above, do the following:

- Draw a bar or number line that represents 0 to 10.

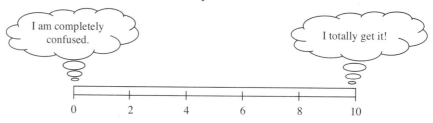

- Color or shade in a portion of the bar that represents your level of understanding and comfort with completing that problem on your own.

If any of your bars are less than a 5, choose *one* of those problems and complete one of the following tasks:

- Write two questions that you would like to ask about that problem.
- Brainstorm two things that you DO know about that type of problem.

If all of your bars are a 5 or above, choose *one* of those problems and do one of these tasks:

- Write two questions you might ask or hints you might give to a student who was stuck on the problem.
- Make a new problem that is similar and more challenging than that problem and solve it.

Making Connections: Course 2

③   WHAT TOOLS CAN I USE?

You have several tools and references available to help support your learning – your teacher, your study team, your math book, and your Toolkit, to name only a few. At the end of each chapter you will have an opportunity to review your Toolkit for completeness as well as to revise or update it to better reflect your current understanding of big ideas.

The main elements of your Toolkit should be your Learning Log, Math Notes, and the vocabulary used in this chapter. Math words that are new to this chapter appear in bold in the text. Refer to the lists provided below and follow your teacher's instructions to revise your Toolkit, which will help make it a useful reference for you as you complete this chapter and prepare to begin the next one.

Learning Log Entries

- Lesson 1.2.3 – Comparing Probabilities
- Lesson 1.2.5 – Adding Fractions with Unlike Denominators

Math Notes

- Lesson 1.1.2 – Perimeter and Area
- Lesson 1.1.3 – Mean
- Lesson 1.1.4 – Median and Mode
- Lesson 1.1.5 – Representations of Portions
- Lesson 1.2.1 – Probability
- Lesson 1.2.2 – Probability: Vocabulary and Definitions
- Lesson 1.2.3 – Additive and Multiplicative Identities
- Lesson 1.2.4 – Equivalent Fractions
- Lesson 1.2.5 – Scaling a Graph
- Lesson 1.3.1 – Fraction ↔ Decimal ↔ Percent

Mathematical Vocabulary

The following is a list of vocabulary found in this chapter. Make sure that you are familiar with the terms below and know what they mean. For words you do not know, refer to the glossary or index. You might also want to add these words to your Toolkit for a way to reference them in the future.

area	equivalent fractions	experimental probability
histogram	mean	median
mode	outcome	percent
perimeter	prime number	probability
repeating decimal	terminating decimal	theoretical probability

Process Words

These words describe problem solving strategies and processes that you have been involved in as you worked in Chapter 1. Make sure you know what each of these words means. If you are not sure, you can talk with your teacher or other students or look through your book for problems in which you were asked to do these things.

brainstorm	choose a strategy	describe
generalize	justify	predict
reason and justify	represent	reverse your thinking
visualize		

Answers and Support for Closure Activity #2
What Have I Learned?

Problem	Solution	Need Help?	More Practice
CL 1-138.	Possible answers include: $\frac{1}{4}, \frac{2}{8}, \frac{3}{12}, \frac{4}{16}, \frac{8}{32}, \frac{12}{48}$	Lessons 1.2.2 and 1.2.3	Problems 1-67, 1-70, 1-93, and 1-108
CL 1-139.	$\frac{6}{15}$ or $\frac{2}{5}$	Lesson 1.2.1 Math Notes boxes in Lessons 1.2.1 and 1.2.2	Problems 1-44, 1-47, 1-58, 1-80, and 1-83
CL 1-140.	$\frac{3}{10}$	Lessons 1.2.4 and 1.2.5 Math Notes box in Lesson1.2.4 Learning Log (problem 1-107)	Problems 1-81, 1-82, 1-103, 1-105, and 1-122
CL 1-141.	a. Two fifths, 0.4, 40% b. One sixth, $0.1\overline{6}$, 16.67% c. Three eighths, 0.375, 37.5%	Lessons 1.1.5, 1.2.3, 1.3.1, and 1.3.2 Math Notes box in Lesson 1.3.1	Problems 1-35, 1-37, 1-38, 1-48, 1-62, 1-78, 1-92, 1-121, 1-126, and 1-134
CL 1-142.	$\frac{8}{12}, \frac{4}{6}$, or $\frac{2}{3}$	Lesson 1.2.4 Math Notes boxes in Lessons 1.2.3 and 1.2.4 Learning Log (problem 1-107)	Problems 1-84 through 1-89, 1-100, and 1-110

Problem	Solution	Need Help?	More Practice

CL 1-143.	a. Perimeter: 14 units
	   Area: 8 square units
	
	b. Perimeter: 18 units
	   Area: 20 square units
	
	c. Perimeter: 46 cm
	   Area: 120 cm
	
	d. Possible arrangement:
	
		Lesson 1.1.2
		
		Math Notes box
		in Lesson 1.1.2
			Problems 1-10,
			1-12, 1-19,
			1-39, and 1-135

CL 1-144.	Mean 3, median 3, mode 1; Cheryl probably cannot use her data to convince her parents because none is 4 or more.	Lessons 1.1.3 and 1.1.4 Math Notes boxes in Lessons 1.1.3 and 1.1.4	Problems 1-18, 1-26, 1-40, and 1-98
CL 1-145.	Kimberly's number is 30. $30 \cdot 3 - 7 = 83$	Lesson 1.1.3	Problems 1-15, 1-16, 1-17, 1-66, and 1-76,

Puzzle Investigator Problems

Dear Students,

Puzzle Investigator Problems (PIs) present you with an opportunity to investigate complex, interesting problems over several days. Their purpose is to focus on the process of solving complex problems. **You will be evaluated on your ability to show, explain, and justify your work and thoughts.** Save **all** of your work, including what does not work, in order to write about the processes you used to reach your answer.

Completion of a PI problem includes four parts:

- **Problem Statement:** State the problem clearly in your own words so that anyone reading your paper will understand the problem you intend to solve.

- **Process and Solutions:** Describe in detail your thinking and **reasoning** as you work from start to finish. Explain your solution and how you know it is correct. Add diagrams when it helps your explanation. Include what you do that does not work and changes you make along the way. If you do not complete this problem, describe what you <u>do</u> know and where and why you are stuck.

- **Reflection:** Reflect about your learning and your reaction to the problem. What mathematics did you learn from it? What did you learn about your math problem solving **strategies**? Is this problem similar to any other problems you have done before? If yes, how?

- **Attached work:** Include <u>all</u> your work and notes. Your scratch work is important because it is a record of your thinking. Do not throw anything away.

PI-1.   SQUARES GALORE

How many squares do you see at right? Can you identify more than 4 squares? How can we know when we have found all the squares? The puzzles below will help you investigate these questions.

a.   How many squares can you find on an 8×8 checkerboard, like the one shown at right? (By the way, there are more than 65 squares.) Organize your work so that you can find patterns that help you to determine how many 1×1 squares, 2×2 squares, and so on, that you can find.

Problem continues on next page. →

PI-1. *Problem continued from previous page.*

    b.   Use your patterns from part (a) to figure out how many squares would be in a design made with square tiles if it is 30 tiles wide and 30 tiles long. Can you do this without drawing a diagram?

    c.   Is there a square made up of square tiles (like the checkerboard) that has only 75 squares overall? What about one that has 120 squares overall? If it is possible, show the square design and explain how you found it. If it is not possible, explain why that design cannot exist.

PI-2.   TOOTHPICK CHALLENGES

This challenge will require you to **visualize** new shapes that can be made from the toothpick designs below. Keep in mind that for no puzzle should you have toothpicks that overlap or "cross" each other. To help you solve the challenges below, you may want to get toothpicks and use them to build models.

    a.   The design at right is made with 16 toothpicks.

          i.   Move only 2 toothpicks so that the result has only 4 congruent (identical) squares.

          ii. Starting with the original design, move 2 toothpicks so that the design has a total of 6 squares. Note: The squares do not need to have the same area.

          iii. Starting with the original design, which 2 toothpicks could you move so that 5 squares of the same size remain? Is there more than one way to do this?

    b.   This time, 9 toothpicks are used to make 4 equilateral triangles at right.

          i.   Move only 2 toothpicks so that the result has only 3 equilateral triangles.

          ii. Starting with the original design, move only 5 toothpicks so that the result has 3 equilateral triangles.

Transformations and Area

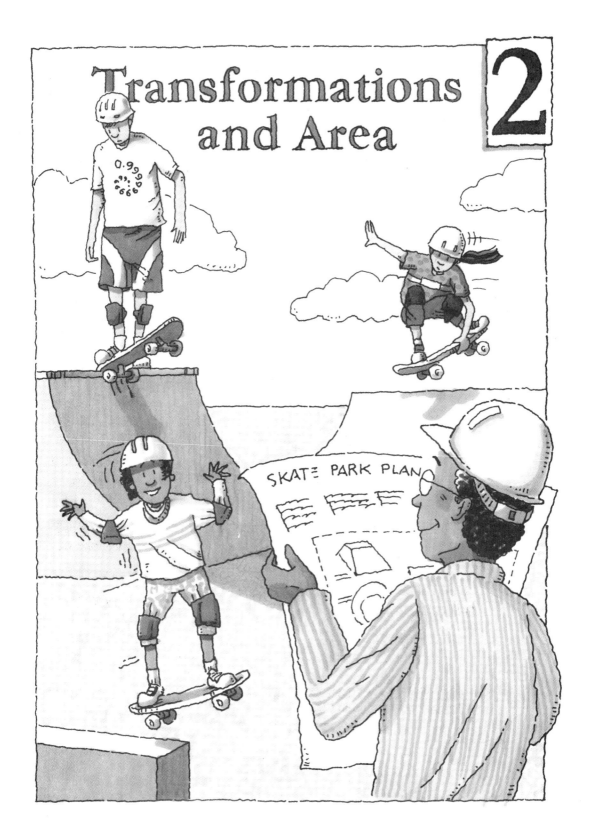

CHAPTER 2   Transformations and Area

While you may not think about how you move objects in daily life, such movements involve changing directions, much like placing a piece in a jigsaw puzzle. In Sections 2.1 and 2.2 you will investigate different kinds of motion on a number line and on a graph. You will begin by describing how a point moves on a number line using addition and subtraction of integers. You will also learn how to give directions to slide, flip, turn, and stretch flat shapes on a coordinate grid and show where the shapes will be after a series of moves.

Section 2.3 focuses on the question, *"How can we use what we know about the area of basic shapes to find the area of complex shapes?"* As you develop new **strategies** for finding the area of shapes, you will be able to solve new problems involving areas of a park.

Guiding Questions

Think about these questions throughout this chapter:

How can I visualize it?

How can I describe the motion?

How can I transform it?

How can I break it into smaller pieces?

How can I rearrange the shape?

In this chapter, you will learn how to:

➢ Connect addition and subtraction of integers to movement along a number line.

➢ Transform shapes by flipping, turning, and sliding them on a coordinate grid.

➢ Describe movement on a graph using coordinates and expressions.

➢ Find the area of shapes, including rectangles, triangles, parallelograms, and trapezoids.

➢ Break complex shapes into smaller pieces in order to find area.

Chapter Outline

Section 2.1   You will describe motion on a number line using integers and will learn how addition and subtraction can help you predict the starting or ending point of a series of moves.

Section 2.2   You will use a technology tool to move a shape on a coordinate grid using slides, flips, and turns, and will use integers to describe those moves.

Section 2.3   You will find the area of different shapes such as parallelograms, triangles, and trapezoids by rearranging them into rectangles.

2.1.1 How does it move?

. . . .

Adding Positive and Negative Numbers

In Chapter 1, you learned about the famous frog-jumping contest that takes place each spring in Calaveras County, California. In the contest, the final measure represents the distance the frog moves away from a starting pad after three separate hops. The three hops can be different lengths and go in different directions.

In this section you will solve problems that involve distances and directions with diagrams and numbers.

2-1.   GETTING THERE

Elliott has been watching Dr. Frog take practice jumps all day. The frog keeps landing 15 feet from the starting pad after making three hops. Answer the questions below to consider ways that the frog can travel 15 feet in three hops.

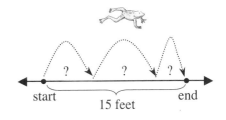

- How many combinations of hops can you find to move Dr. Frog 15 feet from where he started? Show your work with pictures, words, numbers, or symbols.

- Can the frog move 15 feet in three equal hops?

- If two of the frog's hops are 10 feet long, how could you describe the third hop? Is there more than one possibility?

2-2.   Elliott is so interested in the frogs that he is
        developing a video game about them. In his
        game frogs start on a number line like the one
        below. The frogs can hop to the left and to the
        right.

        One game starts with the frog sitting at the
        number 3 on the number line. Use your
        Lesson 2.1.1 Resource Page to help you
        answer Elliott's challenges below.

   a.   If the frog hops to the right 4 units, to the left 7 units, and then to the right
        6 units, where will the frog end up?

   b.   If the frog makes three hops to the right and lands on 10, list the lengths of
        two possible combinations of hops that will get it from 3 to 10.

   c.   Could the frog land on a positive number if it makes three hops to the left?
        Use an example to show your thinking.

   d.   **Additional Challenge:** The frog made two hops of the same length to the
        right and then hopped 6 units to the left. If the frog ended up at 11 on the
        number line, how long were the first two hops?

2-3.   While designing his videogame, Elliott decided to replace some of his long
        sentences describing hops with symbols. For example, to represent where the
        frog traveled and landed in part (a) of problem 2-2, he wrote:

$$3 + 4 + (-7) + 6$$

   a.   How does Elliott's expression represent the words in part (a) of
        problem 2-2? Where did the 3 come from? Why is one number negative?

   b.   If another set of hops was represented by $5 + (-10) + 2 + 1$, describe the
        frog's movements. Where did the frog start, and where did it end up?

   c.   One game used the expression $-5 + 7$. Where does the frog start? Where
        does it end up?

   d.   Another game had a frog start at 12, hop 5 units to the left, 6 units to the
        right, and 9 units to the left. Write an expression to represent the frog's
        motion on the number line. Where did the frog end up?

2-4.   Another frog starts at –3 and hops four times.
        Its hops are listed at right.

Hop Lengths

Right 2 units
Left 7 units
Right 10 units
Left 3 units

   a.   Is it possible for the frog to finish at 2 on the
        number line? Explain.

   b.   If you have not done so already, write an expression (sum) for the frog's
        movements. Where does the frog end up?

   c.   Will the frog land in a different place if it makes its hops in a different
        order? In other words, does it matter which hop the frog takes first,
        second, etc.?

   d.   Kamille says that for the frog to end up at –1, she can ignore the last three
        hops in the list. She says she only needs to move the frog to the right
        2 units. Is she correct? Why?

2-5.   When adding, the order in which the numbers are added does not matter. That
        means that you will get the same answer if you add $2+5$ or if you add $5+2$.
        This property is called the **Commutative Property of Addition**. Read the
        Math Notes box for this lesson and answer the questions below.

   a.   Why does $2+5=5+2$? Use your number line to explain.

   b.   Does the Commutative Property work with negative numbers? Use a
        number line to verify that $-3+10=10+(-3)$.

   c.   Use the Commutative Property to rewrite the expression $6+4+(-3)$ in two
        different ways. Use a number line to show that they all have the same
        value.

2-6.   In part (d) of problem 2-4, Kamille noticed that she could group some of the numbers together first before finding the entire sum. When she grouped the last three hops, she actually calculated the expression $-3 + 2 + (-7 + 10 + (-3))$.

She wonders, "*When adding, will grouping the terms in different ways affect the sum?*"

a.   The expressions below use the same numbers that are grouped differently. Find the sums. Use a number line if it will help. Do you get the same answers?

   i. $5 + (4 + (-1))$ ii. $(5 + 4) + (-1)$

b.   In an addition problem, the numbers that are added can be grouped together in different ways and the sums will be the same. This is called the **Associative Property of Addition**. The Math Notes box for this lesson has information about this property.

Show that $(-2 + 6) + 9 = -2 + (6 + 9)$.

METHODS AND MEANINGS

MATH NOTES

Commutative and Associative Properties of Addition

When two numbers are combined together using addition, changing the order in which they are added does not matte, so $5 + 7 = 7 + 5$. This fact is known as the **Commutative Property of Addition**. This result is generalized using variables as:

$$a + b = b + a$$

Note that subtraction does not satisfy the Commutative Property of Addition since $7 - 5 \neq 5 - 7$.

The **Associative Property of Addition** states that changing the grouping of the numbers does not change the result of the addition. The answer to the problem $(7 + 5) + 9$ is the same as $7 + (5 + 9)$. This is generalized using variables as:

$$(a + b) + c = a + (b + c)$$

Note that subtraction is not associative since $(7 - 5) - 1 \neq 7 - (5 - 1)$.

$$2 - 1 \neq 7 - 4$$

Making Connections: Course 2

2-7.   Lucas' frog is sitting at –2 on the number line.

   a.   His frog hops 4 units to the right, 6 units to the left, and then 10 more units
        to the right. Write an expression (sum) to represent his frog's movement.

   b.   Where does the frog land?

2-8.   Nathan wants you to solve this puzzle: *"I am thinking of a
        number. If you divide my number by three and add –3, you
        will get 4. What is my number?"* Show all of your work.

2-9.   Simplify the following expressions.

   a. $\frac{2}{3} - \frac{1}{6}$ b. $\frac{7}{10} - \frac{1}{5}$ c. $\frac{1}{2} - \frac{3}{4}$

2-10.   One of the topics you will review in
        Chapter 2 is reading graphs. Look at the
        graph at right. This graph shows positive and
        negative values on both axes and it divides
        the plane into four parts, or quadrants. It is
        called a **four-quadrant** graph.

   a.   The coordinates (the *x*- and *y*-values)
        for point *A* are $(-3, 5)$. Explain how
        these numbers tell you the position
        of point *A* using the graph.

   b.   Name the coordinates (x, y) for points *B* and *C*.

   c.   If Samantha moved point *A* 9 units down and 6 units to the right, at what
        point would she end up?

2-11.   Rewrite the following fractions as decimals and decide if they are terminating or
        repeating decimals. Show your work and explain how you made your decision.

   a. $\frac{7}{8}$ b. $\frac{2}{9}$ c. $\frac{4}{7}$ d. $\frac{11}{22}$

2-12.   Copy the sequences and fill in the missing numbers. Explain the pattern in words.

   a.   5, 14, 23, 32, 41, ___, ___, ___

   b.   3, 6, 12, 24, 48, ___, ___, ___

2.1.2 How can I record it?

Adding and Subtracting Integers

Mathematical symbols and expressions are like shorthand. Instead of writing "The sum of positive four and positive seven and negative two," we can write $4 + 7 + (-2)$. These symbols give information about how the numbers are related and can also be used to describe real-life situations.

In this lesson you will use movement on a number line to make sense of expressions involving addition and subtraction.

2-13.   Before you find each sum below, predict whether the answer will be positive, negative, or zero. Then draw a number line on your paper and use it to find the sum. Be ready to share your **strategy**.

   a. $-2 + (-9)$ b. $5 + (-5)$ c. $4 + (-7)$ d. $-6 + 2$

2-14.   Emre is looking at the expression $4 + (-7)$, which his teammate wrote to represent starting at 4 and moving seven units to the left. *"I can also show addition with + and − symbols."* He made the diagram below.

   a.   Why do you think Emre placed four + symbols where he did?

   b.   What do the − symbols represent?

   c.   How does Emre's diagram show that the sum is −3?

   d.   Use the idea of frog hopping to explain why the tiles at right add up to zero.

Making Connections: Course 2

2-15.   Emre's diagram for $-5 + 9 + (-1)$ is shown below.

a.   Copy his diagram on your paper and describe the motion it represents in words.

b.   Circle any "**zeros**" (+ and – symbols that add up to zero). What is left?

c.   What is the sum of $-5 + 9 + (-1)$?

d.   What if the + and – symbols are not on the number line? What if Emre organized the symbols in separate rows, like those shown at right? Does the sum change?

2-16.   Your teacher will give you tiles to represent + and – symbols to use to build expressions. For each part below:

   •   Build the expressions with tiles and find the sum.

   •   **Visualize** the frog hopping on a number line to confirm your answer.

   •   Record your work by drawing the + and – symbols and circling zeros.

a. $6 + (-5) + 2$ b. $-8 + 8 + (-2)$ c. $-7 + (-2)$

2-17.   What if you do not have enough tiles and your number line is not long enough? Without using tiles, add the numbers in each part below. Explain your **strategy**.

a. $32 + (-38)$ b. $-150 + (-50)$ c. $-41 + 28$

2-18.   SUBTRACTION

What is the connection between adding negative numbers and subtraction? Use + and – tiles from your teacher to answer the questions below.

a.   Build $8 + (-2)$ with tiles. Draw a picture on your paper. What is the sum?

b.   How could you use the tiles to simplify $8 - 2$? Talk about this with your team and find the answer. Draw a picture to show your **strategy**.

c.   Compare your answers to parts (a) and (b) above. Explain why they give the same answer.

d.   How could you use a number line to figure out $8 - 2$? Draw a number line on your paper. Be ready to share your ideas with the class.

2-19.   For each part below, simplify the expression using tiles or a number line. If one **strategy** does not work, try a different **strategy**. Be sure to draw a diagram to show your work.

a. $9 - 8$ b. $7 - 11$ c. $-5 - (-2)$ d. $0 - 6$

2-20.   MAKING CONNECTIONS

One way to use + and – tiles to show that $-5 - (-2) = -3$ is shown at right.

a.   Now think about this problem on a number line. How could you start at –5 and make one "hop" to end up on –3? Which direction do you move? How far do you travel?

b.   The symbol "–" can be read aloud as *subtract* or *negative*. But sometimes it makes more sense to translate it as *opposite*. For example, $-5 - (-2)$ can be read as, "Start at –5 and move the *opposite* direction of -2, so move the opposite direction of 'to the left 2'."

Use this idea to help you figure out $4 - (-6)$ on a number line.

c.   Now use + and – tiles to simplify $-10 - (-6)$. Draw a diagram to show this on your paper.

d.   How can you use a number line to simplify $-10 - (-6)$? Show how you get your final answer on a number line.

2-21.   Lani is stuck. She wants to use + and – tiles to simplify $7 - (-2)$. She has 7 + tiles. *"I don't have any negative tiles to take away!"*

a.   Her friend, Carla, told her to try using the tiles at right. Explain why she can use the tiles at right to represent 7.

b.   Use Carla's idea to simplify $7 - (-2)$.

c.   Did subtracting a negative number make the answer larger or smaller? Explain.

2-22.   Find the missing value in each number sentence below.

   a. $-5+3+(-7) =$ ___   b. $4-2-(-3) =$ ___   c. $15+(-30) =$ __

   d. $8 +$ ___ $= 0$ e. $-3-4 = -2 +$ ___   f. $-10 -$ ___ $= 15$

   g. $-22+40 =$ ___   h. $25-75+(-10) =$ ___

   i. $16+5+(-30)-(-5) =$ ___

2-23.   Olivia drew number line diagrams to help her solve several integer problems.
         For each of the problems below, compare her picture to the expression and
         answer these questions:

   •   How does her number line represent the problem?

   •   How is her picture helpful for evaluating the expression? That is, why
        did she stop at zero in parts (a), (b), and (c)?

   •   What other expression(s) could you write to represent her picture?

   a. $5+(-6)$ b. $3-5$

   c. $-7+9$ d. $8+(-6)$

2-24.   Write two different expressions to represent each picture below.

   a.   b.

2-25.   LEARNING LOG

         The symbol for minus ("$-$") can be translated into words
         as *subtract*, *take away*, *negative*, or *opposite*. In your
         Learning Log, explain how you think of this symbol when
         adding and subtracting on a number line. Explain how you
         think of it when you use + and $-$ tiles. Give examples.
         Label this entry "Meanings for $-$" and today's date.

2-26.   Find the missing value in each number sentence.

   a. $4 + (-3) + 3 - 1 = $ ____   b. $-2 - (-4) + 4 = $ ____   c. $5 - $ ___ $= 7$

2-27.   Find the measure indicated in each question below.

   a.   Find the perimeter.   b.   Find the area.

   c.   Find the area and perimeter
         of the rectangle at right.

   2 inches / 8 inches

2-28.   Marguerite wants to convince her parents to raise her monthly allowance. She
         decided to take a quick poll of her five best friends to see what they receive for
         their allowance. Here are the results:

Friend	Allowance
Kari	no allowance
Wanda	$25
Gary	$100
Donna	$20
Jorge	$20

   a.   Calculate the mean, median, and mode for her friends' allowances.

   b.   Her current allowance is $30.00. Which measure of central tendency
         should she use to get her allowance increased? Why?

2-29.   Look at the two units of measure at right.

   a.   Which of them would you use to measure the top
         surface of your desk? Explain your thinking.

   b.   What part(s) of your desk could you measure using the linear unit? Draw a
         picture and show how that unit could be used.

2-30.   In parts (a) and (b) below, copy the number lines and use them to show the solution to the problems.

a.

b.

$5 + (-2)$

$2 - (-1)$

c.   Show $-3 + 4 + (-1)$ on a number line.

d.   Rachel said that $-4 + (-3)$ will be positive because two negatives always give a positive. Draw the problem on a number line, then explain whether you agree or disagree with Rachel.

2-31.   State which direction you should move on a number line from -5 in each expression below. Then simplify each expression.

a. $-5 + (-4)$ b. $-5 - 8$ c. $-5 - (-6)$

2-32.   One of the topics you will soon review in Section 2.2 is graphing shapes. The graph at right is called a **first quadrant graph**. It uses two number lines that only show positive numbers and zero.

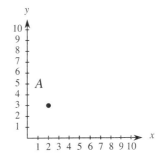

a.   Carefully copy the **axes** (the number lines) and point A on a piece of graph paper.

b.   Plot the points listed below. Then connect them in the order given. Point A is given for you.

$A\ (2,3)$, $B\ (3,7)$, $C\ (7,7)$, $D\ (8,3)$ Then connect D to A.

c.   What is the name of the shape that you drew?

2-33.   Evan's uncle gave him money for his birthday.

a.   Evan plans to put half of the money in his savings account, spend $\frac{1}{5}$ of the money on bubble gum to share with his friends, and buy comic books with the money he has left. What portion of the money will he spend on comic books?

b.   Evan uses some of his comic book money to buy a magazine for \$4. If Evan's uncle gave him \$30, what fraction of this money did he spend on the magazine?

2-34.   Look carefully at the key at right. Which of the keys below could you create by spinning (rotating) the original key? Which keys could you create by flipping (reflecting) the original key?

original

a.   b.   c.   d.

2.1.3   How can I predict the result?

More Integer Operations

So far in this chapter, you have made connections between moving left and right on a number line and integer expressions. Today you will use a technology tool to check your understanding and describe patterns in your results. By the end of this lesson, you should be prepared to answer these target questions:

How can I decide if the frog will hop to the right or to the left?

Why does subtracting a negative number make the original number greater?

How can I tell if the answer will be positive or negative?

2-35.   HOP TO IT

You have learned about how adding and subtracting **integers** (positive and negative whole numbers and zero) moves points on a number line. Today you will practice adding and subtracting integers using a game called "Hop To It" that is available at www.cpm.org/students/technology. After you have played for awhile, think about the following questions and be ready to share your responses with the class. You should be able to **justify** your answers.

a.   When you add two negative numbers, will you get a negative or positive answer? Why does this happen?

.b.   If you add a positive number to a negative number, will you get a negative or positive answer? Why does this happen?

c.   When you subtract a negative number, is your answer greater than or less than the number you started with? Why does this happen?

Making Connections: Course 2

2-36.   Simplify each expression. **Visualize** the movement of a frog on a number line and its landing point. You may want to use the number lines on the Lesson 2.1.1 Resource Page to help you.

a. $-1 + 2$

b. $-5 + 3$

c. $-2 - (-4)$

d. $6 - (-3)$

e. $8 - 9$

f. $6 + (-7)$

g. $4 - (-4)$

h. $3 + (-3)$

i. $-4 - 3$

j. $20 + (-18)$

k. $20 - (-18)$

l. $-30 - (-22)$

2-37.   Predict whether each answer below will be positive or negative. You may want to **visualize** a number line or + and – tiles. Then find the answer to check your prediction.

a. $5 - 10$

b. $2 + (-8)$

c. $-5 - (-6)$

d. $15 + (-4)$

2-38.   **Additional Challenge:** Given the hop lengths –8, –5, 2, –3, and –1, can a frog start at 4 on a number line and end up on –2? You do not need to use all of the hop lengths. Can you find more than one way to do this?

2-39.   LEARNING LOG

In your Learning Log, answer the target questions from the beginning of this lesson. The questions are reprinted for you below. Title this entry, "Subtraction of Integers," and include today's date.

How can I decide if the frog will hop to the right or to the left?

Why does subtracting a negative number make the original number greater?

How can I tell if your answer will be positive or negative?

2-40. Simplify the following expressions. Show your work.

a. $8-(-10)$ 　　 b. $-6-9$ 　　 c. $8-3+(-4)$ 　 d. $0-(-3)$

e. $15-20$ 　　 f. $-9+14$ 　　 g. $11+(-7)$ 　 h. $5-9$

2-41. Solve the number puzzles below.

a. If I add 9 to my number, I get 6. What is my number?

b. If I start at –5 on a number line and end up at –8, what direction did I move? How many units did I move?

c. If I moved to the right 8 and moved to the left 8, what can you tell me about my ending position?

2-42. John has a bag of marbles that contains 12 red marbles, 20 green marbles, and 17 blue marbles.

a. If John pulls one marble out of the bag, what is the probability that it will not be red, that is, P(not red)?

b. What is the probability that he will draw a purple marble, that is, P(purple)?

2-43. Copy and complete each of the Portions Webs below.

a.

b.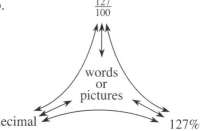

2-44. Find the missing lengths in the problems below. Assume each line segment is subdivided into equal segments. Show your work.

a.

b.

2.2.1 How can I move a shape on a grid?

Rigid Transformations

How can you describe the movement of a figure on a flat surface when it is not moving in a straight line? For example, when you need to move a loose puzzle piece into the puzzle (as shown at right), how can you describe the way its position changes?

Today you will explore mathematical ways of sliding, turning, and flipping an object without changing its size or shape in order to solve challenges. These movements are called **rigid transformations**.

2-45.   KEY IN THE LOCK PUZZLES

Use the transformation buttons (shown at right) with the technology tool "Key-Lock Transformations," to move the key to the keyhole to unlock the door. (The game is available at www.cpm.org/students/technology.)

You will need to tell the computer about how you want the key to move. For example, how far to the left or right and how far up or down do you want the key to slide? Which direction do you want your key to flip?

Your task: For each puzzle, move the key to the keyhole. Remember that to unlock the door, the key must fit exactly into the keyhole and not be upside down! Your key will also not be able to move through walls.

Be sure to record your moves on the Lesson 2.2.1 Resource Page.

Discussion Points

In what direction does the key need to move?

How can we get the key to fit the keyhole?

What information do we need to give the computer so that it moves the key into the lock?

METHODS AND MEANINGS

Adding & Subtracting Integers

Integers are positive and negative whole numbers and zero. One way that integers can be combined is by **adding**, which can be thought of as walking on a number line. If you walk one step left, and then one step back to the right, you end up in the same place as you started. This is represented on the number line as $-1+1=0$. A number and its opposite, like 5 and -5, are called **additive inverses**, and their sum in zero (0).

To **add integers** on a number line, mark the position of the first integer, and then move in the direction of the second integer the number of units indicated. Positive numbers indicate movement to the right, while negative numbers indicate movement to the left. Study the examples below:

Example 1: $-5+(2)$

Example 2: $-6+(-2)$

One method for **subtracting integers** is to use a number line as you did with addition, except that instead of moving in the direction indicated by the second integer, you must move in the opposite direction to "**undo**" that motion. For example, adding -3 would indicate moving to the left on the number line, so **subtracting** -3 would undo that motion, and mean moving to the right on the number line.

Example: $3-(-3)=3+3$

Example: $-2-5=-2+(-5)=-7$

2-46.   Finding patterns is an important problem solving skill used in mathematics. You will use the patterns in Diamond Problems to solve other problems later in the course. Can you discover a pattern for the numbers in each of the four diamonds below?

Copy the Diamond Problems below and use the pattern you discovered to complete each of them.

a.   b.   c.   d.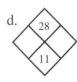

2-47.   Describe what moves you could use to create the transformation of the original image shown at right.

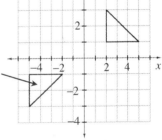

2-48.   Simplify each expression.

    a. $-32 + 10 - (-2)$

    b. $17 + (-50) - 5$ c. $-5 - (-8) - 1$

2-49.   Lisa and Nicole are playing a new version of Toothpicks and Tiles. Instead of showing Nicole a shape so that she has to find the number of toothpicks and the number of tiles, Lisa describes the shape and Nicole has to build it out of tiles.

    Lisa says, *"My shape has 14 tiles and 16 toothpicks."*

    a.   Draw a shape that matches Lisa's description. **Justify** your answer.

    b.   Is there more than one shape that matches this description? If so, sketch a second shape.

2-50.   Thu has a bag with 7 green marbles, 5 blue marbles, and 4 red marbles. For each part below, if the marble selected in replaced before the next marble is drawn, what is the probability that she will draw:

    a.   A red marble?   b.   A red or a green marble?   c.   An orange marble?

2.2.2 How can I move a shape on a grid?

Rigid Transformations on a Coordinate Grid

Have you ever had trouble giving directions? Sometimes describing where something is or how it moved is difficult. For this reason, people often use **coordinate grids**, like the one show at right, to help describe directions by using words like "left" and "down." They can also help you measure distances.

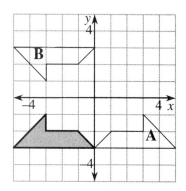

Today you will work with your team to describe movement on a grid. You will also look at ways to describe where an object is on the grid before and after a transformation. As you work, use the questions below to help start math discussions.

Is there a different way to get the same result?

Did we give enough information?

How can we describe the position?

2-51.   While solving the key challenge in Lesson 2.2.1, Rowan made more than one move to change his key from point *A* to point *B* and from point *C* to point *D*, as shown on the graph at right. Both of these keys are shown as triangles on the Lesson 2.2.2 Resource Page.

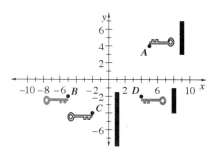

Your task: With your team, describe how Rowan could have moved each key from the starting position to the ending position using slides (also called **translations**), turns (also called **rotations**), and/or flips (also called **reflections**).

- Make sure you provide enough detail to describe the moves completely.

- Try to find more than one way he could have moved each key.

- Be ready to **justify** your ideas with the class.

Making Connections: Course 2

2-52.   WHERE DOES IT LAND?

Felicia found a copy of a puzzle like the one in problem 2-45, but the lock is missing. All she has are the starting points and the moves to unlock the lock. This time her key is shaped like a triangle.

The points are at $A(-5, 0)$, $B(-5, 3)$, and $C(-1, 0)$.

Step 1:   Translate 4 units to the right and 2 units up.

Step 2:   Reflect across the x-axis.

Step 3:   Rotate counter-clockwise 90° about point $(3, -2)$.

Help Felicia find out where the lock is by following her steps. The following questions are designed to help you.

a.   With your team, set up your own coordinate grid on graph paper. The questions below will help. Refer to the Math Notes box at the end of this lesson if your team needs more information about how to set up the graph.

  •   How many **quadrants** (regions) should the graph have? Should it be an "L" graph with only the first quadrant? Or a "T" graph with four quadrants?

  •   How can the **x-axis** (which is horizontal ↔) and **y-axis** (which is vertical ↕) be labeled so we can remember which one is which?

  •   How should the axes be **scaled?** How many units should you use for each side length of a grid square?

b.   Plot triangle *ABC* to represent the key.

c.   Follow Step 1 to translate the triangle. Name the new location of each **vertex**, or corner, of the triangle in the form (x, y).

d.   Complete Step 2. Sketch the triangle in its new position and label the coordinates of each vertex.

e.   Where does her triangle end up? Complete Step 3 on the graph and label the coordinates of each vertex.

2-53.   Could Felicia's team have used different steps to "unlock" her puzzle in problem 2-52? In other words, could she use different moves and still have the key end up in the same final position?

- If it is possible, list a new set of steps that would move her key from the same starting location to the same final position.

- If it is not possible, explain why not.

METHODS AND MEANINGS

Graphing Points on an *xy*-Coordinate Grid

Coordinate axes on a flat surface are formed by drawing vertical and horizontal number lines. The **origin** is the point where the two number lines cross, which is 0 on each axis.

Numerical data can be graphed on a flat surface using **points**. Points on the graph are identified by two numbers in an **ordered pair** written as (x, y). The first number is the *x***-coordinate** of the point and the second number is the *y***-coordinate**.

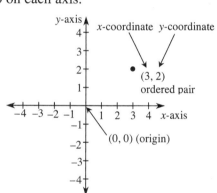

To locate the point $(3, 2)$ on an *xy*-graph, go three units from the origin to the right to mark 3 on the horizontal axis and then, from that point, go 2 units up. To locate the point $(-2, -4)$, go 2 units from the origin to the left to the mark -2 on the horizontal axes and then 4 units down.

Review & Preview

2-54.   Copy these incomplete axes. Label the missing numbers on each number line.

a.   50 — length (cm) — 20 — 0

b.   32 — length (cm) — 0

c.   80 — time (min.) — 0

d.   90 — time (min.) — 0

2-55.   On graph paper draw a coordinate grid with x- and y-axes. Graph shapes A, B, and C as described below.

a.   Shape A is a triangle with vertices $(1,1)$, $(3,3)$, and $(2,4)$.

b.   Shape B is a square with vertices $(2,-1)$, $(4,-1)$, $(2,-3)$, and $(4,-3)$.

c.   Shape C is a rectangle with vertices $(-3,1)$, $(-3,4)$, $(-1,4)$, and $(-1,1)$.

2-56.   On the same grid you used in problem 2-55, slide triangle A four units right and three units up to create triangle D. Write the coordinates of the new vertices.

2-57.   Copy and complete each of the Diamond Problems below. The pattern used in the Diamond Problems is shown at right.

a.   b.   c.   d.

2-58.   After a pizza party, Julia has parts of five pizzas left over. The shaded areas represent the slices that were not eaten. If each pizza was originally cut up into 12 pieces:

pizza A   pizza B   pizza C   pizza D   pizza E

a.   What fraction of pizza A is left?

b.   If all of the pieces were put together, how many whole pizzas could she make? How many extra pieces would she have?

c.   Julia wants to write the amount of pizza left over as a single fraction. How could she do this?

2.2.3 How can I describe it?

Describing Transformations

In Lesson 2.1.2, you used numbers and symbols to describe how a frog moved on a number line. These expressions described the starting place, the motion, and the point where the frog landed. Today, you will write similar expressions to describe transformations on a grid.

2-59. Rosa changed the position of quadrilateral *ABCD* to that of quadrilateral *WXYZ*. "*How did the coordinates of the points change?*" she wondered.

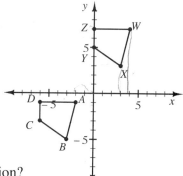

a. Describe how Rosa transformed *ABCD*. Was the shape translated (slid), rotated (turned), or reflected (flipped)? Explain how you know.

b. How far did *ABCD* move? In which direction?

c. Point *B* became point *X*. What are the coordinates of points *B* and *X*? Name them using (x, y) notation.

d. How did the *x*-coordinate of point *B* change? How did its *y*-coordinate change? For each coordinate, write an expression using addition to show the change.

e. **Visualize** translating *WXYZ* 10 units to the right and 12 units up. Where will point *X* end up? *Without counting on the graph*, work with your team to find the new coordinates of point *Y*. Write expressions using addition to show the change.

2-60. Rosa translated a different shape on a grid. Use the clues below to figure out how her shape was moved.

a. The point $(4, 7)$ was translated to $(32, -2)$. Without graphing, describe how the shape moved on the grid.

b. Another point on her original shape was $(-16, 9)$. After the translation, where did this point end up? For each coordinate, write an expression using addition to show the change.

2-61. Rowan transformed triangle *DEF* at right to get triangle *QRS*.

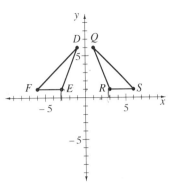

a. Describe how Rowan transformed the triangle. Was the shape translated, rotated, or reflected? Explain how you know.

b. Rowan noticed that the *y*-coordinates of the points did not change. What happened to the *x*-coordinates? Compare the *x*-coordinate of point *D* with the *x*-coordinate of point *Q*. Do the same with points *E* and *R* and with points *F* and *S*. What do you notice?

c. Can you describe the change to all of the *x*-coordinates with addition like you did in problems 2-59 and 2-60? If not, what other operation could you use? Explain.

2-62. What if Rowan reflected triangle *DEF* from problem 2-61 across the *x*-axis (the horizontal axis)? What would happen to the coordinates?

a. First **visualize** how the triangle will reflect across the *x*-axis.

b. Neatly set up a four-quadrant graph on graph paper and plot triangle *DEF* from problem 2-61.

c. Reflect triangle *DEF* across the *x*-axis to get triangle *KLM*.

d. Compare the coordinates of point *D* with point *K*, point *E* with point *L*, and point *F* with point *M*. What do you notice? How can you use multiplication to describe this change?

2-63. In problem 2-61, Rowan noticed that multiplying the *x*-coordinates by –1 reflects the shape across the *y*-axis.

a. Test this **strategy** on a triangle formed by the points $A(-3, 5)$, $B(1, 2)$, and $C(0, 8)$. Before you graph, multiply each *x*-coordinate by –1. What are the new points?

b. Graph your original and new triangle on a new set of axes. Did your triangle get reflected across the *y*-axis?

2-64.   Stella used three steps to move the key on
the graph at right from *A* to *B*. On your
graph paper, draw the key at *A*. (A triangle
can be used to represent the key.) Then
follow the steps Stella wrote below. What
was her last move?

1. *Slide the key to the right 3 units and
up 6 units.*

2. *Reflect the key across the line x = 4.*

3. *???*

2-65.   **Additional Challenge:** Is there a way to use translations to create a reflection
or a rotation? Can reflections be used to move a shape in the same way as a
rotation? To investigate these questions, begin by making a graph like the one
below:

a.   Reflect (flip) the triangle across the *x*-axis.
Then, reflect the new triangle over the
y-axis.

b.   Rotate the original triangle 180° around the
point $(0, 0)$. What you notice?

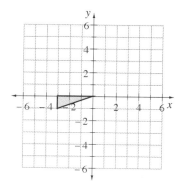

c.   Is there a way to use more than one
reflection step so that at the end, the
triangle looks like it was translated (slid)?
If so, describe the combination of moves
you would use.

2-66.   LEARNING LOG

In your Learning Log, describe what the words *translate*,
rotate, and *reflect* mean in your own words. For each word,
demonstrate the movement with a diagram. Title this entry
"Rigid Transformations" and include today's date.

Ⓜ️ETHODS AND MEANINGS

MATH NOTES

Rigid Transformations

Rigid transformations are ways to move an object while not changing its shape or size, namely: translations (slides), reflections (flips), and rotations (turns). Each movement is described below.

A **translation** slides an object horizontally (side-to-side), vertically (up or down), or both. To translate an object, you must describe which direction you will move it, and how far it will slide. In the example at right, triangle A is translated 4 units to the right and 3 units up.

A **reflection** flips an object across a line (called a **line of reflection**). To reflect an object, you must describe the line the object will flip across. In the example at right, triangle A is reflected across the x-axis.

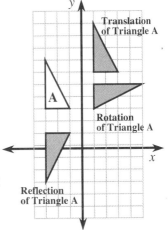

A **rotation** turns an object about a point. To rotate an object, you must choose a point, direction, and angle of rotation. In the example above, triangle A is rotated 90° clockwise (↻) about the origin $(0, 0)$.

2-67. Erin started with one corner of a figure located at $(-4, 5)$ and translated it to end at $(6, 8)$. To find out how far the shape moved horizontally, she decided to find the difference between the two x-coordinates. She wrote: $6 - (-4)$.

a. When Erin simplified $6 - (-4)$ she got 2 as her answer. Is this correct? If not, what is the correct simplification?

b. Write another expression to find out how far the shape moved vertically ($\updownarrow$). Simplify both expressions and describe the translation.

c. Describe each of the translations below.

    i. $(3, -2) \rightarrow (5, -9)$ *ii.* $(-1, 4) \rightarrow (6, -2)$

    iii. $(0, 0) \rightarrow (-4, -7)$ *iv.* $(-2, -9) \rightarrow (2, 9)$

Chapter 2: Transformations and Area

99

2-68.   On grid paper, set up x- and y-axes for a four quadrant graph. Then draw a triangle with vertices at $(1,1)$, $(5,1)$, and $(6,3)$. Label this triangle T.

   a.   Translate (slide) the triangle left 3 units and down 4 units. Label this triangle A and list the vertices.

   b.   Reflect triangle T across the y-axis. Label this triangle B and list the vertices.

   c.   Are triangles T, A, and B congruent (that is, do they have the same shape and size)? Explain.

2-69.   Draw an example of each of the following shapes. Refer to the glossary in the back of the book if you need help.

   a.   rectangle   b.   square   c.   parallelogram

   d.   trapezoid   e.   scalene triangle   f.   right triangle

2-70.   Copy each expression below and simplify it. Be sure to show the steps you use to get the answer.

   a. $\frac{11}{12} - \frac{7}{12}$ b. $\frac{1}{2} + \frac{1}{8} + \frac{3}{4}$ c. $\frac{3}{4} - \frac{1}{6}$

2-71.   Erica is making a quilt like the one shown at right. She is going to give each square to a different person to decorate before she sews them together.

   a.   If she gives people squares at random, what is the probability that she will give her mother a gray square?

   b.   What is the probability that she will give her brother a gray or a black square to decorate?

   c.   What is the area of the white region? What is the perimeter of the white region?

2.2.4 What if I multiply?

Multiplication and Dilation

When an object is translated, rotated or reflected, it stays the same size and shape even though it moves. For this reason, they are called **rigid transformations**. In this lesson you will explore a new transformation that changes how the object looks. As you work today, ask these questions in your team:

> What parts of the shape are changing? What parts stay the same?

> What happens when we multiply by a negative number?

2-72.   PREPARING FOR THE CONTEST

Milo's frog is ready for the frog-jumping contest. If the frog hops three times to the right, and each hop is 5 feet long, then Milo records the jump as $(3)(5) = 15$. This means that the frog ends up 15 feet from its starting position (0 on a number line).

a.   What if each hop is to the left 5 feet? How could Milo change his equation to show this? Discuss this with your team and describe a way to change his equation.

b.   What if the frog hops twice and each hop is 8 feet to the left? Where does the frog end up? How should Milo record the hops?

c.   Milo recorded one set of hops as $(-4)(-2) = 8$. His sister complained, *"Didn't the frog hop to the left?"*

Milo answered, *"No, he did the opposite."* What did he mean? How this is shown in his equation?

2-73.   Describe how Milo's frog hopped based on the expressions below. Assume the frog starts at zero on the number line each time, and that all measurements are in feet. For each part, describe in words how the frog hopped (how far, how many times, and in what direction)? Also find the product, that is, the place the frog lands.

a. $(6)(4)$ b. $(-3)(-7)$ c. $(5)(-1)$ d. $(-1)(5)$

e.   Explain what happens when you multiply a positive number by a negative number. What happens when you multiply a negative number by a negative number?

2-74.   When all of the *x*- or *y*-coordinates of each vertex of a shape are changed by adding or subtracting the same numbers, the shape translates (slides) to a new position on the coordinate grid.

How does the shape change when the *x*- and *y*-coordinates are doubled? Use the directions below to help you answer this question.

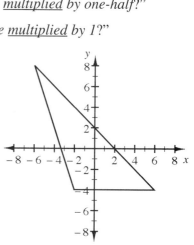

a.   Plot the following points on graph paper: $(2,1)$, $(3,1)$, $(5,5)$, $(2,5)$. Connect the points to make a quadrilateral.

b.   Without graphing, predict how you think the figure would change if the *x*- and *y*-coordinates were multiplied by two and then plotted.

c.   Test your prediction by doubling the coordinates from part (a) and plotting them on your graph paper. Was your prediction correct?

d.   With your team members look at the figure you just graphed. Transforming a graphed shape by multiplying each coordinate by the same number is called a **dilation**. With your team, discuss how this figure compares to the original. Be specific!

2-75.   INVESTIGATING DILATIONS

The students in Ms. Stanley's class were studying what happens to the graph of a shape when each coordinate is multiplied by the same number. They came up with the following questions:

- *"What happens when each coordinate is <u>multiplied</u> by one-half?"*

- *"What changes when the coordinates are <u>multiplied</u> by 1?"*

- *"What happens when the coordinates are all <u>multiplied</u> by –1?"*

a.   Use the shape at right to investigate the questions above. Use graph paper to make the dilations.

b.   How did the figure change in each of the investigations? Explain what your team learned about the three questions you investigated.

Making Connections: Course 2

2-76.   In problem 2-75, you investigated questions about multiplying coordinates that were posed by other students.

a.   With your team, write a different question about the effect of multiplying the coordinates of a shape on a grid. This question might start, *"What happens when you multiply…"*

b.   On graph paper, investigate your question by multiplying the coordinates of the shape in problem 2-75 as you described in your question.

c.   What happened? Write a **conjecture** — that is, an educated guess based on the evidence in the last two problems — to answer your question.

(M)ETHODS AND MEANINGS

MATH NOTES

Mixed Numbers and Fractions Greater Than One

The number $4\frac{1}{3}$ is called a **mixed number** because it is composed of a whole number, 4, and a fraction, $\frac{1}{3}$.

The number $\frac{13}{3}$ is a called a **fraction greater than one** because the numerator is larger than the denominator and so its value is greater than one. (Sometimes such fractions are called *improper fractions* but this is just an historical term. There is nothing wrong with the fraction itself.) The fraction $\frac{13}{3}$ is equal to the mixed number $4\frac{1}{3}$.

Whether to write a number as a mixed number or a fraction greater than one depends on what arithmetic operation(s) you are performing. For some arithmetic operations — especially multiplication and division — you will usually want to use fractions greater than one.

2-77. Louis is dilating triangle *ABC* at right. He multiplied each *x*-coordinate and *y*-coordinate of triangle *ABC* by −2.

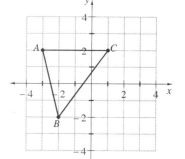

a. What are the new coordinates of the points?

b. Graph Louis' new triangle.

c. Describe how triangle *ABC* changed.

2-78. Linh has a bag of beads that contains 10 glass beads, 7 metal beads, 15 plastic beads, and 3 clay beads. For each part below, if the bead selected is replaced before the next draw, what is the probability that she will pull out a:

a. Metal bead? b. Bead that is not plastic?

c. Glass or plastic bead?

2-79. Gracie loves to talk on the phone, but her parents try to limit the amount of time she talks. They decided to keep a record of the time she spends on the phone each day. For the past nine days the data was: 120, 60, 0, 30, 15, 0, 0, 10, and 20.

a. Find the mean, median, and mode for the information.

b. Which of the three measures in part (a) might give Gracie's parents the most accurate information about her phone use? Why do you think so?

2-80. If the line segment at right is subdivided into equal parts, what is the length of the marked portion of the line?

2-81. Read the Math Notes box for this lesson. Then, rewrite each number below as a single fraction greater than one.

a. $1\frac{1}{11}$ b. $3\frac{2}{5}$ c. $2\frac{4}{15}$

Extension Activity   What can I create?

Using Rigid Transformations

In the last several lessons you have described translations using coordinates, and developed **strategies** for determining where an object started when you know how it was translated and its final position. In this lesson, you will continue to practice transforming objects on a coordinate grid by translating (sliding), rotating (turning), and reflecting (flipping). As you work, **visualize** what each object will look like after the transformation and use the graph to check your prediction.

2-82.   BECOMING AN ARTIST

Have you ever seen directions for drawing a cartoon figure such as a face? Usually these directions start by helping you to put some basic shapes together to form an outline. Then they give you ideas for how to finish the drawing. An example showing how you could draw a dinosaur is at right.

Your task: Obtain Extension Activity Resource Page A from your teacher. On it, you will find shapes A, B, and C provided. Follow the directions below to create a design. Whenever one of the shapes is mentioned below, start with the original shape on the left side of the paper. The final result of each step is part of the outline of the design.

Once you have finished following all of the directions, describe the picture that is formed. Then use the outline to create a cartoon drawing complete with color and other details.

- Draw a rectangle with vertices $(5,0)$, $(9,0)$, $(9,8)$, and $(5,8)$.

- Translate circle A so that its center is at $(7,6)$. Describe how the shape moved.

- Rotate (turn) triangle C 180° clockwise about the point $(-6,3)$. Record the coordinates of the new vertices. Then add 15 to each x-coordinate and graph the final result. What transformation does "adding 15" represent?

- Reflect (flip) triangle B across the y-axis.

Problem continues on next page. →

2-82.   *Problem continued from previous page.*

- A new shape, triangle D, has vertices at $(-7, 13)$, $(-8, 11)$ and $(-6, 11)$. Translate triangle D so that its top vertex is at $(7, 4)$.

- Translate triangle C to the right 11 units. Then reflect the result across the horizontal ($\leftrightarrow$) line that goes through $y = 3$.

- Translate circle A so that the *x*-coordinates increase by 13 units and the *y*-coordinates increase by 11 units.

2-83.   CREATE A DESIGN

Now create your own design using basic shapes A through F on the Extension Activity Resource Page C. Write complete directions at the bottom of your resource page (such as those in problem 2-82) for creating your design. Make sure you provide all the necessary information.

2-84.   **Additional Challenge:**
Visualize a pattern of squares covering a coordinate grid as show at right. What transformations could you make that would move the whole pattern so that the squares and lines in the pattern line up exactly over other squares and lines?

2-85.   Sketch the graph at right on your paper.

a.   Write directions to translate the original triangle to make the new triangle.

b.   What are the coordinates of the vertices (corners) of the new shape?

c.   On your graph, reflect the original triangle over the *y*-axis. What are the coordinates of the new triangle?

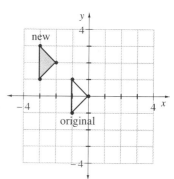

Making Connections: Course 2

2-86.   Copy each Portions Web below and fill in the missing parts.

a.

b.
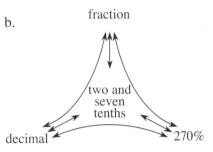

2-87.   Copy and complete each of the Diamond Problems below. The pattern used in the Diamond Problems is shown at right.

a.

b.

c.

d.

2-88.   Craig is practicing his baseball pitching. He kept track of the speed of each of his throws yesterday, and made the histogram at right.

a.   Can you tell the speed of Craig's fastest pitch? Explain.

b.   Between what speeds does Craig usually pitch?

c.   Based on this data, what is the probability that Craig will pitch the ball between 70 and 75 miles per hour?

2-89.   How many different rectangles can you draw with an area of 16 square units? What is the perimeter of each one? Show your work.

2.3.1 How big is the part?

Multiplication of Fractions

You often only need part of something. You might need part of a gallon of gasoline to fill the tank of a scooter, part of a can of paint to finish covering a wall, or part of a piece of paper to complete an assignment.

But what happens when you need a part of a part? Cooks, construction workers, and city planners often need to find part of something that is already a part of something else.

As you work with your team to find parts of parts, be sure to draw diagrams and clearly label all of the pieces in them so that you know what they represent. Think about the following questions:

How can I represent it?

What does each part represent in the situation?

2-90.   PLANNING FOR THE PARK

The city council is trying to decide how to budget for mowing the city park shown in the diagram at right. The park is all grass except for an activity area, picnic area, and basketball court.

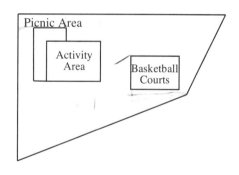

a.   What information does the council need in order to make its decision?

b.   Can you determine how much grass will need to be mowed? Why or why not?

c.   In this section, you will develop new tools that will help you find the area of irregular shapes with portions removed, like this park. At this point, what do you know about finding the area of shapes? Individually reflect about what you know.

Making Connections: Course 2

2-91.   **SKATE PARK**

Someone has given our community money for a
new activity area in the city park that will include
a skate park with a pyramid. The City Council
wants to build the activity area soon, but there are
some limits to the actual design. According to the
donor, $\frac{3}{4}$ of the activity area must be used for the
skate park, and $\frac{1}{3}$ of the skating section should be
reserved for a pyramid.

a.   Use a whole index card to represent the entire activity area. How can you
show the $\frac{3}{4}$ portion that will be the skate park? How can you show that $\frac{1}{3}$
of the skate park region will be a pyramid?

b.   Determine what fraction of the activity area should be reserved for the
pyramid.

c.   Label all parts of the diagram and be prepared to share your thinking with
the class.

2-92.   In the Skate Park problem (2-91), you drew a diagram to represent the situation
in the activity area. The index card represented the whole activity area.

a.   To create her diagram, Dalia divided her index card into four equal
columns. Then, she divided the card into three equal rows in the other
direction and drew lines across the card. Copy her diagram onto your
paper, then:

- Color the fraction *of the activity
  area (card)* that represents the
  skate park with one color.

- Color the fraction *of the skating
  section* that will be the pyramid
  with a new color.

- Determine what fraction of the activity
  area will be covered by the pyramid.

b.   The fraction of the skate park that is reserved for a pyramid can be
represented by the multiplication problem $\frac{1}{3} \cdot \frac{3}{4}$. With your team, discuss
and decide how this expression is related to the diagram you drew using the
index card in problem 2-91 or to Dalia's diagram. Record your conclusions
on your paper.

c.   What is a way to multiply $\frac{1}{3} \cdot \frac{3}{4}$? Does this **strategy** give you the answer
you found in part (b) of problem 2-91?

2-93.   GREATEST GREENSPACE

The mayor of your city has just announced
he will give an award of $1500 to the
neighborhood that can build the largest new
park. As part of the city planning team, you
are in charge of looking at the applications
and choosing the winner.

The two neighborhoods with the best
applications are West Vale and Cozy
Corner. West Vale will build a park that
measures $\frac{3}{5}$ mile by $\frac{1}{2}$ mile. Cozy Corner
has an open space for a park that measures
$\frac{1}{3}$ mile by $\frac{4}{5}$ miles.

a.   Without calculating, predict which park you
      think will be bigger. Why do you think so?

b.   Will either park have an area more than one square mile? Will either have
      an area less than $\frac{1}{2}$ square mile? How do you know?

c.   How can the West Vale Park (that will be $\frac{3}{5}$
      mile by $\frac{1}{2}$ mile) be represented in this 1 square
      mile diagram? Copy the diagram and work
      with your team to represent this park as a
      portion of 1 square mile.

1 mile

d.   What would the area of the West Vale Park be?
      Use your diagram to help you.

e.   Draw the Cozy Corner Park as a portion of 1 square mile and find its area.

f.   Which park is larger? **Justify** your answer.

2-94.   The mayor is donating land to build a new park that is $\frac{2}{3}$ mile on one side by
         $2\frac{1}{2}$ miles on the other.

a.   Draw a picture to represent the park. Label each side length.

b.   Divide the shape into smaller pieces and find the area of each piece.

c.   What will be the total area of the new park (in square miles)?

2-95.   A number, such as $2\frac{1}{2}$, which is composed of a whole number and a fraction, is called a **mixed number** because it has two whole units and $\frac{1}{2}$ of another whole.

   a.   How many halves are in $2\frac{1}{2}$?

   b.   How can you rewrite the fraction $2\frac{1}{2}$ as a single fraction (greater than one) so you can use it in a multiplication problem?

   c.   Write and solve a multiplication problem to represent the park in problem 2-94. Show all work and include a diagram.

2-96.   Erik is painting the fence at the park. With the first can of paint he covered an area that measures $\frac{2}{5}$ the length of the fence and $\frac{1}{2}$ the distance from the top of the fence to the ground.

   a.   What portion of the fence surface area has he covered? Be ready to explain your team's **strategy** for finding the area through pictures and equations.

   b.   How many more cans of paint will he need to finish the job? Show how you found your answer.

   c.   If the full area that Erik will paint is 1400 square feet, how many square feet has he painted so far?

2-97.   Zac is making cookies, but he does not have enough flour to make a full recipe. The full recipe calls for $\frac{2}{3}$ cup of brown sugar.

   If Zac is making $\frac{3}{5}$ of the full recipe, how much brown sugar should he use?

   a.   Represent the $\frac{2}{3}$ cup of brown sugar with a diagram.

   b.   Represent the portion of brown sugar that Zac needs if he makes only $\frac{3}{5}$ of the recipe.

   c.   What math operation should Zac use to find the amount of brown sugar he needs? Write an expression and find a solution.

2-98.   Simplify the following fraction expressions. Show all of your work.

a. $\frac{3}{4}+\frac{2}{3}$ b. $\frac{7}{8}-\frac{1}{4}$ c. $\frac{3}{5}\cdot\frac{1}{3}$ d. $\frac{4}{7}\cdot\frac{2}{3}$

2-99.   What is the length of the marked portion of each line segment? Copy the segment onto your paper before finding the missing length. Assume the entire line segment is subdivided into equal sections.

a.   b.   c.

2-100.   On Saturday, Stella worked for two hours helping her mother around the house. She spent $\frac{1}{3}$ of her time doing laundry, $\frac{1}{4}$ of her time cleaning, and the rest of her time working in the yard. How much of her time was spent in the yard? Show all your work. Use a diagram if it would help.

2-101.   Draw a coordinate grid and plot the following points: $A(-1,-1)$, $B(2,2)$, $C(4,-2)$. Connect the points. Which point could you move to make this an obtuse triangle (a triangle with one angle greater than $90°$)? What would be the new point?

2.3.2 What if it's not a rectangle?

Decomposing and Recomposing Area

In previous classes you have had experience with finding the area of squares and other rectangles, but what about finding the area of irregular shapes? Landscape designers, floor tilers, and others often have to deal with areas that are made of several shapes combined into one. As you work on the problems in this lesson, you will need to **visualize** the new shapes, and predict what they will look like after they are changed.

As you work through this section, it will be important to describe how you **see** different shapes and to organize your work to show your thinking. Ask each other these questions to get discussions started in your study team:

What other shapes can we **see** in this figure?

Where should we break this shape apart? How should we rearrange the pieces?

Will the area change?

2-102. RECTANGLE PUZZLE

Corey and Morgan were given two shape puzzles and asked to find the area of each one. They know how to find the area of a rectangle, but they have never worked with these shapes.

Corey and Morgan would like to rearrange each figure to make it into a single rectangle. Using a Lesson 2.3.2 Resource Page, help them decide how to cut each shape into pieces that they can put back together as *one* rectangle.

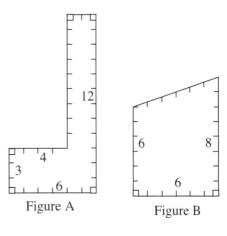

Figure A   Figure B

- On your own, **visualize** and **strategize** how to cut each shape into pieces that will make a rectangle.

- Discuss and decide on one **strategy** to try with your team.

- Cut and rearrange each shape into a rectangle to test your **strategy**.

2-103. Find the area of Figures A and B from problem 2-102. Does it matter if you use the original or rearranged shape? Be sure to show your calculations.

2-104. Find the area of each of the pieces that you made when you cut up the original Figure A. How does the sum of these areas compare to the area of the larger rectangle you found for Figure A in problem 2-103? Why?

2-105. Compare each of the rearranged rectangles that your team made with the rectangles of other teams in your class.

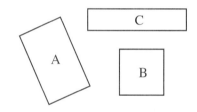

a. To talk about rectangles, it is useful to have words to name the different sides. What are some of the words you have used to name the sides of a rectangle?

b. The words "length" and "width" are only used to describe rectangles and not used for other shapes that you will study. This book will use the words **base** and **height** instead. Often the bottom side is called the base when a rectangle is shown in a horizontal position, like rectangle C above, but "base" can actually refer to any side of the rectangle. Once the base is chosen, the height is either side that is perpendicular (at a right angle) to it. Read the Math Notes box in this lesson for more examples.

c. Are all of the rectangles your class created for the figures from problem 2-102 the same? Use the words *base* and *height* to discuss similarities and differences between the rectangles.

d. Do all of the rearranged rectangles for each figure have the same area? Why or why not?

2-106. LEARNING LOG

In your Learning Log, explain why rearranging a shape might be a good **strategy** to find the area of an unusual shape. Title this entry "Rearranging Shapes to Find Area" and include today's date.

2-107. **Additional Challenge:** How can rectangles help you find the area of the irregular shapes below? Talk about what rectangles you **see** in the shapes and how the areas of those rectangles can help you find the total area. All angles are right angles.

a. Find the shaded area.

9 m

2 m

10.5 m

25 m

b.

18 m

5 m

6 m

7 m

3 m

2 m

21 m

METHODS AND MEANINGS

MATH NOTES

Base and Height of Rectangles

Any side of a rectangle can be chosen as its **base**. Then the **height** is either of the two sides that intersect (meet) the base at one of its endpoints. Note that the height may also be any segment that is perpendicular to (each end forms a 90° angle with) both the base and the side opposite (across from) the base.

In the first rectangle at right, side $\overline{BC}$ is labeled as the base. Either side, $\overline{AB}$ or $\overline{DC}$, is a height, as is segment $\overline{FE}$.

In the second rectangle, side $\overline{GJ}$ is labeled as the base. Either side, $\overline{HG}$ or $\overline{IJ}$, is a height, as is segment $\overline{MN}$. Segment $\overline{GL}$ is not a height, because it is not perpendicular to side $\overline{HI}$.

2-108. Use the following directions to create a mystery letter! On a piece of graph paper, use a ruler to draw a four-quadrant graph. Scale each axis from 6 to –6. Plot these points and connect them in order to create a rectangle: $(2,1)$, $(2,4)$, $(3,4)$, $(3,1)$. Be sure to connect the last point to the first point. Then:

  a. Rotate the rectangle $90°$ clockwise ($\circlearrowright$) about the point $(2,1)$ and draw the rotated rectangle.

  b. Reflect the new rectangle over the line $y = 2$ and draw the reflected rectangle.

  c. Name the letter of the alphabet that your graph resembles.

2-109. Copy and complete the Portions Web at right.

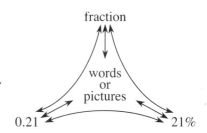

2-110. For each shape drawn below, choose one of the names on the list above them that best describes that shape. Be as specific as you can. If you do not remember what one of the shape names means, you might want to look in the glossary of this book for more information.

right triangle	scalene triangle	obtuse triangle
equilateral triangle	parallelogram	rectangle
rhombus	trapezoid	acute triangle

a.   b.   c.   d.

2-111. Melissa collected the date for all of her friends' birthdays. The histogram shows what she found out. Make a list of the months when her friends' birthdays occur and how many birthdays there are in each month.

Making Connections: Course 2

2-112. Bianca is trying to find the area of this rectangle. She already measured one side as 10 cm. Which other length(s) could she measure to use in her area calculation? Explain your **reasoning**.

2.3.3 Can I make a rectangle?

Area of Parallelograms

In Lesson 2.3.2, you worked with your study team to rearrange two irregular shapes into rectangles in order to find their areas more easily. Today you will use a technology tool (available at www.cpm.org/students/technology) to investigate the question: *Can all shapes be rearranged to make rectangles?* As you work, **visualize** what each shape will look like cut into pieces and how those pieces could fit back together to make a rectangle. Ask yourself these questions while you investigate:

How can I break this shape apart?

How can I rearrange the pieces of the shape to make a new shape?

2-113. CHANGE IT UP

What kinds of shapes can be rearranged to make rectangles? If one complete rectangle is not possible, can any shape be divided into a few different rectangles?

Using the technology tool Area Decomposer (available at www.cpm.org/students/technology) and the Lesson 2.3.3A Resource Page provided by your teacher, figure out which shapes can be changed into rectangles. If you find a way to rearrange the shape on the computer, record your work on the resource page by:

- Drawing lines on the original shape to show the cuts you made.

- Drawing the rectangle made out of the cut pieces.

- Finding the area of the shape.

2-114.   REARRANGING CHALLENGE — PARALLELOGRAMS

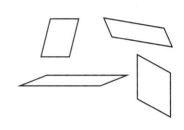

The shapes at right are each an example of a
parallelogram, that is, a quadrilateral with two
pairs of opposite parallel sides. With your
partner, decide if there is a **strategy** for cutting
and rearranging *any* parallelogram that will
always change it into a rectangle. To start, set
the technology tool to show you a parallelogram
like one of those shown at right.

While one person controls the computer, the other (or
others) should show on the Lesson 2.3.3C Resource
Page how the parallelogram was cut and rearranged.
Remember that everyone should share ideas about
how to try to cut and rearrange the shape. Make sure
that each person has an opportunity to control the
computer during the investigation.

a.   How can you cut and rearrange the parallelogram so that you end up with a
     rectangle? Draw your cuts on the original figure, then draw what the final
     rectangle looks like. Use arrows to show where the pieces move.

b.   Will this cutting **strategy** work for any parallelogram? Show the cuts that
     you would make, and use arrows to show where the pieces would move, on
     a new sketch of a different parallelogram. Use your picture to explain a
     general strategy.

2-115.   AREA OF A PARALLELOGRAM

Lydia encountered the following
parallelogram on her homework
assignment. The problem asked her to
find the area of the shape.

Lydia decided to cut and rearrange the shape to make a rectangle (like she did in
problem 2-114). However, she was not sure what the measurements of that
rectangle would be.

a.   With your team, figure out what the base and height of Lydia's new
     rectangle will be. Which side did you use for the height? How do you
     know which side is the height? Draw a diagram to show how you know.

b.   What is the area of the parallelogram? Show your work.

Problem continues on next page. →

Making Connections: Course 2

2-115.   *Problem continued from previous page.*

c.   What about other parallelograms? For example, the parallelogram at right has lengths marked b, c, and h.

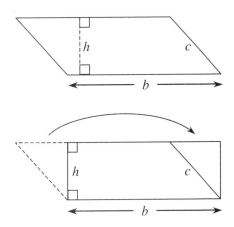

What will be the base of the new rectangle? What will be its height? Talk with your team about the difference between the parts labeled h and c.

d.   How would you find the area of the rectangle? Which lengths would you use? Why?

e.   What is the area of the parallelogram? That is, if A represents the area of the parallelogram, use the variables in the picture to write a formula for calculating the area of any parallelogram.

METHODS AND MEANINGS

MATH NOTES

Parallelogram Vocabulary

Two lines in a plane (a flat surface) are **parallel** if they never meet no matter how far they extend. The distance between the parallel lines is always the same. The marks " >> " indicate that the two lines are parallel.

The **distance** between two parallel lines or segments is the length of a line segment that is **perpendicular** (its ends form right angles) to both parallel lines or segments. In the diagram at right, h is the distance between the two parallel lines. It is also called the **perpendicular distance**.

A **parallelogram** is a quadrilateral (a four-sided figure) with two pairs of parallel sides. Any side of a parallelogram can be used as a base. The height (h) is perpendicular to one of the pairs of parallel bases (b), as in the example at right.

2-116. Use any of your new **strategies** to find the area of the parallelograms below. The information in the Math Notes Box may help.

a.

20 in.

25 in.

20 in.

b.

8 mm   10 mm

10 mm

2-117. Camille had a very fun birthday party with lots of friends and family attending. The party lasted for three hours. If $\frac{3}{8}$ of the time was spent playing games, 50% of the time was spent eating, and the remainder of the time was spent opening presents, draw a diagram and make calculations to show the amount of time spent opening presents.

2-118. Copy and complete each of the Diamond Problems below. The pattern used in the Diamond Problems is shown at right.

a.

−8   −6

b.

−96

12

c.

0.3

0.5

d.

−20

−1

2-119. Copy each expression and then simplify it without a calculator. Be sure to show all steps.

a. $7\frac{5}{8} + 2\frac{9}{16}$

b. $2\frac{7}{8} + 6\frac{1}{6}$

c. $8 - 6\frac{2}{5}$

2-120. Insert whole numbers from 0 to 9 (each digit may only be used once and 6 and 8 are already used) in the blanks below to make the largest number possible. Then repeat the process to make the smallest number possible. Record each answer using numbers and words.

__ 8. __ 6 __

Making Connections: Course 2

2.3.4 What if I add to the shape?

Area of Triangles

So far in this chapter you found the area of different shapes by dividing them into smaller pieces and then putting the pieces back together to make rectangles. In this lesson you will look at **strategies** for making shapes larger in order to find their areas. As you work today, consider these questions:

How can I make a rectangle?

How are the areas related?

Which lengths help me find the area?

2-121.   AREA CHALLENGE — TRIANGLES

Think about how you might find the area of the obtuse triangle shown at right.

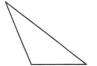

a.   Can you cut and rearrange this shape to make a rectangle?

b.   What if you had two copies of this triangle? What shapes could you make by putting the copies together? To find out:

- Get a set of triangles from the Lesson 2.3.4A Resource Page.

- Carefully cut out the obtuse triangle by cutting along the sides of the figure.

- Find the person in your team who has a triangle that matches yours in size and shape. This person will be your partner.

- Work with your partner to combine the two triangles into a four-sided shape. Sketch the shapes that you create on your paper.

- Decide if each shape can be easily formed into a rectangle by cutting and rearranging.

c.   What about triangles that are not obtuse? Cut out the other two triangles from the resource page. Work with the same partner to combine the two acute triangles. Sketch your results. Can any of your arrangements be formed into a rectangle?

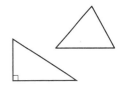

d.   Repeat the process you used in part (c) for the two right triangles.

2-122.   Look carefully at the shapes you found in problem 2-121 that can be cut and rearranged into rectangles.

    a.   What lengths would you need to know to find the area of each rectangle? Where can you find those lengths on the parallelograms before you rearrange them into rectangles? Draw and label them on your sketches.

    b.   How is the area of each parallelogram related to the area of the two triangles that made it?

    c.   Darla created the shape at right out of two triangles and has measured and labeled some of the lengths. Which measurements should she use to find the area of the shaded triangle? What is the area?

    d.   Where else could you draw the height on Darla's shape?

2-123.   Leticia is looking at a triangle (see her figure at right). *"I know how it can be copied and made into a parallelogram, which can then be made into a rectangle,"* she said, *"But when I look at this shaded triangle, I see it inside a rectangle instead."*

    What fraction of the rectangle is this triangle? Work with your team to **justify** your ideas. Be sure to include a labeled diagram as part of your explanation.

2-124.   Describe how to find the area of *any* triangle. That is, when a triangle has a base of length b and a height of length h, what expression will calculate the area of the triangle?

2-125.   **Additional Challenge:** On graph paper, graph $\triangle ABC$ if A is at $(-2, -3)$, B is at $(-2, 5)$, and C is at $(3, 0)$.

    a.   What is the length of the base of $\triangle ABC$? Label side AB with its length in grid units.

    b.   What is the height of $\triangle ABC$? Draw this length on your graph and label it.

    c.   What is the area of $\triangle ABC$? Show how you get your answer.

    d.   If you formed a parallelogram using a copy of $\triangle ABC$ with the triangle on your graph, where would the fourth vertex be? Is there more than one possible answer?

Making Connections: Course 2

2-126.   LEARNING LOG

In your Learning Log, describe how to find the areas of
parallelograms and triangles. This entry does not ask for
simply writing a formula. Instead, for each description:

- Sketch an example shape.

- Show how you found the area.

- Explain how finding the area of each shape is the same and how it is
  different.

Label this entry, "Area of Parallelograms and Triangles" and include today's
date.

ETHODS AND MEANINGS

MATH NOTES

Area of a Parallelogram

A parallelogram can be decomposed
and rearranged into a rectangle with the same
base length and height. Since the area of a
shape does not change when it is cut apart and
its pieces are put together in a different
arrangement (a principle called **conservation
of area**), the area of the parallelogram must
equal the product of its base and height.

Therefore, to find the area of a
parallelogram, find the product of the length
of the base (b) and the height (h).

$$A = b \cdot h$$

Review & Preview

2-127.   Simplify each multiplication problem below.

a. $\frac{5}{8} \cdot \frac{2}{3}$

b. $\frac{3}{4} \cdot \frac{2}{5}$

2-128.　Find the area of each parallelogram. Show all of your work. Use the Math Notes box if you need help.

a.

b.

2-129.　Find the area of the following triangles. Show all your work.

a.

b.

2-130.　Simplify the expressions below.

a.　$8 - 13 - (-4)$　　　　b.　$4 - (-7) + (-2)$　　　　c.　$-7 + 3 - 20$

2-131.　Copy the trapezoid at right on grid paper.

a.　Find the length of the bottom base (segment CD), the length of the top base (segment AB), and the distance between the two bases. Use grid units.

b.　Use what you learned about cutting up figures to find the area of the trapezoid.

2-132.　Draw a coordinate grid, then plot and connect the following points: $A(-3,1)$, $B(-1,3)$, $C(4,2)$, $D(2,0)$.

a.　What is the shape you created?

b.　Reflect the shape across the x-axis. List the coordinates of the new points.

c.　Multiply each coordinate of the original shape by three. Graph the dilated shape. What are the new coordinates of the points?

2.3.5 How can I find the area?

Area of Trapezoids

In this chapter, you have used the process of cutting apart and rearranging shapes to help you find their areas. You have also made some shapes larger to help find their area. In this chapter you have developed several different **strategies** for finding the area of shapes. For example, you have found the sum of the areas of multiple smaller parts, rearranged smaller parts into rectangles to find area, and made shapes bigger in order to find their area. In this lesson you will focus on how to **choose a strategy** to find the area of a new shape: a trapezoid. As you work with your team, practice **visualizing** how each shape can be changed or rearranged. Ask each other these questions:

What **strategy** should we **choose**?

Which lengths are important?

2-133. AREA CHALLENGE — TRAPEZOIDS

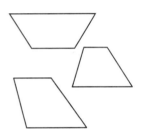

So far in this chapter, you have learned how to find the area of an unfamiliar shape by cutting and rearranging pieces to form a parallelogram or rectangle. Will these **strategies** work to find the area of a **trapezoid** (a shape like the ones at right, with four sides and at least one pair of opposite sides that are parallel)?

To investigate how to find the area of this new shape, get a set of three trapezoids from the Lesson 2.3.5A Resource Page.

Your task: Work with your team to identify at least two ways to rearrange a trapezoid into another shape (or set of shapes) for which you could find the area. Then discuss how you could find the area of each original trapezoid. Use the Discussion Points below to get started.

Discussion Points

How can we cut and rearrange a trapezoid into another shape for which you can find the area?

What shapes can we make from two congruent (identical) trapezoids?

Which lengths are needed to find the area?

How is the area of each original trapezoid related to the area of the other shapes you created?

2-134. Sheila thinks she can make a trapezoid into a parallelogram (and then a rectangle). She started by folding her trapezoid so that the two parallel sides lined up. She then cut along the fold line (the dashed line in the picture).

    a. Fold and cut one of your trapezoids in the way Sheila did. What two new shapes have you created?

    b. How can Sheila rearrange her two pieces to make one parallelogram? Sketch her shape.

    c. Locate the base and the height of the parallelogram. Where could she find these lengths on her original trapezoid?

2-135. AREA OF A TRAPEZOID

Dejon's homework tonight includes a problem where he has to find the area of the trapezoid at right.

    a. Draw a copy of Dejon's trapezoid on your paper. Then choose a way to form a parallelogram. Sketch the rearrangement on your paper and label the base and height of the parallelogram.

    b. Find the lengths on the trapezoid that make the base of the parallelogram. These lengths are called the **bases** of the trapezoid.

    c. Where can you **see** the height of the parallelogram on the trapezoid? What does it measure?

    d. Find the area of the new parallelogram or rectangle. How is this area related to the area of the trapezoid? Explain how you found your answer.

    e. If you have not already done so, find the area of the trapezoid.

2-136.   PARK PROBLEM REVISITED

At the beginning of Section 2.2, your
team looked at problem 2-90, Planning
for the Park. In this park, the city
planners are trying to figure out the size
of the grassy area that they need to mow
so they can determine the mowing costs
for their budget.

Using what your team now knows about
finding the areas of rectangles,
parallelograms, triangles, and trapezoids,
and using the Lesson 2.3.5CB Resource
Page, calculate the area of the park that
will need to be mowed. Assume that all
angles that appear to be right angles are
right angles. If you have time, find two
different ways to find the total area. Be
sure to show all of your work so that you
can explain your **strategies** to other teams.

2-137. Use any of your new **strategies** to find the area of the shapes below. The information in the Math Notes boxes may help. Assume the shape in part (a) is a parallelogram, and the shape in part (b) is a trapezoid.

a.

5 in.
←4 in.→

b.
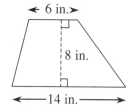
← 6 in.→
8 in.
←—14 in.—→

2-138. Carmen is drawing a card from a standard deck of playing cards. What is the probability that:

a. She will draw a heart?

b. She will *not* draw a club?

2-139. Complete the Portions Webs below.

a.

$\frac{17}{100}$
seventeen hundredths
decimal   percent

b.
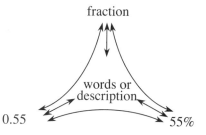
fraction
words or description
0.55   55%

2-140. One-third of a rectangular playground is designed for young children. In that part of the playground, a play structure covers $\frac{2}{5}$ of the children's space.

a. Represent the portion of the playground that is the play structure with a drawing.

b. Represent the problem with multiplication.

c. What fraction of the total playground is the play structure? Show all of your work.

2-141. Christina collected the ages of the players on her softball team. The team ages were: 10, 12, 14, 13, 12, 11, 13, 12, 11, 12, 12, and 13. Christina wants to describe the players' ages in an article for the school newspaper. Since she did not want to list all of the ages, should she use the range or a measure of central tendency (mean, mode, median) to describe them? **Justify** your choice.

2.3.6 How do I calculate it?

Order of Operations

If you know the length of the base and height of a triangle, how do you find its area? Some people **reason** this way: *Since I know that two of the triangles can make a parallelogram, then the area of the triangle must be half the area of the parallelogram. Therefore, it is half the product of the length of the base and the length of the height.*

However, this relationship can also be written as a **rule**, such as $A = \frac{1}{2}bh$, where A represents the area of the triangle, b represents the length of the base, and h represents the height of the triangle.

There are many other relationships that can be written with symbols that you may have seen before. Perhaps one of the most famous rules is Einstein's formula $E = mc^2$, relating energy, mass, and the speed of light. Work with your team to use some rules you already know to find a quantity.

2-142. FUNKY TRAPEZOID RULES

During a discussion in Lesson 2.3.5, some students in Mrs. Cho's class wrote different rules to find the area (A) of the trapezoid at right. Their rules are reprinted below.

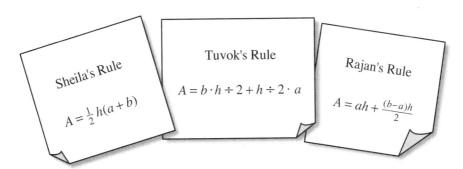

Sheila's Rule
$A = \frac{1}{2}h(a+b)$

Tuvok's Rule
$A = b \cdot h \div 2 + h \div 2 \cdot a$

Rajan's Rule
$A = ah + \frac{(b-a)h}{2}$

a. Trace the trapezoid on your paper and label its side lengths. Explain how Sheila may have rearranged the trapezoid to build her rule. That is, why did she add the lengths a and b together in her rule? Why did she multiply by $\frac{1}{2}$?

b. Pick one of the other rules and explain how the student may have built the rule. Use a diagram to show how the trapezoid might have been cut apart and rearranged.

2-143.   Your teacher will provide your team with a diagram of a trapezoid with the values of *a*, *b*, and *h* labeled.

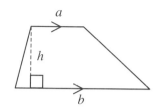

a.   Find the area of your team's trapezoid using each rule from problem 2-142. Each person in your team should use each rule to find the area, rather than splitting the work among team members.

b.   Do each of the rules give you the same area? If not, use problems 2-144 through 2-147 to help your team find any errors in your work.

Further Guidance

2-144.   An expression represents mathematical relationships using numbers, letters, and/or symbols. The rules for simplifying expressions are called the **order of operations**. These rules state that operations like addition and multiplication are performed in a specific order when calculating the value of expressions. Review the Math Notes box for order of operations at the end of this lesson. Then answer the questions below.

a.   Axel was solving for the area of a trapezoid using Tuvok's rule. In Axel's trapezoid, $h = 4$, $a = 3$, and $b = 8$. Axel substituted numbers into the equation that he was using and circled the terms. It looked like this:

$$b \cdot h \div 2 \; + \; h \div 2 \cdot a$$
$$8 \cdot 4 \div 2 \; + \; 4 \div 2 \cdot 3$$
$$\boxed{8 \cdot 4 \div 2} + \boxed{4 \div 2 \cdot 3}$$

b.   Copy Axel's work on your paper. Evaluate each **term** (part of the expression) in Axel's expression, and then add the terms together to get the area of his trapezoid.

2-145.   Copy Tuvok's rule below on your paper and substitute the measures of the trapezoid your teacher gave you into his rule.

$$A = b \cdot h \div 2 + h \div 2 \cdot a$$

a.   What **operations** (addition, subtraction, multiplication, or division) are used in Tuvok's rule?

b.   Addition and subtraction separate terms. Therefore, Tuvok's rule has two terms. Circle the terms on your paper.

c.   Calculate the value of the terms separately and add the results. Remember that multiplication and division are performed in order from left to right.

Making Connections: Course 2

2-146.   Copy Sheila's rule below on your paper and substitute the measures of the trapezoid your teacher gave you into her rule.

$$A = \tfrac{1}{2} h(a+b)$$

a.   What operations are being used in Sheila's rule? If any multiplication is not marked, you may want to add a " · " symbol.

b.   Is $\tfrac{1}{2}h$ multiplied by a, the sum of a and b, or b? How do you know?

c.   One way to show the different quantities within a single term is to circle the separate parts as shown at right.

   •   Find the value of $(a+b)$ for your trapezoid.

   •   Multiply h by $\tfrac{1}{2}$, then multiply the result by the value of $(a+b)$ to find the area of your trapezoid.

2-147.   Copy Rajan's rule (below) on your paper and substitute the measures of the trapezoid that your teacher gave you into his rule:

$$A = ah + \frac{(b-a)h}{2}$$

a.   In your rule, circle the terms.

b.   In the term $\frac{(b-a)h}{2}$, there is a group that must be calculated first. What is it?

c.   Calculate the area of your trapezoid by following the order of operations.

═══════   *Further Guidance*   ═══════
                section ends here.

2-148.   Problem 2-142 used three different ways to represent the area of a trapezoid with bases a and b and height h.

Sheila wonders if there are different ways to write some of the other formulas she has developed in the chapter. She checked with her class and found that there were at least two ways that the formula for the area of a triangle was written. They are shown below. Are these formulas the same? How do you know?

$$A = bh \div 2 \quad \text{and} \quad A = \tfrac{1}{2}bh$$

2-149. Science, economics, and business are just a few of the fields that often describe relationships with rules (or formulas). For each part below, substitute the given values into the rule, then follow the order of operations to find the value of the remaining variable.

    a. FALLING OBJECTS

        $h = \frac{1}{2}gt^2$, where h is the height an object falls (in feet), g is gravity (in feet per square seconds), and t is time (in seconds).

        Let $g = 32$ feet/sec^2 and $t = 10$ seconds. Find the height in feet.

    b. SIMPLE INTEREST

        $I = prt$, where I is the interest, p is the starting value (in dollars), r is the interest rate per year, and t is the number of years the interest is added to the account.

        Let $p = \$50$, $r = 0.085$ per year, and $t = 2$ years. Find the interest earned in dollars.

    c. CONVERSION FROM CELSIUS TO FAHRENHEIT

        $C = \frac{5(F-32)}{9}$, where C is degrees in Celsius and F is degrees in Fahrenheit.

        Let $F = 212$ degrees. Find the temperature in degrees Celsius.

    d. **Additional Challenge:** ENERGY OF A MASS

        $E = mc^2$, where E is the amount of energy in an object (in joules), m is its mass (in kilograms), and c is the speed of light (in meters per second).

        Let $m = 2$ kilograms and $c = 300,000,000$ m/s. Find the amount of energy in the object in joules.

2-150.   LEARNING LOG

In your Learning Log, describe how to find the area of trapezoids. For your description, sketch an example shape and include work showing how you found the area. Label this entry, "Area of Trapezoids" and include today's date.

METHODS AND MEANINGS

Order of Operations

A **numerical term** is a single number, or numbers multiplied together. A **numerical expression** is a combination of numbers and operation symbols such as $+, -, \cdot, \div$. Examples of numerical terms include 4, $3(6-3)$, $\frac{5+4}{2}$, 10^2, and $-\frac{1}{2}(5-9)$.

A numerical expression is a sum or difference. To evaluate an expression:

Example:

$$3(6-3\cdot1) + 4\cdot5^2 - \frac{13-3}{2}$$

1. *Circle* the parentheses or any other grouped numbers, and then circle the terms inside the grouping. See note below.

$$3\boxed{(6-3\cdot1)} + 4\cdot5^2 - \boxed{\frac{13-3}{2}}$$

$$3\boxed{(\boxed{6}-\boxed{3\cdot1})} + 4\cdot5^2 - \boxed{\frac{13-3}{2}}$$

2. *Simplify* each term in the parentheses.

$$3(3) \quad + \quad 4\cdot5^2 \quad - \quad \frac{10}{2}$$

3. *Circle* the terms in the expression.

$$\boxed{3(3)} \quad + \quad \boxed{4\cdot5^2} - \boxed{\frac{10}{2}}$$

4. *Simplify* each term until it is one number by:

$$\boxed{9} \quad + \quad \boxed{4(25)} - \boxed{5}$$

$$9 \quad + \quad 100 \quad - \quad 5$$

- Evaluating each exponential (e.g., 5^2).

$$109 - 5 = 104$$

- Multiplying and dividing from left to right.

5. Finally, *combine* terms by adding and subtracting left to right.

Note: In the example above, $\frac{13-3}{2}$ is treated as $\frac{1}{2}(13-3)$, that is, a term with parentheses.

Review & Preview

2-151. Find the area of these trapezoids.

a.

4 cm
8 cm
13 cm

b.

16 mm
11 mm
21 mm

Chapter 2: Transformations and Area

133

2-152. Simplify each expression. You may want to refer to the Math Notes box for help.

 a. $16 - 5(3 - 1)$

 b. $31 \cdot 4 + 18 \cdot 6$

 c. $3(2^2) - 8 \cdot 1$

 d. $4 \cdot 5 - 2^2 + 3(5 - 4)$

2-153. Copy each expression and simplify it. Be sure to show the steps you use to get the answer.

 a. $\frac{19}{20} - \frac{1}{4}$

 b. $\frac{22}{25} - \frac{7}{10}$

 c. $\frac{9}{32} + \frac{7}{8}$

2-154. Graph the points $X(-3, 5)$, $Y(-2, 3)$ and $Z(-1, 4)$. Connect them to make a triangle.

 a. Reflect the triangle over the y-axis. What are the new coordinates of point Z?

 b. Translate the original triangle down six units and right 3 units. What are the new coordinates of point Y?

 c. Dilate the original triangle by multiplying each coordinate by -1. Describe the new shape you create.

2-155. Identify the length of the missing section of each line. Assume that the lines are divided into equal parts.

 a.

 b.

 c.

Chapter 2 Closure   What have I learned?

Reflection and Synthesis

The activities below offer you a chance to reflect
about what you have learned during this chapter.
As you work, look for concepts that you feel very
comfortable with, ideas that you would like to learn
more about, and topics you need more help with.
Look for connections between ideas as well as
connections with material you learned previously.

①   SUMMARIZING MY UNDERSTANDING

This section gives you an opportunity to show what you know about certain
math topics or ideas. Your teacher will give you directions for exactly how to
do this and will provide you with instructions about how to summarize your
understanding of transformations and **undoing** transformations. In this activity,
you will use a triangle to review transformations.

Predict and Order: Predict how
each transformation will change
or move the shape. Select an
order for the four
transformations and predict
what the new coordinates of the
vertices will be after each step.

Tracy Triangle's Transformation Travels

Apply Transformations: Follow the transformation steps you described on the
graph. Use color and written descriptions to show how each transformation
alters the shape and its position on the coordinate grid. Check that the
coordinates you predicted were correct.

Tracy Triangle's Transformative Travels	Tracy Triangle's Transformative Travels
Add 5 to each x-coordinate	Multiply each y-coordinate by -1.
Tracy Triangle's Transformative Travels	**Tracy Triangle's Transformative Travels**
Multiply each coordinate by 2	Add -8 and then 3 to each x-coordinate Add 9 and -4 to each y-coordinate

Problem continues on next page. →

① *Problem continued from previous page.*

Undo Transformations: To get the triangle back to the original position, **undo** your transformations. You may choose to **undo** *each* transformation step or to find a new series of steps to return the shape to its original position. Show, using color, symbols, and written descriptions, how each transformation changes the shape's size and position on the coordinate grid.

② WHAT HAVE I LEARNED?

Working the problems in this section will help you to evaluate which types of problems you feel comfortable with and which ones you need more help with.

Solve each problem as completely as you can. The table at the end of this closure section provides answers to these problems. It also tells you where you can find additional help and practice on problems like them.

CL 2-156. The histogram at the right shows the weights of the frogs entered in the Jumping Frog Jubilee.

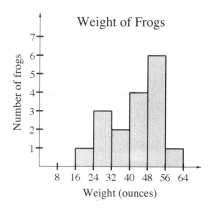

a. How many frogs weigh more than two pounds (32 ounces)?

b. What is the most common weight for the frogs?

c. What is the weight of the largest frog(s)?

CL 2-157. Find the mean, mode, range, and median of the values:

$$8, 13, 6, -1, 10, 0, -3, 5, 7, 1$$

CL 2-158. Copy the graph at right on your paper. You will need a second graph for List II. Complete each list of transformation steps you could use to move triangle B back to where it started at position A, and show each transformation on your graph.

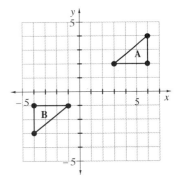

List I	List II
1. Rotate triangle B 180° about point (−1, −1)	1. Reflect triangle B across the y-axis
2. ?	2. ?
	3. ?

CL 2-159. Neatly graph the points (−2, 9), (−3, 7) and (−5, 10) on a four-quadrant graph. Connect them to make a triangle. Then, for each transformation described below:

- Write and simplify an expression to find the new coordinates.

- Check your answer on your graph.

a. Slide the triangle right 4 units and down 6 units.

b. Reflect the triangle across the y-axis.

CL 2-160. George is playing a game, but the spinner is incomplete. Help him figure out what fraction is missing.

CL 2-161. Multiply $\frac{2}{3} \cdot \frac{1}{2}$. You may want to copy and complete the diagram at right to show your work.

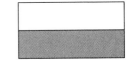

CL 2-162. Mary has a bag of colored tiles. There are 8 red tiles, 7 blue tiles, 9 yellow tiles, and 12 green tiles. If she reaches into the bag, what is the probability of picking a:

a. Yellow tile?   b. Green tile?   c. Purple tile?

CL 2-163. Copy each shape below on your paper, then find its area and perimeter. Show all your work.

a.

b.

c.

CL 2-164. For each of the problems in this section of closure, do the following:

a. Draw a bar or number line like the one below that represents 0 to 10.

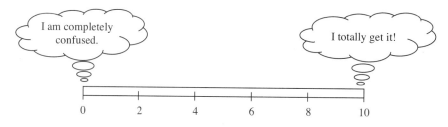

b. Color or shade in a portion of the bar that represents your current level of understanding and comfort with completing that problem on your own.

c. If any of your bars are less than a 5, choose *one* of those problems and do one of the following tasks:

- Write two questions that you would like to ask about that problem.

- Brainstorm two things that you DO know about that type of problem.

d. If all of your bars are a 5 or above, choose one of those problems and do one of these tasks:

- Write two questions you might ask or hints you might give to a student who was stuck on the problem.

- Make a new problem that is similar and more challenging than that problem and solve it.

③ WHAT TOOLS CAN I USE?

You have several tools and references available to help support your learning – your teacher, your study team, your math book, and your Toolkit, to name only a few. At the end of each chapter you will have an opportunity to review your Toolkit for completeness as well as to revise or update it to better reflect your current understanding of big ideas.

The main elements of your Toolkit should be your Learning Log, Math Notes, and the vocabulary used in this chapter. Math words that are new to this chapter appear in bold in the text. Refer to the lists provided below and follow your teacher's instructions to revise your Toolkit, which will help make it a useful reference for you as you complete this chapter and prepare to begin the next one.

Learning Log Entries

- Lesson 2.1.2 – Meanings for –
- Lesson 2.1.3 – Subtraction of Integers
- Lesson 2.2.3 – Rigid Transformations
- Lesson 2.3.2 – Rearranging Shapes to Find Area
- Lesson 2.3.4 – Area of Parallelograms and Triangles
- Lesson 2.3.6 – Area of Trapezoids

Math Notes

- Lesson 2.1.1 – Commutative and Associative Properties of Addition
- Lesson 2.2.1 – Adding and Subtracting Integers
- Lesson 2.2.2 – Graphing Points on an xy-Coordinate Grid
- Lesson 2.2.3 – Rigid Transformations
- Lesson 2.2.4 – Mixed Numbers and Fractions Greater Than One
- Lesson 2.3.2 – Base and Height of Rectangles
- Lesson 2.3.3 – Parallelogram Vocabulary
- Lesson 2.3.4 – Area of a Parallelogram
- Lesson 2.3.5 – Area of a Triangle
- Lesson 2.3.6 – Order of Operations

Mathematical Vocabulary

The following is a list of vocabulary found in this chapter. Some of the words have been seen in the previous chapter. The words in bold are the words new to this chapter. Make sure that you are familiar with the terms below and know what they mean. For the words you do not know, refer to the glossary or index. You might also want to add these words to your Toolkit for a way to reference them in the future.

area	**associative property**	**commutative property**
coordinate grid	**coordinates**	**expression**
integers	**lengths**	**mixed numbers**
origin	**parallelogram**	**quadrant**
quadrilateral	**reflection**	**rigid transformation**
rotation	**term**	**translation**
trapezoid	**triangle**	**vertex**
x-axis	**y-axis**	

Process Words

The list of words below are problem solving strategies and processes that you have been involved in throughout the course of this chapter. Make sure you know what it means to do each of the following. If you are not sure, look through your book for problems when you were asked to think in the following ways.

brainstorm	choose a strategy	decompose
describe	explain your reasoning	justify
predict	rearrange	reverse your thinking
test your prediction	visualize	

Answers and Support for Closure Activity #2
What Have I Learned?

Problem	Solution	Need Help?	More Practice
CL 2-156.	a. 13 frogs b. between 49 and 56 ounces c. between 57 and 64 ounces	Lesson 1.1.4	Problems 1-23, 1-28, 2-88, and 2-111
CL 2-157.	mean: 4.6 median: 5.5 mode: none range: 16	Lessons 1.1.3 and 1.1.4 Math Notes boxes in Lessons 1.1.3 and 1.1.4	Problems CL 1-44, 2-28, 2-79, and 2-141
CL 2-158.	List I: 2. Translate (slide) triangle B right 4 units and up 3 units. List II: 2. Reflect triangle B across the *x*-axis. 3. Translate triangle right 2 units and up 1 unit. 	Lessons 2.2.1, 2.2.2, and 2.2.3 Math Notes box in Lesson 2.2.3 Learning Log (problem 2-66)	Problems 2-47, 2-51, 2-52, 2-59 through 2-64, 2-68, 2-85, 2-132, and 2-154
CL 2-159.	a. x: $-2+4=2$, y: $9-6=3$; $(2,3)$ x: $-3+4=1$, y: $7-6=1$; $(1,1)$ x: $-5+4=-1$, y: $10-6=4$; $(-1,4)$ b. y-coordinates remain the same. x: $-2 \cdot (-1)=2$; $(2,9)$ x: $-3 \cdot (-1)=3$; $(3,7)$ x: $-5 \cdot (-1)=5$; $(5,10)$ 	Lessons 2.2.1, 2.2.2, and 2.2.3 Math Notes box in Lesson 2.2.3 Learning Log (problem 2-66)	Problems 2-47, 2-51, 2-52, 2-55, 2-59 through 2-64, 2-68, 2-77, 2-85, 2-108, 2-132, and 2-154

Problem	Solution	Need Help?	More Practice
CL 2-160.	$\frac{4}{15}$	Lessons 1.2.4 and 1.2.5 Math Notes box in Lesson 1.2.4 Learning Log (problem 1-107)	Problems CL 1-140, 2-9, 2-98, and 2-153
CL 2-161.	$\frac{2}{6}$ or $\frac{1}{3}$	Lesson 2.3.1	Problems 2-93, 2-94, 2-98, and 2-127
CL 2-162.	a. $\frac{9}{36}$ or $\frac{1}{4}$ b. $\frac{12}{36}$ or $\frac{1}{3}$ c. 0: There are no purple tiles; impossible	Lessons 1.2.1 and 1.2.2 Math Notes boxes in Lessons 1.2.1 and 1.2.2	Problems CL 1-139, 2-42, 2-50, 2-71, 2-78, and 2-138
CL 2-163.	a. $A = 45$ sq in., $P = 33$ in. b. $A = 374$ sq cm, $P = 80$ cm c. $A = 48$ sq mm, $P = 36.5$ mm	Lessons 2.3.2 through 2.3.5 Math Notes boxes in Lessons 2.3.2 through 2.3.5 Learning Log (problems 2-106, 2-126, and 2-150)	Problems 2-102, 2-112, 2-115, 2-116, 2-124, 2-128, 2-129, 2-135, 2-137, and 2-151

Making Connections: Course 2

Puzzle Investigator Problems

PI-3.   SIERPINSKI TRIANGLES

Fractals are geometric structures developed by repeating a process over and over. A famous example of a fractal is the **Sierpinski Triangle**, shown below. To create this design, start with a triangle, as shown in Figure 1. Then find and connect the midpoints of all of the sides of the triangle, subdividing it into four smaller triangles. Shade all but the central triangle as shown in Figure 1.

Then repeat the process by finding and connecting the midpoints of the shaded triangles of Figure 1. Shade all but the center triangles, as shown in Figure 2. If this process is continued infinitely, the result is the Sierpinski Triangle.

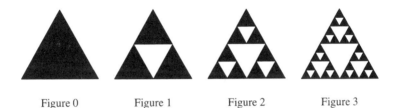

Figure 0   Figure 1   Figure 2   Figure 3

a.   On the PI-3 Resource Page (which can be downloaded at www.cpm.org/students), shade in the next figure in the sequence.

b.   For Figures 1 through 4, write a fraction to represent the amount of the entire triangle that is shaded. As you work, look for patterns. What is happening to the numerator and denominator of the fraction? What is happening to the amount shaded?

c.   Use your pattern to predict what portion of Figure 5 and Figure 6 in the sequence will be shaded.

d.   The shaded portion of Figure 2 could be written as $\left(\frac{3}{4}\right)^2$. Rewrite the other figures in this form. According to this pattern, what should the value of $\left(\frac{3}{4}\right)^0$ to be? Explain why.

e.   Is there any figure that will have less than 10% shaded? If so, use your pattern to explain how you know.

PI-4.   FAIR SHARES?

Three students baked cookies to share the next day and put them on a plate. However, Latisha woke up in the middle of the night and ate one-third of the cookies and went back to sleep. A little while later, Susan woke up, ate one-third of what was left and fell asleep. Then Hieu woke up, ate one-third of what was left, and went back to sleep. When all three students woke up, they discovered 8 cookies were left.

a. How many cookies did they bake? Drawing diagrams may help.

b. What if there had been four students instead? Solve the problem again where four students bake cookies and each of them wakes up separately and eats one-fourth of the cookies that are left. This time, assume that at the end, 81 cookies were on the plate. How many cookies did they bake?

c. For each situation above, compare the original number of cookies to the final number of cookies left. What is their relationship?

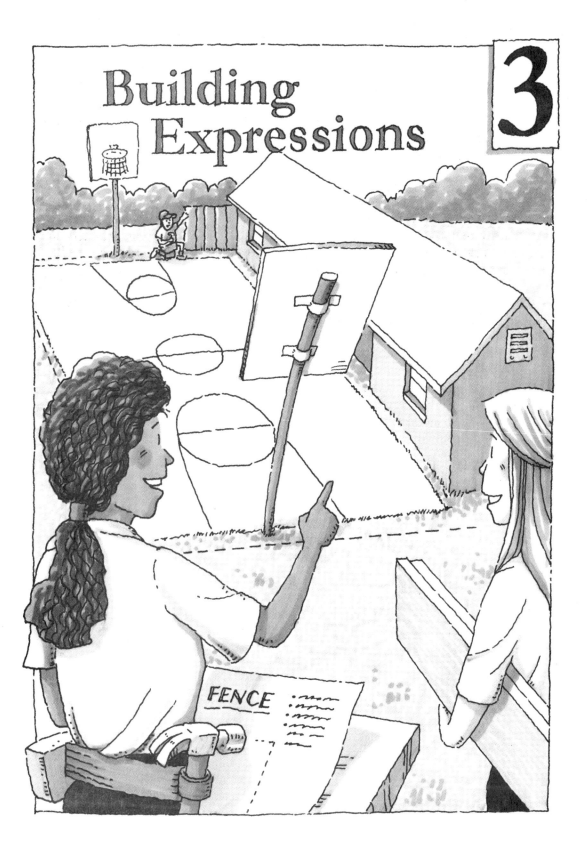

Building
Expressions

3

FENCE

CHAPTER 3   Building Expressions

You may have heard the saying, "Mathematics is a universal language." This is sometimes said because mathematics uses symbols (like letters and numbers) to describe mathematical ideas and relationships in **general** ways to understand specific cases. For example, a statement like, "*I am exactly 3 years older than my cousin,*" describes a **general** relationship that is true for any specific age of your cousin. To represent **general** relationships like this, you will use variables (like x) and build expressions (like $x + 3$).

Section 3.1 begins building expressions by using a new tool called "algebra tiles." You will use a variable to help you describe the perimeter and area of shapes built with tiles when one dimension is unknown or can represent various lengths.

Guiding Questions

Think about these questions throughout this chapter:

How can I write it?

How can I represent the relationship?

How can I organize my thinking?

Are these representations equivalent?

In Section 3.2, you will use variables to represent a single unknown number in different contexts, such as the balance of your bank account or the number of minutes you spend doing homework. You will learn about the 5-D Process, a **strategy** to organize your thinking that can help you solve problems.

In this chapter, you will learn how to:

> ➢ Combine like terms and simplify variable expressions.

> ➢ Use a variable to represent any number.

> ➢ Substitute a given value for a variable and evaluate an expression.

> ➢ Solve situational problems using the 5-D Process.

Chapter Outline

Section 3.1 This section introduces algebra tiles and uses their area and perimeter to develop the skills of building expressions and combining like terms. Variable expressions will be simplified and evaluated for given values.

Section 3.2 This section will introduce the 5-D Process as a problem-solving method. You will learn how to understand a problem by drawing, describing, and defining its elements. You will learn **strategies** that will help you throughout the course and lead to writing and solving equations later in the course.

3.1.1 What is the area?

Area of Rectangular Shapes

Mathematics can be used to describe patterns in the world. Scientists use math to describe various aspects of life, including how cells multiply, how objects move through space, and how chemicals react. Often, when scientists try to describe these patterns, they need to describe something that changes or varies. Scientists call those quantities that change **variables**, and represent them using letters and symbols.

In this course you will spend time learning about variables, what they can represent, and how they can serve different purposes. To start, you will use variables to describe the dimensions and area of different shapes and begin to organize those descriptions into **algebraic expressions**.

As you work with your teammates, use the following questions to help focus your team's discussion:

How can we organize groups of things?

What is the area?

Which lengths can vary?

3-1. Find the area of each rectangle below. Show your work. In part (b), each small square in the interior of the rectangle represents one square unit.

a.
15 cm

25 cm

b.

c.
0.75 m

1.8 m

d. Explain your method for finding the area of a rectangle.

3-2. AREA OF ALGEBRA TILES

Your teacher will provide your team with a set of
algebra tiles. Remove one of each shape from the
bag and put it on your desk. Trace around each
shape on your paper. Look at the different sides of
the shapes.

a. With your team, discuss which shapes have the
same side lengths and which ones have
different side lengths. Be prepared to share
your ideas with the class. On your traced
drawings, color code lengths that are the same.

b. Each type of tile is named for its area. In this course we will say that the
smallest square has a side length of 1 unit, so its area is 1 square unit. We
will call this tile "one" or the "unit tile." Can you use the unit tile to find
the side lengths of the other rectangles? Why or why not?

c. If the side lengths of a tile can be measured
exactly, then the area of the tile can be
calculated by multiplying these two lengths
together. The area is measured in square units.
For example, the tile at right measures 1 unit by
5 units, so it has an area of 5 square units.

The next tile at right has one side length that is
exactly one unit long. If we cannot give a
numerical value to the other side length, what
can we call it?

d. If we agree to call the unknown length "x," label the side lengths of each of
the four algebra tiles you traced. Find each area and use it to name each
tile. Be sure to include the name of the type of units it represents.

Making Connections: Course 2

3-3. Jeremy and Josue have each sketched three *x*-tiles on their papers.

Jeremy has labeled each tile with an *x*. *"They are three x-tiles, each with dimensions 1 by x, so the total area is 3x square units,"* he said.

Josue labeled the dimensions, that is, length and width, of each tile. His sketch shows six *x*-lengths.

Jeremy's sketch   Josue's sketch

          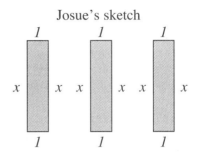

a. Why do the two sketches each show a different number of *x* labels on the shapes?

b. When tiles are named by their area, they are named in square units. For example, the *x* by *x* tile (large square) is a shape that measures x^2 square units of area, so we call it an x^2-tile.

What do the six *x*'s on Josue's sketch measure? Are they measures of square units?

3-4. When a collection of algebra tiles is described with mathematical symbols it is called a **variable expression**. Take out the tiles shown in the picture below and put them on your table.

- Use mathematical symbols (numbers, variables, and operations) to record the area of this collection of tiles.

- Write at least three different variable expressions that represent the area of this tile collection.

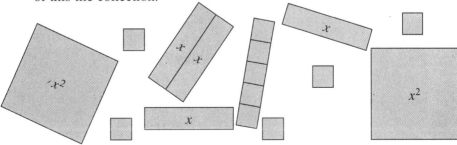

3-5.   Take out the tiles pictured in each collection below, put them on your table, and
        work with your team to find the area as you did in problem 3-4.

a.

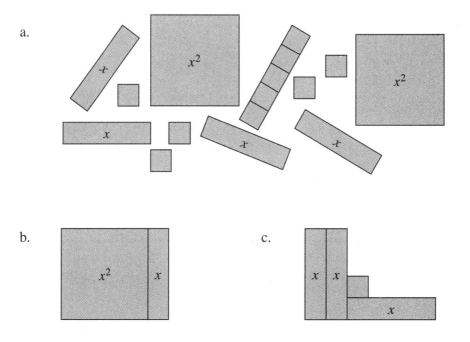

b.   c.

d.   Is the area you found in part (a) the same or different from the area of the
      collection in problem 3-4? **Justify** your answer using words, pictures, or
      numbers.

3-6.   Build each collection described below with algebra tiles and use them to help
        you to answer the questions.

a.   If a person combined a collection of three x^2-tiles, two x-tiles and five unit
      tiles with one x^2-tile and two x-tiles, how many of each tile would they
      have?

b.   If a student started with three x^2-tiles, two x-tiles and five unit tiles and
      removed two x^2-tiles, two x-tiles and three unit tiles, what would remain?

Ⓜ ETHODS AND MEANINGS

MATH NOTES

Area of Trapezoids

There are multiple ways to divide a trapezoid and rearrange the pieces into a parallelogram with the same area. For example, the trapezoid can be divided parallel to its two bases to create two smaller trapezoids that are each half of the height of the original trapezoid. Those two pieces can be rearranged into a parallelogram, as shown below.

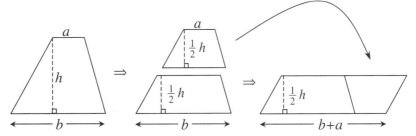

Therefore, to find the **area of a trapezoid**, find the product of half of the height (h) and the sum of the two bases (a and b).

$$A = \tfrac{1}{2} h(a + b)$$

Review & Preview

3-7. Sketch the shape made with algebra tiles at right on your paper. Then answer parts (a) and (b) below.

a. Find the area of the shape.

b. If the algebra tiles were rearranged into a different shape, how would the area change?

3-8.   Your team forgot to clean up their algebra tiles and now they are all over your desk.

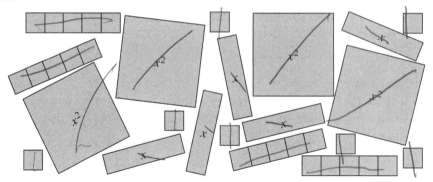

Sort the tiles so that they are in groups that are all the same and write a sentence explaining how many of each type of tile you have.

3-9.   Suppose that a triangle is created on a graph by connecting points *A*, *B*, and *C* below. Marika, Kimiku and Marcus want to move triangle *ABC* five units to the left and four units down. Write an integer expression to record how the shape moves and find the new coordinates for each vertex.

a. $A(-1, 3)$ b. $B(5, -1)$ c. $C(0, 1)$

3-10.   Find the area and perimeter of the shape at right.

3-11.   Find the area of each square with the given side lengths.

a.   4 cm × 4 cm

b.   10 in. × 10 in.

c.   12 km × 12 km

d.   5 units × 5 units

e.   Describe the method you used to find the area of the squares.

Making Connections: Course 2

3.1.2 What is a variable?

Naming Perimeters of Algebra Tiles

How much homework do you have each night? Some nights you may have a lot, while other nights you may have no homework at all. The amount of homework you have varies from day to day. In mathematics we use letters such as x and y, called **variables**, to represent quantities that are not constant.

In Lesson 3.1.1 you used variables to name lengths that could not be precisely measured. Using variables allows you to work with lengths that you do not know exactly. Today you will work with your team to write expressions to represent the perimeters of different shapes using variables. As you work with your teammates, use the following questions to help focus your team's discussion:

Which lengths can vary?

How can we see the perimeter?

How can we organize groups of things?

3-12. TOOTHPICKS AND ALGEBRA TILES

In Chapter 1, you played the game "Toothpicks and Tiles." However, this time, you will play it using algebra tiles!

Work with your team to find the "tiles" (the area) and "toothpicks" (the perimeter) for the following figures.

a.   b.   c.

d. What is different about the shape in part (c)?

e. Is the perimeter of the shape in part (c) greater or less than the perimeter of the shape in part (a)? Explain your thinking.

3-13.   The perimeter of each algebra tile can be written as an
         expression using variables and numbers.

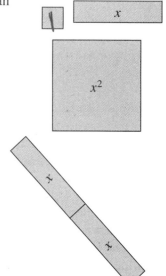

         Write at least two different expressions for the
         perimeter of each tile shown at right.

    a.   Which way of writing the perimeter seems
         clearest to you? What information can you get
         from each expression?

    b.   Lisa wrote the perimeter of the collection of
         tiles at right as $2x + 1 + 2x + 1$ units, but her
         teammate Jody wrote it as $4x + 2$. How are
         their expressions different?

    c.   Which expression represents the perimeter?

3-14.   The expressions that you have written to
         represent area and perimeter are made up
         of **terms**. A **term** may be a single number,
         variable, or product of numbers and
         variables such as $3x$, x^2, 8, $-2xy$, or
         $6(x - 7)$.

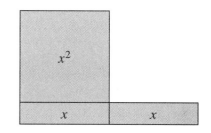

         For the shape at right, one way to write the
         perimeter would be to include each side
         length in the sum:

$$P = x + x + x + 1 + x + x + 1 + x$$

    a.   How many x lengths are represented in this expression? How many unit
         lengths?

    b.   **Combining like terms**, that is, terms that contain the same variable, is a
         way of simplifying an expression. Rewriting the perimeter of the shape
         above as $P = 6x + 2$ **combines** the separate x-terms as $6x$ and combines the
         units in the term 2.

         If you have not already done so, combine like terms for the perimeter of the
         different algebra tiles in problem 3-13.

Making Connections: Course 2

3-15.   Using algebra tiles, on your desk, make the shapes shown below. Trace each shape and label the length of each side on your drawing. With your team, find and record the total perimeter and area for each shape. If possible, write the perimeter in more than one way.

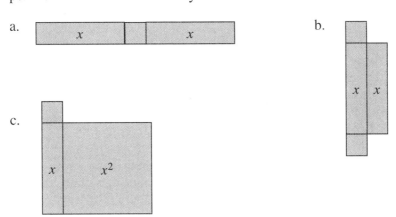

a.

b.

c.

3-16.   In problem 3-15, x is a variable that represents a number. The value of x determines the size of the perimeter and area of the shape.

Using the shapes from the previous problem, sketch and label each shape with the new lengths given below. Rewrite the expressions with numbers and simplify them to determine the perimeter and area of each shape.

a. $x = 6$ units for all three shapes

b. $x = 2$ units for all three shapes

c.   Compare your method for finding perimeter and area with the method your teammates used. Is your method the same as your teammates? If so, is there a different way to find the perimeter and area. Explain the different methods.

3-17.   LEARNING LOG

In your Learning Log, explain what a variable is in your own words. What does it mean for the length of an x-tile to be a variable? What is an expression? Use examples with drawings to illustrate your statements. Title this entry "Variables" and include today's date.

METHODS AND MEANINGS

Naming Algebra Tiles

Algebra tiles help us represent unknown quantities in a concrete way. For example, in contrast to a 1×5 tile that has a length of 5 units, like the one shown at right, an x-tile has an unknown length. We can represent its length with a symbol or letter (like x) that represents a number, called a **variable**. Because its length is not thought to be fixed, the x-tile could be 6 units, or 5 units, or 0.37 units long.

5 units

1 unit

1 unit

←Can be any length→

Algebra tiles can be used to build **algebraic expressions**. An algebraic expression is similar to numerical expressions defined in Chapter 2, but its terms include variables. The three main algebra tiles are shown at right. The large square has a side of length x units. Its area is x^2 square units, so it is referred to as an x^2-tile.

The rectangle has length of x units and width of 1 unit. Its area is x square units, so it is called an x-tile.

The small square has a side of length 1 unit. Its area is 1 square unit, so is called a one or unit tile. Note that the unit tile in this course will not be labeled with its area.

3-18.   Natalie and her little sister, Coco, found an old trunk
        in the attic. They decided to explore the contents of
        the trunk. It had 25 baseball cards, three hats, four
        pair of gloves, five books, two photo albums, one
        pair of boots and two hairbrushes.

        The girls want to organize the objects into two
        groups of things that are alike. Help them sort the
        objects and explain how you created the two groups.

3-19.   Find the perimeter of the figure at right.

3-20.   Copy the diagrams of algebra tiles below on your
        paper. Then find the perimeter of each shape.

        a.

        b.

3-21.   Paige traveled to Australia and is making her favorite bread
        recipe. She usually bakes the bread in a 350°F oven. She
        is surprised to learn that the oven temperatures in Australia
        are measured in degrees Celsius. Using the formula at
        right and the order of operations, help Paige determine how
        she should set the oven in degrees Celsius.

        $C = \frac{5(F-32)}{9}$

3-22.   Simplify the following expressions.

        a. $\frac{2}{5} - \frac{1}{6}$ b. $\frac{3}{7} - \frac{7}{14}$ c. $\frac{5}{8} - \frac{2}{3}$

3-23.   Mr. Hill has a deck of math flashcards that include addition, subtraction, and multiplication problems. Twenty-five cards show addition problems, 30 are subtraction problems, and 45 are multiplication problems.

   a.   What is the probability of drawing a card with an addition or subtraction problem on it?

   b.   If Mr. Hill adds 40 division flashcards to the deck, what will P(division) be?

   c.   In the new deck, which is greater: the probability of drawing an addition or subtraction flashcard, or the probability of drawing a multiplication or division flashcard? **Justify** your conclusion.

3.1.3   How can I rewrite it?

Combining Like Terms

In Lesson 3.1.2, you looked at different ways the perimeter of algebra tiles can be written, and created different expressions to describe the same perimeter. Expressions that represent the same perimeter in different ways are called **equivalent**. Today, you will extend your work with writing and rewriting perimeters to more complex shapes. You will rewrite expressions to determine whether two perimeters are equivalent or different. As you work today, keep these questions in mind:

Are there like terms I can combine?

How can I rearrange it?

How can I see (**visualize**) it?

3-24.   Build each of these shapes using algebra tiles and look carefully at the lengths
of the sides:

a.   Sketch each figure on your paper and color code
the lengths that are the same. Which figures have
side lengths that are different than those you have
measured before? How are they different?

b.   Label each length on your paper. Discuss with your team how to label the
new lengths. Explain your **reasoning**.

c .   Find the perimeter of each figure. Write the perimeter in simplest form by
combining the like terms.

3-25.   In any expression, the number that tells you how
many of each variable or quantity you have is
called a **coefficient**.

$$3x^2 + 4x + 6$$

coefficient

constant

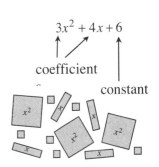

For example, for the expression that describes the
collection at right, the coefficient "3" shows that
there are three x^2-tiles, and the coefficient "4"
shows that there are four x-tiles. The 6 is the
constant, because it shows the number of units.

Answer each question below for each of the perimeters you found in
problem 3-24.

•   How many x (or y) lengths are there in the perimeter?

•   How do you **see** the coefficient of x (or y) in your expression and in the
shape?

•   What is the constant in the expression? How do you **see** the constant in the
shape?

3-26.   HOW MANY PERIMETERS?

Erik cannot keep his hands off the algebra tiles! He has made several different shapes, each one using the same tiles. *"Will every shape I create with these tiles have the same perimeter?"* he wonders.

Help Erik investigate by making different shapes with your team. Your shapes must follow these rules:

Shares a complete side

Does not share a complete side

- Shapes must use exactly three tiles: a one tile, an x-tile, and an x^2-tile.

- Tiles must share a complete side. An example of tiles that do, and do not, share complete sides is shown at right.

a.   Rearrange the tiles until each teammate has a shape that follows the rules and has a different perimeter. Discuss why the perimeters are different. Trace each shape, color-code the sides, and label their lengths. Write an expression for the perimeter of each shape and simplify it by combining like terms.

b.   Are other perimeters possible with the same pieces? As you find others:

- Trace the shapes.

- Color-code and label the sides.

- Write the perimeter in simplest form.

Be prepared to share your list of perimeters with the class.

c.   Are there different shapes that have the same perimeter? Why or why not?

3-27.   **Additional Challenge:** Build this shape out of algebra tiles. Then, on grid paper, draw the shape when x is equal to each of the lengths below.

a. $x = 5$ units   b. $x = 3$ units

c. $x = 2$ units   d. $x = 1$ unit

3-28.   LEARNING LOG

In your Learning Log, describe what a "term" is in math. Using algebra tiles, make up an example to explain how to combine like terms. Why is it useful to combine like terms? Title this entry "Combining Like Terms" and include today's date.

Making Connections: Course 2

MATH NOTES

METHODS AND **M**EANINGS

Combining Like Terms

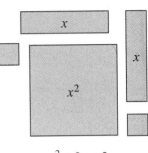

A **term** is an expression that contains a single number (called a **constant**), single variable, or the product of numbers and variables. This course uses tiles to represent variables and constants. Combining tiles that have the same area to write a simpler expression is called **combining like terms**. See the example shown at right.

$$x^2 + 2x + 2$$

More formally, **like terms** are two or more terms that have the same variable(s), with the corresponding variable(s) raised to the same power.

Examples of like terms: $2x^2$ and $-5x^2$, $4ab$ and $3ab$.

Examples that are *not* like terms: 5 and $3x$, $5x$ and $7x^2$, a^2b and ab.

When you are not working with the actual tiles, it helps to **visualize** them in your mind. You can use these images to combine those terms that are the same. Here are two examples:

Example 1: $2x^2 + x + 3 + x^2 + 5x + 2$ is equivalent to $3x^2 + 6x + 5$

Example 2: $3x^2 + 2x + 7 - 2x^2 - x + 7$ is equivalent to $x^2 + x + 14$

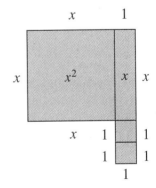

When several tiles are pushed together and form a more complicated figure, the area of the new figure is the sum of the areas of the individual pieces, and the perimeter is the sum of the lengths around the outside. Area and perimeter expressions can be **simplified**, or rewritten, by combining like terms.

For the figure at right the perimeter is:
$x + 1 + x + 1 + 1 + 1 + 1 + 1 + x + x = 4x + 6$ units

3-29. Find the perimeter of each figure made of algebra tiles below.

a.

b.

c.

3-30. Copy and simplify each expression.

a. $6 + (-18)$ b. $12 + (-25)$ c. $-9 + (-9)$ d. $-12 + 6 + 15$

3-31. Find the mean, mode, range, and median of the values:

$$12, 4, -2, 0, 9, -2, 1, 7, 8, 2.$$

3-32. Sketch the collection of algebra tiles that is described by the following expression. Rewrite the area of the collection by combining like terms.

$$7x + 2x^2 + 3x^2 + 3 + x$$

3-33. Copy and complete the portions web at right by including a picture, decimal, and percent representation of $\frac{9}{20}$.

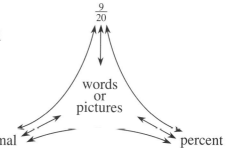

3.1.4 What can a variable represent?

Evaluating Variable Expressions

In the past three lessons, you have learned how to find the perimeter and area of a shape using algebra tiles. Today, you will challenge the class to find the perimeter and area of shapes that you create. As you work, keep in mind these questions:

Which lengths are constant?

Which lengths can change?

3-34. Use the perimeter expressions you found in problem 3-29 to answer the questions below.

a. Determine each perimeter if $x = 5$ units.

b. Determine each perimeter if $x = 2\frac{1}{2}$ units.

c. Using a technology tool or grid paper as directed by your teacher, carefully draw each shape with the specified length of x units.

3-35.   SHAPE CHALLENGE

You and your team will choose four algebra tiles that
will be used to build a shape to challenge your
classmates. You may choose whatever tiles you would
like to use as long as you use exactly four tiles.

As a team, decide on the shape you want to make.
Experiment with different shapes until you find one you
think will have a challenging perimeter and area for your
classmates to find. Then, to share your challenge with
the class:

  • Build the shape with algebra tiles in the middle of your team so everyone
    can see it.

  • Get an index card from your teacher. On one side, neatly draw the shape
    and label each side.

  • Write a simplified expression for the perimeter and for the area on the
    same side of the card. This will be the answer key. Show all of your
    steps clearly.

  • Turn the card face down so the answer is hidden, put the names of your
    team members on the top of the card, and then put it beside the shape you
    built with your algebra tiles.

Remember, your work needs to be clear enough for your classmates to
understand.

Follow your teacher's directions to complete challenges created by other teams.
As you look at their shapes, sketch them on your paper. Work with your team
to label the sides and find the perimeter and area of each shape. Be sure to
combine like terms to make the expressions as simple as possible.

3-36.   Choose two of the shapes from problem 3-35. Sketch each shape and label it
         with its perimeter and area. Do not forget the correct units. It is not necessary
         to draw the figures to scale. Rewrite each expression with the values given
         below and then evaluate it.

         a. $x = 1.5$ units   b. $x = 3\frac{3}{4}$ units

3-37.   LEARNING LOG

In your Learning Log, sketch a complex shape made out of
algebra tiles (you might choose one from the Shape
Challenge). Explain your **strategies** for finding the area
and perimeter of the shape. Use color, arrows, and labels
to explain your work. Title this entry "Perimeter and Area
Using Algebra Tiles" and include today's date.

METHODS AND MEANINGS

Evaluating Expressions

The word **evaluate** indicates that the value of an expression
should be calculated when a variable is replaced by a numerical
value.

For example, when you evaluate the
expression $x^2 + 4x - 3$ for $x = 5$, the result is:

$$(5)^2 + 4(5) - 3$$
$$25 + 20 - 3$$
$$42$$

Using the expression $3x^2 - 5x + 2$ for $x = 4$, the result is:

$$3(4)^2 - 5(4) + 2$$
$$3(16) - 5(4) + 2$$
$$48 - 20 + 2$$
$$30$$

In each case remember to follow the order of operations.

3-38.　Sketch the algebra tile shape at right on your paper. Write an expression for the perimeter of the shape, then find the perimeter for each of the given values of x.

a.　$x = 7$ units

b.　$x = 5.5$ units

c.　$x = \frac{7}{3}$ units

3-39.　Copy each expression and simplify it. Show all of your steps.

a.　$1.234 + 0.58 + 5.316$

b.　$6.1 - 1.536$

c.　$4.8(0.6)$

3-40.　Multiply $\frac{4}{5} \cdot \frac{1}{3}$. You may want to show your thinking with a diagram.

3-41.　On a coordinate grid, graph these points to create a triangle:

$$(-2, 3),\ (3, -2),\ (-2, -2)$$

a.　What kind of triangle is it?

b.　Where could you add a fourth point so that when the points are connected you will make a rectangle?

c.　What point can you add to create a trapezoid?

d.　Translate the original triangle 5 units to the left and 4 units down. Label the coordinates of the vertices of the new triangle.

3-42.　Simplify each expression.

a.　$-\frac{4}{5} + \frac{3}{10}$

b.　$2\frac{5}{8} - 1\frac{1}{3}$

3.1.5 Are they related?

Perimeter and Area of Algebra Tile Shapes

People often assume that area and perimeter are related. It seems reasonable that if the area of a shape gets bigger (or smaller), then its perimeter should also get bigger (or smaller). But is this always true? In Chapter 1 you learned that the "tiles" could stay the same, but you could increase the "toothpicks" by changing the arrangement of squares. In this lesson you will continue to investigate whether there is a relationship between perimeter and area using algebra tiles.

As you work with your team, it is important that you share your ideas so that you are able to understand many different ways of **seeing** the shapes. Be prepared to **justify** how you are finding perimeters and how you are simplifying the expressions. Ask yourself these questions to help you to explain your **reasoning**:

How can I see the perimeter?

Where am I adding (or covering) length?

How can I rearrange the tiles?

3-43.   HOW MANY PERIMETERS?

Obtain a set of algebra tiles from your teacher. For each problem below, use exactly three x-tiles to build a shape with the specified perimeter. Sketch the shapes on your paper, label the sides, and show how you combined like terms. Be prepared to **justify** your answer.

a. $P = 2x + 6$ b. $P = 4x + 2$

c. $P = 6x + 2$

3-44.   Look at the shapes you made in problem 3-43. How do the areas of each of the shapes compare? How do the perimeters compare? Explain.

3-45.   Build and sketch a shape with an area of $x^2 + x$ square units and a perimeter of $6x$ units.

3-46.   The shapes you made in problem 3-43 each had a different perimeter, but each
          one used the same algebra tiles. Can you make more than one perimeter with
          any collection of algebra tiles? Assume the tiles share a complete side.
          Consider the three different sets of tiles listed below:

          Collection I: one x^2-tile and one x-tile

          Collection II: one x^2-tile and one unit tile

          Collection III: two x^2-tiles

     a.   With your team, make shapes with each pair of tiles that have different
          perimeters. Make as many different perimeters as you can. Remember, a
          perimeter is only different if the expression is different after you combine
          like terms. Each time you create a new perimeter, write it down and sketch
          the shape.

     b.   When the areas of two shapes are the same, are the perimeters equal? If so,
          explain why. If not, give an example in which they are not.

3-47.   Build the shape at right in the center of your table, and sketch it on your paper.

     a.   Write an expression for the perimeter of the shape.

     b.   Where could you add another unit tile to the shape without
          changing the perimeter? Decide with your team where to
          put it, then sketch the new shape on your paper. Label the
          sides and find the perimeter.

     c.   Are the areas of the two shapes the same or different? Explain your
          reasoning.

3-48.   **Additional Challenge:** In the shape at right, one
          of the x lengths on the x^2-tile is partially
          covered by three 1-unit lengths. What happens to
          the perimeter if x has a value less than 3?
          Investigate this by answering the questions below.

     a.   Write an expression for the perimeter and for the area of the shape.

     b.   Use your expressions to predict the perimeter and area of the shape when
          $x = 4$, $x = 3$, $x = 2$, and $x = 1$.

     c.   Draw the algebra tile diagram on grid paper to **scale**, using each of the four
          side lengths. In other words, first draw all of the sides of length x so that
          they are 4 units long. Then, draw the diagram again and make all of the
          sides of length x just 3 units long. Do the same for $x = 2$ and $x = 1$.

     d.   Use your diagrams to measure the actual area and perimeter of each shape.
          What do you notice? Can you explain why this happens?

Review & Preview

3-49. Evaluate each expression for the given value.

a. $2a - 7$ when $a = 3$

b. $10 + 4m$ when $m = -2$

c. $9 + (-2n)$ when $n = 4$

d. $\frac{x}{2} + 5$ when $x = 6$

3-50. The Kennedy High School cross-country running team ran the following distances in recent practices:

> 3.5 miles, 2.5 miles, 4 miles, 3.25 miles, 3 miles, 4 miles, and 6 miles.

Find the mean, median, and mode of the team's distances.

3-51. Sketch the rectangle at right on your paper. Calculate the perimeter and area for the given x-values.

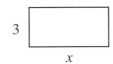

a. $x = 5$

b. $x = 9$

c. $x = 4.6$

3-52. Where would the point $(11, -18)$ be after each transformation described below? Write an integer expression to find each new coordinate.

a. Reflect $(11, -18)$ across the x-axis, then reflect that point across the y-axis.

b. Translate $(11, -18)$ 5 units to the right and 3 units down.

3-53. Set up a 4-quadrant graph and graph the points below to make the 4-sided shape $PQRS$.

$$P(-2, 4) \quad Q(-2, -3) \quad R(2, -2) \quad S(2, 3)$$

a. What shape is $PQRS$?

b. Find the area of the shape.

3.2.1 How can I draw it?

Describing Relationships Between Quantities

You may not know it, but you use mathematical thinking every day. You think mathematically when you figure out if you can afford items you want to buy, or when you read a graph on a web page. You also think mathematically when you double a recipe or when you estimate how much longer it will take to get somewhere based on how far you still have to go. Math can describe many of the relationships in the world around you.

Building your interpretation skills and developing ways to represent situations will help you solve problems. In this section you will learn new ways to show your thinking when using math to solve problems. As you work today, think about the following questions:

How can I represent this with a diagram?

Who has more? Who has less?

3-54.   Sometimes using the same words in a slightly different way can change their meaning. Read and compare the two situations below.

Situation 1	Situation 2
Myra has 15 marbles. This is ten less than Dahlia.	Myra has 15 marbles. Dahlia has ten less than Myra.

a. For each situation, draw a picture to represent the marbles each girl has. What is the difference between the problems?

b. In which problem does Myra have more marbles than Dahlia?

c. How many marbles does Dahlia have in Situation 1 above? How many does she have in Situation 2?

Making Connections: Course 2

3-55.   Ellie is building a dollhouse. She has boards
         that are two different lengths. One long
         board is 7 inches longer than the total length
         of three of the short boards.

   a.   Draw a picture showing how the short and
         long boards are related.

   b.   What are some possible lengths of her
         boards?

   c.   If one of the long boards is 50 inches long, how long is a short board? Be
         ready to share your thinking with the class.

3-56.   Now read and compare Problems A and B below.

Problem A	Problem B
Dianna has $16. Jairo has twice as much money as Dianna. Who has more money?	Dianna has $16. She has twice as much money as Jairo. Who has more money?

   a.   Represent each problem with a diagram.

   b.   Compare the amount of money Jairo has in part (a) to the amount he has in
         part (b). Explain how you know in which situation he has more money.

3-57.   Now you are going to **reverse** your thinking. Examine the pictures below, then
         use words to describe the relationship you see in the pictures. Assume the
         lengths that appear to be equal are equal.

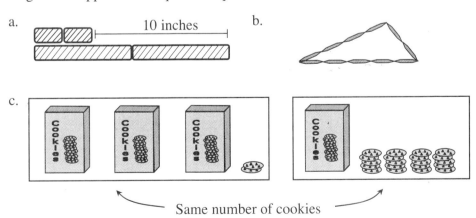

3-58. Richard, Arielle and Kristen just measured how tall they are in feet. Their heights are shown in the bar graph at right.

Decide which statements below are true and which statements are false. Rewrite the false statements to make them true.

a. Richard is one foot shorter than Kristen.

b. Arielle is twice as tall as Richard.

c. Kristen is one foot taller than twice Arielle's height.

d. The sum of the three children's height is 10 feet.

3-59. **Additional Challenge:** Represent this description with a picture.

Ellen is gluing tiles on the four vertical sides of a rectangular planter box. The longer side of the box is covered by six more than two times as many tiles as the shorter side.

3-60. Find the area of each figure below.

a.

b.

Making Connections: Course 2

3-61.　Find the missing information from the following relationships.

a.　Mark has downloaded four times as many songs on his music player as Chloe. If Mark has 440 songs, how many songs does Chloe have?

b.　Cici likes to collect shoes, but she only has half the number of pairs of shoes that her friend Aubree has. If Cici has 42 pairs of shoes, how many pairs of shoes does Aubree have?

c.　Tito walked three more miles than Danielle. If Danielle walked 2 miles, how far did Tito walk?

3-62.　Evaluate the expression $10 - 2x$ for the given x-values.

a.　$x = 2$　　　　　b.　$x = \frac{1}{2}$　　　　　c.　$x = -2$

3-63.　Copy and complete each of the Diamond Problems below. The pattern used in the Diamond Problems is shown at right.

a.

b.

c.

d.

3-64.　Complete a Portions Web, described in Lesson 1.1.5, for each number below.

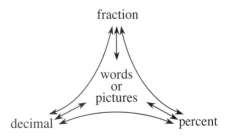

a.　0.25

b.　$\frac{3}{4}$

c.　$33\frac{1}{3}\%$

3.2.2 How can I organize it?

Solving a Word Problem

You have seen that being able to draw diagrams and describe relationships is helpful for solving problems. In this lesson, you will learn another way to organize your thinking as you solve word problems.

3-65.   FENCING THE BASKETBALL COURT

The Parent Club at Post Falls Middle School needs 183 feet of fencing to go around the rectangular outdoor basketball court behind the school gym. They will only need to place a fence on three sides of the court because the wall of the gym will form the fourth side. The length of the court is 32 feet more than the width. One of the shorter sides will be 5 feet shorter than the other one to leave room for a gate.

Your task: Determine how much fencing will be used on each side of the court. Be prepared to **justify** your answer and show all of your work. Be sure that someone who is not on your team can read and understand your work.

Discussion Points

What information do we know in the problem?

What do we need to figure out?

What diagram can we draw to represent this situation?

How did we organize our work?

How can a wrong answer help us revise our thinking?

3-66. If another team came to look at your paper for problem 3-65, could they understand your work? Why or why not? What else could you do to make it so that someone else could make sense of your work just by looking at it?

3-67. Daniel, Donald, and Debra decided to organize their thinking in a table using a method they call the 5-D Process. Get a Lesson 3.2.2A Resource Page from your teacher that shows their work. Then answer some of the following questions during the whole class discussion.

- *"What are the students <u>Describing and Drawing</u>?"*
- *"What is in the <u>Define</u> column?"*
- *"What is the <u>Do</u> column used for?"*
- *"What are they trying to <u>Decide</u>?"*
- *"What might the <u>Declare</u> section be for?"*

3-68. While one team was working on problem 3-65, they decided to see if a width of 30 feet would use all of the 183 feet of fencing. They figured out that, with a 30-foot width, the length would be 62 feet and the side with the gate would be 25 feet. Only 117 feet of fencing would be used.

What is a logical number that they should try next for the width so that all of the fencing is used? Explain your **reasoning**.

3-69. Finish problem 3-65 using the 5-D Process. Continue the chart you looked at in problem 3-67 to find the answer.

3-70. Use the steps of the 5-D Process to organize and solve each of the parts below. The Lesson 3.2.2C Resource Page may help you set up your table. Be sure to show each of the "D" steps clearly in your solution process.

a. Laura takes very good care of her vehicles. She owns a blue van and a red truck. Although she bought them both new, she has owned the truck for 17 years longer than the van. If the sum of the ages of the vehicles is 41 years, how old is the van and how old is the truck?

b. Ryan is thinking of a number. When he multiplies this number by 6 and then subtracts 15 from the answer, he ends up with his original number. What number is Ryan thinking of?

3-71. Sketch the algebra tile shape shown at right on your paper. Then:

- Write an expression for the area of the shape.

- Write and simplify an expression for the perimeter of the shape.

- Calculate the area and perimeter of the shape for each value of x.

a. $x = 7$ b. $x = 2.5$ c. $x = 15$

3-72. Copy and simplify each expression.

a. $7 \cdot (-2)$ b. $-3 \cdot 10$

c. $4 \cdot (-3)$ d. $-8 \cdot (-6)$

3-73. What fraction of one hour (60 minutes) is represented by the following numbers of minutes? Simplify each fraction whenever possible. A sketch of a clock might help you.

a.   10 minutes   b.   15 minutes   c.   30 minutes   d.   20 minutes

3-74. Write a sentence that describes the relationship in words. For example, "$5, $8" could be $8 is three more than $5.

a. $13, $39   b.   25 feet, 17 feet   c.   38 lbs., 19 lbs.

3-75. Find the missing parts of each number line. Assume that the lines have been split into equal parts.

a.   b.   c.

3.2.3 How do I use the 5-D Process?

Strategies for Using the 5-D Process

Math is used to solve challenging problems that apply to daily life. For example, how much fresh water is on the planet? How many area codes (for telephone numbers) are needed in a city? Where should a city build transportation lines such as city bus systems and subways to reduce traffic on the freeways? Mathematics can provide helpful insights for the solutions.

When trying to solve a new and challenging problem, it is useful to have a **strategy**. The 5-D Process that you learned about in Lesson 3.2.2 will often work when you are trying to solve a problem you have not seen before.

In this lesson you will practice using this process to solve more word problems and you will compare the different ways that your classmates use the 5-D Process to help them. Be sure to write your work neatly and be prepared to **justify** your **reasoning**.

As you work using the 5-D Process, consider the following questions:

How can we describe the problem?

How can we decide how to label the columns?

How can we organize the columns?
How can we decide which quantity to start with?
Does it matter which one we choose?

How can we decide which number to try first?

Your team may be asked to present your responses to one or more of the target questions above at the end of this lesson.

3-76.   A **scalene triangle** has three unequal side lengths. The medium-length side is 7 cm longer than the shortest side. The longest side is twice as long as the shortest side. The total perimeter is 39 cm. What are the lengths of the sides of the triangle?

3-77.   Travis and Angela were playing a Guess My Numbers game. Angela told Travis, "I'm thinking of two positive numbers. The difference of my numbers is 4 and the product of my numbers is 96. What are my numbers?" Help Travis find Angela's numbers.

3-78.   The Potter Valley basketball team did not record how many baskets each player made during the last game. Jenny remembers that she made three times as many baskets as Grace. Alexis knows that she made six more baskets than Grace. Joan thinks that she made 4 fewer baskets than Grace. Tammy is sure that she made the same number of baskets as Joan. Altogether the five players made 40 baskets. How many baskets did each player make?

3-79.   Ramon was studying pond life in Doyle Park. In two hours, he counted four more frogs than turtles. The number of crayfish he counted was three more than twice the number of turtles. In total, he counted 54 turtles and crayfish. How many frogs were there?

3-80.   Dawn is trying to find the dimensions of a parallelogram. She knows that the base is one unit less than twice the height of the shape. The area is 91 square units. How long are the base and height?

3-81.   Ms. Pacheco, Mr. Edwards, and Mr. Richards are three math teachers at Turner Middle School. Ms. Pacheco is three years older than Mr. Richards. Mr. Edwards is twice as old as Mr. Richards. The sum of Mr. Richard's age and Mr. Edwards' age is 81. How old is each person?

3-82.   **Additional Challenge:** If one side of a square is increased by 12 feet and the side connected to it is decreased by three feet, a rectangle is formed. The perimeter of the rectangle is 62 feet. How long was the side of the original square?

3-83.   With your team, re-read the focus questions for this lesson, reprinted below:

How can we describe the problem?

How can we decide how to label the columns?

How can we organize the columns?
How can we decide which quantity to start with?
Does it matter which one we choose?

How can we decide which number to test first?

Discuss the **strategies** you use with the 5-D Process as a team. Be prepared to share your ideas with the class.

METHODS AND MEANINGS

Solving Problems with the 5-D Process

MATH NOTES

The **5-D Process** is an organized method to solve problems. The D's stand for Describe, Define, Do, Decide, and Declare. An example of this work is shown below.

Problem: The base of a rectangle is 13 centimeters longer than the height. If the perimeter is 58 centimeters, find the base and the height of the rectangle.

Describe/Draw: The shape is a rectangle and we are looking at the perimeter.

height

base

	Define	Do	Decide
	Height (trial)	Base (height + 13)	Perimeter 2(base) + 2(height)	58?
Trial 1:	10	10 + 13 = 23		66 is too high

Use a trial value.

Use the relationships stated in the problem to determine the values of the other quantities (such as base and perimeter).

Decide if the answer is correct. Revise and make another trial until you find the correct answer.

Trial 2:	7	7 + 13 = 20	2(20) + 2(7) = 54	too low
Trial 3:	8	8 + 13 = 21	2(21) + 2(8) = 58	correct

Declare: The base is 21 centimeters and the height is 8 centimeters.

3-84. If the total area of this algebra tile shape is 168 square units, how long is each side? To find out how long the x side must be, copy the diagram and table and answer the questions below.

Describe/Draw

	Define		**Do**	**Decide**
	Side #1	Side #2	(Side one)·(Side	Area = 168?
Trial 1:	10	12		
Trial 2:				

Declare:

a. Describe how the lengths of the two sides are related to each other.

b. Which side of the rectangle does Side #2 represent?

c. Use the 5-D Process to complete the table. Find the length of the two sides of the rectangle.

3-85. Evaluate the expression $5 + (-3x)$ for the given x-values.

a. $x = 3$ b. $x = \frac{1}{3}$ c. $x = -3$

3-86. Troy has a number cube with the numbers 1 through 6 on it. If each side is equally likely to appear when he rolls the cube, find the following probabilities. (Note: When two or more numbers are multiplied, each of the numbers is a factor of the product.)

a. P (rolls a 2)   b. P (rolls an odd number)

c. P (rolls a factor of 6)

3-87. Simplify the following expressions using the order of operations.

    a. $3(8-4)+4^2-(2+3)$ b. $7\cdot4-3\cdot8+2^2-6$

    c. $7-(-3)+(-4+3)$ d. $-6-4(3\cdot2)+5^2$

3-88. Write expressions for the perimeter and the area of this algebra tile shape. Then simplify each expression by combining like terms.

3.2.4 How can I represent it?

Using Variables to Represent Quantities in Word Problems

In Section 2.1, you used variables to help you describe the perimeter of tiles. In that situation x could be stretched to represent any positive number. Today you will continue to use the 5-D Process as you solve word problems and you will use a variable to represent the unknown value in the problem.

Think of these questions as you work on the problems today:

What is the problem asking?

What is the relationship between the quantities involved?

How can I choose which part of the problem to represent with a variable?

3-89. Thu has one mini-box of Choco-Blasters, and Warren gave her three more pieces. Samara has two mini-boxes of Choco-Blasters and she gave six pieces to Will. Now Thu and Samara have the same number of Choco-Blasters left.

How many Choco-Blasters are in a mini-box? Assuming all mini-boxes of Choco-Blasters have the same number of pieces in them, use the 5-D Process to solve this problem.

3-90.   Allen's team was working on a problem but did not have time to finish it. They also did not follow the teacher's directions for showing work in the Define section. Discuss with your team what information you can get from Allen's table below.

	Define		Do	Decide
	Length	Width	Double each side and add together	Target perimeter = 36?
Trial 1:	3	9	$2(3)+2(9)=24$	Too small
Trial 2:	4	?		

a.   Is there enough information in Allen's table to finish the problem? Why or why not?

b.   What would you need to know in order to complete Trial 2? Explain your thinking.

3-91.   Allen's teammate, Scott, was also working on problem 3-90, but he organized his table differently. As Scott explained his table to Allen, he used the pattern in the first two trials to represent the quantities with a variable, x.

Look at the table below.

a.   How is it different from Allen's chart?

b.   What does the x in the table represent?

c.   Describe the relationship between the length and the width in words.

d.   Where did the expression $x+x+(2x+3)+(2x+3)$ come from? Explain your thinking.

	Define		Do	Decide
	Length	Width	Add all 4 sides together	Target perimeter = 36?
Trial 1:	3	$2(3)+3$	$3+3+9+9=24$	Too small
Trial 2:	6	$2(6)+3$	$6+6+15+15=42$	Too large
	x	$2(x)+3$	$x+x+(2x+3)+(2x+3)$	

182   *Making Connections*: Course 2

3-92.   Izzy's team used a 5-D table to solve a problem that involved **consecutive integers**, which are integers that follow each other on a number line. The numbers 1, 2, 3, …, 14, 15, 16, …, or −5, −4, −3, ... are all examples of consecutive integers. The table below shows part of their work on the problem.

Copy the chart and finish the problem. Apply Scott's idea from problem 3-91 to add variable summaries in the chart after you find a solution.

	Define			Do	Decide
	1st number	2nd number	3rd number	Add all numbers together	Target sum = 57
Trial 1:	15	$15+1$	$15+2$	$15+16+17=48$	Too small
Trial 2:	20	$20+1$	$20+2$	$20+21+22=63$	Too large

3-93.   Meiko saw someone's expressions in the 5-D Process table below and wanted to **reverse** the process. The problem involved a bag of green, red, and blue marbles.

	Define			Do	Decide
	Green	Red	Blue	Total Marbles	Total = 71?
Trial 1:	15				
	x	$x-2$	$2x+5$	$x+(x-2)+(2x+5)$	

a.   One of the variable expressions describes how the number of red marbles compares with the number of green marbles. How can you describe this relationship in words?

b.   Based on the variable expressions, use words to describe how the number of blue marbles compares with the number of green marbles.

c.   How many total marbles are in the bag?

d.   If there are 15 green marbles in the bag, how many red and blue marbles are in the bag? Show your work.

3-94. Camille knew that a triangle had one side with a length of 16 inches and another side was 20 inches. She did not know the length of the third side, but she did know that the perimeter was five times the length of the unknown side. How long is the unknown side?

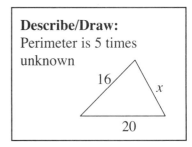

Describe/Draw:
Perimeter is 5 times unknown

Copy the table below and complete the chart. You may add as many rows as you need to solve the problem. Remember to summarize the relationships with a variable line and to complete the Declare sentence.

	Define		Do	Decide
	Unknown Side	Perimeter	Compare sum to perimeter	Same?
Trial 1:	5	5(5)	$5 + 16 + 20 \overset{?}{=} 25$ $41 \neq 25$	No

Declare:

3-95. Margaret was working on the problem below:

Michael earned four times as much money last summer as his sister Mackenzie. Together they earned $475. How much did each person earn?

The table below shows the first two trials Margaret made. Based on the results, work with your study team to suggest a number she should try next. (You do not need to solve the problem.) Is it **reasonable** for different members of your team to suggest different numbers?

- Are there some numbers that would not be helpful? Explain.

	Define		Do	Decide
	Mackenzie's earnings	Michael's earnings	Add both of their earnings together	Target sum = $475
Trial 1:	$50	4($50)	$50 + $200 = $250	Too small
Trial 2:	$100	4($100)	$100 + $400 = $500	Too large

3-96. Dawn and Myrna's father has asked them to build a rectangular pen for their dog. They have 74 feet of fencing. They want the length to be one more than twice the width. Use the 5-D Process to help Dawn and Myrna find the dimensions (both length and width) of the pen.

Making Connections: Course 2

3-97.   **Additional Challenge:** Use the 5-D Process to find three consecutive integers that have a product of 3360.

3-98.   LEARNING LOG

In your Learning Log, describe how you decide which number to use as your first trial in the 5-D Process. Then explain how you use the results of your first trial to choose your next trial number. You may want to include an example from your recent work to help you explain. Title this entry, "Defining and Deciding" and label it with today's date.

MĒTHODS AND MEANINGS

MATH NOTES

Consecutive Integers

Consecutive integers are integers that come "one after another" in order (that is, without skipping any of them). For example: 11, 12, and 13 are three consecutive integers. The numbers 10, 12, 14, and 16 are four **consecutive even integers** because in counting up from 10, no even numbers are skipped. Likewise, 15, 17, and 19 are **consecutive odd integers**.

At times in algebra it is necessary to represent a list of consecutive integers. To represent any list in **general** we must use variables, and it is common to let x represent the first integer. See the examples of how to write a list of consecutive integers below:

Three consecutive integers: $x,\ x+1,\ x+2$

Three consecutive odd integers: $x,\ x+2,\ x+4$

Three consecutive even integers: $x,\ x+2,\ x+4$

Note that consecutive even integers and odd integers look alike because both even integers and odd integers are two apart.

3-99. Think about the mathematical process you use as you solve the following problems. Show your work and your solutions.

a. If there are 100 students in a room and 40 of them are boys, how many are girls?

b. If there are 17 blue and white stripes on a flag and 9 of them are blue, how many are white?

c. If there are 250 pennies and dimes in a box and 130 of them are pennies, how many are dimes.

d. Now **generalize**: Imagine you know how many items you have in a collection of two types of things. If you know how many of one of the items you have, how could you find how many of the other item you have?

3-100. Copy and simplify each expression.

a. $-2 + 5$

b. $(-4) \cdot (6)$

c. $4 - (-3)$

d. $10 + (-2) - 7$

e. $-5 - 3(2 - 6)$

f. $(3 - 3)(10^2 - 11)$

3-101. Daisy and Alexandra each have a group of algebra tiles on their desks as described below.

Daisy has these tiles: $x, x, x^2, 1, x^2, x, x^2$, and x

Alexandra has $x^2, x, 1, 1, 1, x, x^2, x$, and 1.

a. Sketch each girl's tiles.

b. If the girls put their tiles together, how many of each type of tile will they have? Write an expression that represents this sum.

3-102. Rewrite each percent as a fraction and each fraction as a percent.

a. 20%

b. $\frac{2}{5}$

c. 75%

d. $\frac{2}{3}$

3-103.   Manuel used Pattern Blocks to build the shapes below. The block marked "A" is a square, "B" is a trapezoid, "C" is a rhombus (a parallelogram with equal sides) and "D" is a triangle. Find the area of Manuel's shapes.

a.

b.

3.2.5 How can I solve it?

More Word Problem Solving

So far in Section 3.2, you have been using a 5-D Process as a way to organize and solve problems. Today you will continue using this process to solve problems in a variety of situations.

As you work, use the following questions to focus your team's discussion:

What is the problem asking?

What is the relationship between the quantities involved?

How can we decide which part of the problem to represent as *x* ?

What if a different quantity were represented with *x*?

3-104.   According to many sources, insects are the most diverse group of animals on the planet. The number of species is estimated at between six and ten million and insects are said to represent more than half of all known living organisms and potentially over 90% of the differing life forms on Earth.

The following problems are about insects and other creepy crawly creatures. Use your math skills to find out some fascinating facts about them. Your teacher will assign your team one of the following problems to solve. Be prepared to present your solution, including all steps of your 5-D solving process, to the class.

a.   Many insects migrate (travel) between their summer and winter homes. The Desert locust migrates about 800 miles farther then the Monarch butterfly every spring and the Pink-spotted hawkmoth migrates about 200 miles less than four times the distance of the Monarch butterfly every spring. Laid end to end, the distances traveled by a Monarch butterfly, a Desert locust, and a Pink-spotted hawkmoth is about 12,600 miles every spring. How far does each species travel?

b.   Bees, wasps, and ants all live in colonies that have a queen. The queen of the colony is really the mother of all the insects in the colony. During the spring and summer, many eggs are laid in bee, wasp, and ant colonies all over the world. This is sometimes easy to see when there is a bee, wasp, or ant colony close to your house or school because there will be lots of these insects in the area.

   Queen bees lay about double the number of eggs in a day that queen ants lay. Queen wasps lay about 600 fewer eggs a day than queen ants do. An average queen bee, ant, and wasp together lay about 2,600 eggs a day. How many eggs would each type of queen lay in one day?

c.   Flies cannot see much past 24 to 36 inches, but that is not because they do not have lots of lenses in each eye. Dragonflies even have more! In one eye, dragonflies have two thousand more that seven times the number of lenses that houseflies have in one eye. If one housefly eye and one dragonfly eye together have 34,000 lenses, how many lenses do houseflies have in one eye? How many do dragonflies have in one eye?

Problem continues on next page. →

Making Connections: Course 2

3-104.   *Problem continued from previous page.*

d.   Think you do not have enough room to farm? Think again. You could farm worms under your desk with a commercially available worm farm that measures 16" x 16" x 28". You can buy the worms online. At 1200 worms per pound you could start your own business just like John did. He's not good at keeping his records, however, and needs your help.

John buys his worms from two online stores, Worm Heaven and Wiggles R Us. John remembers that he ordered 1200 more than twice as many worms from Worm Heaven as he did from Wiggles R Us. He also knows he has 18,000 worms. How many worms did he order from each store.

e.   There are many kinds of animals that live in and on our bodies, called parasites. Some of the longest parasites live in our intestines. Two of these parasites are roundworms and tapeworms. Their lengths can be quite different depending on how long they have been living in someone's body!

One of the longest tapeworms ever measured was three feet less than seven times the length of the longest roundworm ever measured. If you laid these two worms end to end, they would measure an amazing 69 feet! How long was the tapeworm and how long was the roundworm?

f.   Did you know that most of the states in this country have official state insects and butterflies? Out of 30 states, the three most common insects are Monarch butterflies, honeybees, and ladybugs. The number of states that have Monarch butterflies as their official insect is one more than the number of states that have ladybugs as their official insect. The number of states that have honeybees as their official insect is three times the number of states with ladybugs as their state insect minus one. How many states have each kind of insect as their state insect?

3-105. The number of girls at Middle School Cyber Summer Camp was six more than twice the number of boys. There were a total of 156 middle school students at the camp. Use the 5-D Process to find the number of boys and the number of girls at camp.

3-106. The daily high temperatures in degrees Fahrenheit for the last two weeks in Grand Forks, North Dakota were: 7, 1, −3, 0, 4, −1, −2, 5, 7, 7, −3, −2, −4, −5.

    a. Calculate the mean temperature.

    b. Calculate the mode of the data.

    c. Calculate the median temperature.

    d. Which measure of central tendency do you think best represents the weather in Grand Forks? Why?

3-107. On graph paper, graph the shape that has coordinates $(-2, -1)$, $(1, 2)$, and $(-2, 3)$.

    a. Predict the coordinates of the shape after it is translated three units to the right and one unit down. Check your prediction on the graph.

    b. Dilate the original shape by multiplying both the x- and y-coordinates by 2.

    c. Reflect the original shape over the y-axis. What are the new coordinates?

3-108. Which expressions are equivalent to the perimeter of the shape? How do you know?

    a. $x + 3 + 3x + 1$ b. $2x + 4 + x$

    c. $4x + 4$ d. $2x + 2 + 2x + 2$

Chapter 3 Closure   What have I learned?

Reflection and Synthesis

The activities below offer you a chance to reflect on
what you have learned during this chapter. As you
work, look for concepts that you feel very comfortable
with, ideas that you would like to learn more about, and
topics you need more help with. Look for connections
between ideas as well as connections with material you
learned previously.

①   SUMMARIZING MY UNDERSTANDING

You have been working with finding
areas and perimeters of triangles,
rectangles, trapezoids, parallelograms,
and shapes created by algebra tiles.
This section gives you an opportunity
to showcase what you know about
area and perimeter. Your teacher will
provide you with instructions about
how to create a "magic book." In this
book you will summarize your
understanding of area and perimeter as
well as show how your understanding

can be used to find areas and perimeters of various shapes.

Assemble the Book: Follow your teacher's instructions to create a special
book. It will become clear later why this is called a "magic book."

What are Area and Perimeter? Use your Toolkit, textbook, and other
classroom resources to explain what you know about area. Include an
explanation about how the area formulas for triangles, parallelograms, and
trapezoids are related to the area of a rectangle. Diagrams might be helpful.

In your magic book, also explain what you know about perimeter. Be
specific about the information you need to know about a shape in order to
determine its perimeter.

Area and Perimeter Examples: Follow your teacher's instructions to reveal
the hidden portion of the book. In this region of the book, show how to find
the area and perimeter of the eight shapes in the booklet. Note: It might be
easier to show the connections between the shape, its area, and its perimeter
if you redraw the shape.

②   WHAT HAVE I LEARNED?

Working the problems in this section will help you to evaluate which types of problems you feel comfortable with and which ones you need more help with.

Solve each problem as completely as you can. The table at the end of this closure section has answers to these problems. It also tells you where you can find additional help and practice on problems like them.

CL 3-109. Matt moved Triangle A on the graph at right to match up with Triangle B in three moves. Follow the steps Matt wrote below. What was his final move?

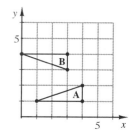

1. *Slide the triangle up 3 units.*

2. *Reflect the triangle across the line y = 4.*

3. *?*

CL 3-110. Using a method of your choice, find the products of the following fractions.

a. $\frac{3}{4} \cdot \frac{1}{4}$ b. $\frac{4}{5} \cdot \frac{4}{3}$

CL 3-111. Copy each figure below on your paper. Assume that the shape in part (a) is a parallelogram. Find the area and perimeter of each shape. Show all your work.

a.

b.

CL 3-112. Sketch the shape made with algebra tiles at right on your paper. Then answer parts (a) through (c) below.

a.   Find the perimeter of the figure.

b.   Find the area of the figure.

c.   If the algebra tiles were rearranged how would the area change?

CL 3-113. Julia has two children who are four years apart in age. Julia is four times older than her youngest child. The sum of the ages of Julia and her children is 76 years. Use the 5-D Process to find the ages of Julia and each of her children.

CL 3-114. Robert found a spinner for a game that was not completely labeled. The spinner is shown at right. Help Robert figure out what fraction of the spinner is missing.

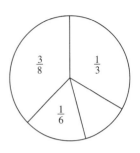

CL 3-115. Evaluate each expression for the given variable.

a. $3a - 7$ when $a = 2$

b. $8 + 5m$ when $m = -2$

c. $13 + (-3n)$ when $n = 4$

d. $\frac{x}{3} + 2$ when $x = 6$

CL 3-116. Copy and simplify each expression.

a. $7(5 - 1) + (-3) - 2^2$

b. $2 \cdot 7 + (-5)(3) - 4$

c. $6 - (-2) + (-5 + 8)$

d. $-2 + 3(3 \cdot 2) - 3^2$

CL 3-117. For each of the problems above, do the following:

- o Draw a bar or number line that represents 0 to 10.

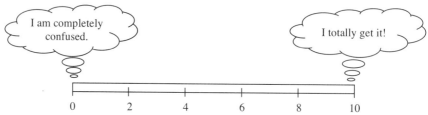

- o Color or shade in a portion of the bar that represents your level of understanding and comfort with completing that problem on your own.

If any of your bars are less than a 5, choose *one* of those problems and do one of the following tasks:

- o Write two questions that you would like to ask about that problem.

- o Brainstorm two things that you DO know about that type of problem.

If all of your bars are a 5 or above, choose one of those problems and do one of these tasks:

- o Write two questions you might ask or hints you might give to a student who was stuck on the problem.

- o Make a new problem that is similar and more challenging than that problem and solve it.

③   WHAT TOOLS CAN I USE?

You have several tools and references available to help support your learning – your teacher, your study team, your math book, and your Toolkit to name only a few. At the end of each chapter you will have an opportunity to review your Toolkit for completeness as well as to revise or update it to better reflect your current understanding of big ideas.

The main elements of your Toolkit should be your Learning Log, Math Notes, and the vocabulary used in this chapter. Math words that are new to this chapter appear in bold in the text. Refer to the lists provided below and follow your teacher's instructions to revise your Toolkit, which will help make it useful for you as you complete this chapter and as you work in future chapters.

Learning Log Entries

- Lesson 3.1.2 – Variables
- Lesson 3.1.3 – Combining Like Terms
- Lesson 3.1.4 – Perimeter and Area Using Algebra Tiles
- Lesson 3.2.4 – Defining and Deciding

Math Notes

- Lesson 3.1.1 – Area of Trapezoids
- Lesson 3.1.2 – Naming Algebra Tiles
- Lesson 3.1.3 – Combining Like Terms
- Lesson 3.1.4 – Evaluating Expressions
- Lesson 3.2.3 – Solving Problems With the 5-D Process
- Lesson 3.2.4 – Consecutive Integers

Mathematical Vocabulary

The following is a list of vocabulary found in this chapter. The words in bold are the words new to this chapter. It is a good idea to make sure that you are familiar with these words and know what they mean. For the words you do not know, refer to the glossary or index. You might also want to add these words to your Toolkit for a way to reference them in the future.

5-D process	**algebraic expression**	**coefficient**
combining like terms	**constant**	**consecutive integers**
equivalent	evaluate	factor
simplified	term	**variable**

Process Words

These words describe problem solving strategies and processes that you have been involved in as you worked in this chapter. Make sure you know what each of these words means. If you are not sure, you can talk with your teacher or other students or look through your book for problems in which you were asked to do these things.

calculate	decide	declare
define	describe	draw
evaluate	illustrate	organize
predict	represent	reverse your thinking
rewrite	simplify	visualize

Answers and Support for Closure Activity #2
What Have I Learned?

Problem	Solution	Need Help?	More Practice
CL 3-109.	Slide the triangle left 1 unit.	Lessons 2.2.1 and 2.2.2 Math Notes box in Lesson 2.2.3 Learning Log (problem 2-66)	Problems CL 2-158, 3-9, 3-52, and 3-107
CL 3-110.	a. $\frac{3}{16}$ b. $\frac{16}{15}$	Lesson 2.3.1	Problems CL 2-161, and 3-40
CL 3-111.	a. Area: 21 square meters Perimeter: 25 meters b. Area: 99 square feet Perimeter: 40.85 feet	Lessons 2.3.2 through 2.3.5 Math Notes boxes in Lessons 2.3.2 through 2.3.5 Learning Logs (problems 2-126 and 2-150)	Problems CL 2-163, 3-10, 3-19, 3-60, and 3-103
CL 3-112.	a. $P = 4x + 6$ units b. $A = x^2 + 2x + 2$ square units c. The area would not change.	Lessons 3.1.1, 3.1.2, 3.1.3, and 3.1.5 Math Notes boxes in Lessons 3.1.2 and 3.1.3 Learning Logs (problems 3-28 and 3-37)	Problems 3-7, 3-13, 3-14, 3-15, 3-20, 3-24, 3-29, 3-38, 3-45, 3-71, 3-88, and 3-108
CL 3-113.	Julia is 48. The children are 12 and 16.	Lessons 3.2.2, 3.2.3, 3.2.4, and 3.2.5 Math Notes box in Lesson 3.2.3 Learning Log (problem 3-98)	Problems 3-67 through 3-70, 3-76 through 3-81, 3-89 through 3-96, 3-104, and 3-105

Problem	Solution		Need Help?	More Practice
CL 3-114.	$\frac{3}{24}$ or $\frac{1}{8}$		Lessons 1.2.4 and 1.2.5 Math Notes box in Lesson 1.2.4 Learning Log (problem 1-107)	Problems CL 1-140, and CL 2-160
CL 3-115.	a. −1 b. −2 c. 1 d. 4		Lesson 3.1.4 Math Notes box in Lesson 3.1.4 Learning Log (problem 3-17)	Problems 3-34, 3-38, 3-49, 3-62, and 3-85
CL 3-116.	a. 21 b. −5 c. 11 d. 7		Lessons 2.1.1, 2.1.2, 2.1.3, and 2.3.6 Math Notes boxes in Lessons 2.2.1 and 2.3.6 Learning Log (problem 2-39)	Problems 2-152, 3-30, 3-72, 3-87, and 3-100

Puzzle Investigator Problems

PI-5. WEIGHING PUMPKINS

Every year at Half Moon Bay, there is a pumpkin contest to see who has grown the largest pumpkin for that year.

Last year, one pumpkin grower (who was also a mathematician) brought 5 pumpkins to the contest. Instead of weighing them one at a time, he informed the judges, "*When I weighed them two at a time, I got the following weights: 110, 112, 113, 114, 115, 116, 117, 118, 120, and 121 pounds.*"

Your task: Find how much each pumpkin weighed.

PI-6. PASCAL'S TRIANGLE

The number pattern started at right is called **Pascal's Triangle**. While it looks like a simple arrangement of numbers, it has many interesting patterns within it. In this challenge, you will learn more about the hidden patterns of Pascal's Triangle.

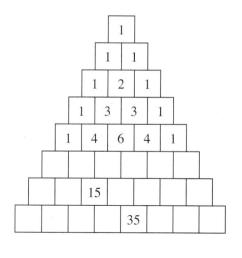

a. Using the PI-6 Resource Page (which you can download at www.cpm.org/students), use the patterns to complete the missing numbers. Some of the numbers are given so you can check your work.

b. What is the sum of the 20th row of the triangle? Can you find this without extending the triangle? <u>Explain</u> how you found your answer.

c. Using a see-through highlighter, color in the squares that contain odd numbers. Describe the pattern that emerges.

d. Find at least three other patterns in Pascal's Triangle that you have not described so far.

e describe how to find the value of a blank square.

Proportional
Reasoning
and Statistics

4

CHAPTER 4   Proportional Reasoning and Statistics

How often do you need to compare one thing to another? Perhaps you compare prices when you are buying something or you compare heights of the basketball players on the court. In mathematics, comparing one thing to another is an important **strategy** to learn about how they are related. We do it when dealing with ratios, fractions, decimals, percents, and similar figures.

You will begin comparing parts and wholes in Section 4.1. You will use these relationships to find percentages, something that you use in your daily life.

In Section 4.2, you will return to the Calaveras Frog Jumping Contest data and use new analysis tools to compare groups of frogs. You will also look at ways to display and interpret data.

Guiding Questions

Think about these questions throughout this chapter:

What's the relationship?

How can I represent the data?

What is the part?

What is the whole?

Section 4.3 will have you investigate how shapes change using mathematics you already know. You will also determine the unknown length of a side in a figure when given information about the lengths of other sides in the figure and in related figures.

In this chapter, you will learn how to:

➢ Find and use percentages to solve problems.

➢ Use measures of central tendency, histograms, stem-and-leaf plots, and box-and-whisker plots to compare data.

➢ Compare shapes and use similarity to find missing side lengths of polygons, especially triangles.

Chapter Outline

Section 4.1 This section introduces a linear diagram that you will use to represent relationships between parts and the whole to solve problems.

Section 4.2 This section introduces you to multiple ways of representing data, including histograms, stem-and-leaf plots, and box-and-whisker plots. You will compare sets of data using these representations.

Section 4.3 This section will introduce similarity and congruence for polygons.

4.1.1   How can I find a percentage?

Part-Whole Relationships

Food labels tell you about what is in the food you eat. The nutrition facts label lists the percentages of vitamins and minerals in each serving. But often it does not tell you exactly how much of each vitamin or mineral is in the food or how much you should have each day to be healthy.

If you know how much Vitamin C is in a serving, can you figure out how much is needed in a day? To help you answer questions like that, this section will develop **strategies** that will help you find information about parts and wholes.

Nutrition Facts

Serving Size 1 cup (228g)
Serving Per Container 4

Amount Per Serving	
Calories 250	Calories from Fat 110

	% Daily Value*
Total Fat 12g	18%
Saturated Fat 3g	15%
Cholesterol 30mg	10%
Sodium 470mg	20%
Total Carbohydrate 31g	10%
Dietary Fiber 0g	0%
Sugars 5g	
Protein 5g	

Vitamin A	4%
Vitamin C	2%
Calcium	20%
Iron	4%

4-1.   WHAT ARE YOU EATING?

The government has created guidelines for how much of various vitamins, minerals, and other substances a person should eat or drink each day to be healthy. These guidelines are then used to create labels (like the one shown above) to inform the public about the nutritional content of food.

According to the sample label above, one serving of Cheesy Mac macaroni and cheese contains 20% of the recommended daily amount of calcium. Doctors recommend a person have a total of 1300 mg calcium each day. How many milligrams of calcium are in one serving of Cheesy Mac?

Your task: With your team, determine how many milligrams of calcium are in one serving of Cheesy Mac macaroni and cheese. Look for more than one way to solve the problem, and be ready to explain all of your **reasoning**.

Discussion Points

What information do we have about the part?

What do we know about the whole?

How could we represent this situation with a number line?

Further Guidance

4-2.   To help you represent the situation in problem 4-1, copy the number line below on your paper.

Recommended Daily Intake of Calcium

0%   100%

a.   With your team, decide how to **partition** the line (divide it into equal parts) so that 20% is shown. Why did you choose to make that number of parts? Is there another way that you could have divided the line?

b.   The recommended daily intake of calcium is 1300 milligrams. Where should 1300 milligrams be labeled on the number line? Add this number to your diagram and **justify** your decision.

c.   Use your diagram to help you decide how much calcium is in one serving of Cheesy Mac. Record your thinking.

Further Guidance section ends here.

4-3.   One way to write a percentage is as a **ratio** (comparison) of parts out of 100. For example, the ratio $\frac{20}{100}$ represents 20 parts out of 100 total parts.

a.   Jill represented the amount of calcium in one serving of Cheesy Mac with the ratio $\frac{260}{1300}$.

   • What does the 260 represent?

   • What does the 1300 represent?

b.   The ratios $\frac{20}{100}$ and $\frac{260}{1300}$ are two different ways to compare the calcium in one serving to the recommended daily amount. How can you show that the ratios are equivalent (the same)?

4-4. One granola bar contains 4 g of dietary fiber. The label says that 4 g is 16% of the daily recommended amount. Louis decided to draw a diagram like the one below to understand this situation.

Recommended Daily Intake of Fiber

a. Copy the diagram on your paper and add the label for 16%.

b. How many grams of fiber are recommended each day? How can you show this with equal ratios?

c. What percent of fiber should Louis get from other foods? Why is this percent equivalent to the ratio $\frac{21 \text{ g}}{25 \text{ g}}$?

d. What other amounts are missing on the diagram? Add labels for all parts, percents, and the whole.

e. Chris is eating cookies that contain 12 g of dietary fiber, which he says is 48% of the recommended daily amount. How can you use ratios to check that 12 g is equivalent to 48%?

4-5. One large carrot contains approximately 6 mg of Vitamin C. The recommended daily intake of Vitamin C is 60 mg. Resa wanted to find out what percentage of her daily Vitamin C she gets from one carrot. She started with a line divided into 10 parts.

Recommended Daily Intake of Vitamin C

a. Why do you think she divided the line segment into 10 parts?

b. Copy the diagram on your paper and fill in the missing labels.

c. The ratio $\frac{6 \text{ mg}}{60 \text{ mg}}$ represents the portion of Vitamin C in one large carrot. Work with your team to find this ratio in the diagram. Where do you see each amount? What other ratio could you write that would be equal to this?

d. Use the diagram to help you find and write at least two more ratios on the number line that are equal to each other.

4-6.   Resa was mixing blue and red paint to create purple paint. She created the drawing below to show the portions of blue paint to red that she used.

a.   What does the picture tell you about the paint mixture? What statements can you make?

b.   If you have not stated it yet, what percent of the paint is blue? What percent of the paint is red? **Justify** your answer.

4-7.   **Additional Challenge:** Turner Middle School has 110 boys. Fifty-six percent of the students in the school are girls. How many students go to this school?

a.   Create a model like Resa's from problem 4-5. Label the percentage of girls, the percentage of boys, and the number of boys on your drawing, as well as 0% and 100%.

b.   How many students go to the school? How do you know?

c.   How many girls go to the school? Explain your **reasoning**.

4-8.   **Additional Challenge:** Regina is making paper flowers as decorations for the fall dance. She has made 40 flowers so far, and she is 16% finished. If she plans to finish making 70% of the flowers tonight, how many more will she need to make? Show your work.

MᴇᴛHODS AND MᴇANINGS

Equivalent Ratios

A **ratio** is a comparison of two amounts. A ratio can be written in words, as a fraction, or with colon notation. Most often in this course we will write ratios as fractions or state them in words.

For example, if there are 28 students in a math class and 15 of them are girls, we can write the ratio of the number of girls to the number of students in the class as:

15 girls to 28 students $\frac{15 \text{ girls}}{28 \text{ students}}$ 15 girls : 28 students

You used a Giant One to write equivalent fractions in Chapter 1. To rewrite any ratio as an **equivalent ratio**, write it as a fraction and multiply it by a fraction equal to one. For example, you can show that the ratio of girls to students is the same for a larger classroom using a Giant One like this:

$$\frac{5 \text{ girls}}{9 \text{ students}} \cdot \frac{3}{3} = \frac{15 \text{ girls}}{27 \text{ students}}$$

Equivalent fractions (or ratios) can be thought of as families of fractions. There are an infinite number of fractions that are equivalent to a given fraction. You may want to review the basis for using a Giant One — the Multiplicative Identity — in the Math Note in Lesson 1.2.3.

4-9.   Find the missing values on the diagram below. Assume that the line is evenly divided.

4-10.   A fish tank that holds 80 gallons of water is 55% full.

   a.   Create a drawing like Louis' in problem 4-4 to represent this situation.

   b.   How many gallons are in the tank now? How many more gallons are needed to fill the tank?

4-11.   Fill in the missing numbers in each number sentence.

   a. $\frac{5}{8} \cdot \frac{3}{3} = \frac{?}{?}$ b. $\frac{9}{15} \cdot \frac{?}{?} = \frac{?}{60}$ c. $\frac{7}{20} \cdot \frac{?}{?} = \frac{?}{110}$ d. $\frac{44}{100} \cdot \frac{?}{?} = \frac{?}{60}$

   e.   What **strategies** did you use to find the numbers in the Giant One in parts (b), (c), and (d)?

4-12.   Okie is a western lowland gorilla that lives at the Franklin Park Zoo near Boston, MA. He loves to finger paint and many of his paintings have been sold because their colors are so interesting. One painting was sold for five times the amount of a second, and a third was sold for $1500. If the total sale was for $13,500, how much did the most expensive painting sell for?

   Set up a 5-D Process table and solve the problem. Then represent the relationships using a variable.

4-13.   Simplify the following expressions.

   a. $\frac{2}{3} + \frac{4}{5}$ b. $\left(\frac{4}{5}\right)\left(\frac{2}{3}\right)$ c. $\frac{4}{5} - \left(-\frac{2}{3}\right)$

4-14.   Lucy keeps track of how long it takes her to do the newspaper crossword puzzle each day. Her recent times (in minutes) were:

   8   22   19   12   18   19   10   35   12   19   16   21

   a.   What is the median of her data?

   b.   What is the mode?

4.1.2 What is the percentage of the whole?

Finding and Using Percentages

How are sales advertised in different stores? In a clothing store, items are often marked with signs saying, "20% off" or "40% discount." In a grocery store, sale items are usually listed by price. For example, pasta is marked, "Sale price 50¢," or boxes of cereal are marked "$2.33 each." In the clothing store you are able to see how much the discount is, but the price you will pay is often not stated. On the other hand, sometimes in the grocery story it is not possible to tell the size of the discount. It might only be a small fraction of the original price.

The actual dollar amount of the discount and the percentage comparing it to the whole are important information that help you decide if you are getting a good deal. Today you will create complete information about a sale situation from the information given in a problem.

By the end of this lesson, you will be expected to answer the following target questions:

How can I find a percentage of a whole?

How can I find a percent if you have two parts that make a whole?

How can I find the whole amount if you know the parts?

4-15.   Marisa is always looking for a great deal while shopping. She found a sale rack where all of the jeans are marked 40% off. Her favorite jeans regularly cost $65.

a.   To figure out if she has enough money to buy a pair of jeans, Marisa decides to estimate. She thinks that the jeans will cost approximately $30. Is her estimate reasonable? Explain your thinking.

b.   To find the exact answer, Marisa created the diagram below. How could she add marks to evenly partition the line? Partition the line and calculate the missing values.

Problem continues on next page. →

4-15.   *Problem continued from previous page.*

    c.   How much money will Marisa save? What is the price she will have to pay?

    d.   Marisa wants to check her answer from part (c). How could she use the amount she saved and the original price to verify that she received a 40% discount?

4-16.   At the same sale, Kirstin sees a shirt that originally cost $50 on sale for just $37.50.

    a.   Estimate the percentage of the discount on the shirt.

    b.   Draw a diagram to represent this situation. Label all the parts.

    c.   What percent is the discount on Kirstin's shirt?

    d.   What is the relationship between the discount, sale price, and the original price? Write a statement that shows the relationship between the sale price, discount, and original price.

4-17.   So far in this section, you have used a linear model to represent percent problems in various contexts.

    a.   Obtain a Lesson 4.1.2 Resource Page (available at www.cpm.org/students) and use the linear models to find parts and wholes when different types of information are provided on the diagrams.

    b.   For each diagram, write at least three statements describing how parts and percentages are related. Some statements are started for you.

4-18.   When Kirstin was about to pay for her clothes, she realized that she had forgotten to include an 8% sales tax.

    a.   The belt Kirstin wants to buy costs $15 and she does not have paper to draw a linear model. To estimate tax, she figured that calculating 10% would be close enough. Explain how Kirstin might find 10% of $15 without a linear model.

    b.   Calculate exactly how much the 8% sales tax will cost Kirstin. What will be the total amount she will have to pay to the store?

                        Making Connections: Course 2

METHODS AND MEANINGS

MATH NOTES

Part to Whole Relationships

Percentages, fractions, and decimals are all different ways to represent a portion of a whole or a number. Portion-whole relationships can also be described in words.

We can represent a part to whole relationship with a linear model like the one below. To solve a percentage problem described in words, you must first identify three important quantities: the percent, the whole, and the part of the whole. One of the quantities will be unknown. A diagram can help to organize the information. For example:

> There are 220 boys in the 8th grade class. If boys make up 40% of the 8th graders, how many students are in the whole class?

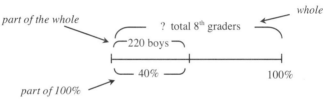

Once the parts have been identified, you can use **reasoning** to extend the part to the whole. For example, if 220 students are 40% of eighth graders, then 10% must be $220 \div 4 = 55$. Then 100% must be $55 \cdot 10 = 550$ students. Another way to solve the problem is to find the ratio of 220 boys to the whole (all students) and compare that ratio to 40% and 100%. This could be written

$$\frac{40}{100} \cdot \boxed{} = \frac{220}{?}, \text{ then } \frac{40}{100} \cdot \boxed{\frac{5.5}{5.5}} = \frac{220}{?}$$

so the total number of 8th graders is 550.

To remember how to rewrite decimals or fractions as percents and percents as fractions or decimals, refer to the Math Notes box at the end of Lesson 1.3.1.

4-19.   A shade of orange paint is made with 5 parts red paint
         and 15 parts yellow paint.

         a.   What percent of the paint is red?

         b.   What is the simplified ratio of yellow to red paint?

4-20.   Janelle earned 90% on a test and got 63 points. How many total points were
         possible on the test? Draw a diagram to organize your information before
         solving the problem.

4-21.   Use graph paper to solve the following problem.

         a.   Draw a four-quadrant graph and label each axis. Plot the following ordered
              pairs: $(-3, 2)$, $(-8, 2)$, $(-10, 8)$, $(-5, 8)$. Connect the points in the order
              given as you plot them, then connect the fourth point to the first one.

         b.   Describe the shape on your graph. What is its area?

4-22.   Copy and simplify each expression.

         a. $7 + (-3)$ b. $(10)(-5)$ c. $-5 + 6$ d. $(-2) \div (-2)$

4-23.   When solving a problem about the perimeter of a rectangle using the 5-D
         Process, Herman built the expression below.

         $$\text{Perimeter} = x + x + 4x + 4x \text{ feet}$$

         a.   Draw a rectangle and label its sides based on Herman's expression.

         b.   What is the relationship of the base and height of Herman's rectangle?
              How can you tell?

         c.   If the perimeter of the rectangle is 60 feet, how long are the base and height
              of Herman's rectangle? Show how you know.

4.2.1 How can I compare the data?

Measures of Central Tendency

You are exposed to a huge amount of information every day in school, in the news, in advertising, and in other places. It helps to have tools to be able to understand what different data mean. In this section, you will turn your attention to what you can learn (and not learn) from data.

4-24. JUMPING FROG JUBILEE

In Chapter 1 you examined results of the Calaveras County Frog Jumping Contest, and saw that the 2009 competition winner jumped 20.5 inches farther than the 2008 winner. Do you think that the winner in 2009 was a special frog? Or were the frogs in 2009 in general better jumpers than the frogs in 2008?

With your team, brainstorm ways that you could compare the two groups of frogs. Recall some of the measures of central tendency from Chapter 1.

2008		2009	
Frog Name	**Jump Length**	**Frog Name**	**Jump Length**
Skeeter Eater	231.5 in.	For the Sign	252 in.
Warped	230 in.	Alex Frog	236.5 in.
Greg Crome Dome	229 in.	Shakit	231.5 in.
R.G.	227 in.	Six Mile Shooter	226.75 in.
The Well Ain't Dry	221.5 in.	Spare the Air Everyday	223.25 in.
Winner	220.5 in.	Hooper	223.25 in.
7 lb 8 oz. Baby	217 in.	Jenifer's Jumper	222.25 in.
Delbert Sr.	216.5 in.	Dr. Frog	185.25 in.

a. Look at the 2008 and 2009 data above (or on the Lesson 4.2.1 Resource Page). What was the **range** (the span of smallest and largest values) of the jumps in each year? What does this tell you about the frog jumps?

b. What was the typical jump length of the frogs each year? How did you find this value?

c. Were the jumps all about the same, or were some jumps **outliers** (data that is much higher or lower than the others)? Name any outliers and why you think they are outliers.

d. Describe how the frogs jumped in each year as completely as you can. Was one year's frogs a better group of jumpers than the other? How do you know?

4-25. How can other representations help you analyze the data? Use the Representing Data technology tool (available at www.cpm.org/students/technology) to create histograms of the data from problem 4-24. Set the bin size of each histogram to 10 inches. Then compare the histograms and answer the questions below as a team or class.

a. How does each histogram organize the data? For example, why is the column between 220 and 230 inches for 2008 four units tall? Why is the 2009 column between 230 and 240 two units tall?

b. What new statements can you make based on the histograms that you did not see when the data was in a list? Is there information that is easier to see in the histogram?

c. The technology tool shows the mean and median of the data below the histogram. However, if those were not labeled, is there a way to determine the median or mean from a histogram alone? Explain.

4-26. How does changing the data affect the mean, median, or mode? Use the 2009 data from problem 4-25. For each of the following changes to the data, predict:

- How would the mean of the data change?

- How would the median change?

- How would the mode change?

Be sure to **justify** your prediction. Only after your team has made a prediction should you calculate or use the technology tool to test your idea. Remember to start with the original 2009 data for each part.

a. What if the 9th place jump length for 2009 (which was 182 inches) was included in the data?

b. What if the 8th place jump length for 2009 was 201 inches instead?

c. What if the 1st place frog was disqualified and only the remaining 7 frogs were included in the data?

Making Connections: Course 2

4-27.   Efren has been keeping data on the Calaveras Frog Jumping Contest for several years. Look carefully at the **stem-and-leaf plot** he made for the top 8 jumpers in 2007, shown at right.

2007 Frog Jump Winners Stem-and-Leaf Plot

Note: 22 | 1 means 221 inches

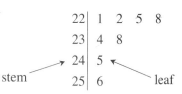

A **stem-and-leaf plot** displays data by ordering it from least to greatest. All of the digits except the last one form the **stem** (in this case, the tens and hundreds places) and the last digit (in this case the ones) forms the **leaf**. The leaf portion is arranged in order from least to greatest.

a.   What is the **minimum** (smallest) value? What is the **maximum** (largest) value?

b.   Are there any outliers in the data?

c.   Is it possible to find the **median** of the data in the stem-and-leaf plot? If so, find the median. If not, explain why not.

d.   Is it possible to find the **mean** with the stem-and-leaf plot? Calculate it and explain what the mean tells you about the frog jumps in 2007.

e.   Create a new stem-and-leaf plot for the 2006 data below. Use your plot to identify the **median** and the **mode**.

2006	
Frog Name	**Jump Length**
Clausenn's Cuzor	235 in.
Whipper	222 in.
Me Me Me Me	212 in.
Haren's Heat	212 in.
Midnight Croaker	209 in.
Alex's Hopper	208 in.
Oh Sweet Sue	205 in.
Humpty Jumpty	204 in.

4-28.   **Additional Challenge:** A visitor to the
frog jumping contest told of another
similar contest he attended. He made the
statements about the frogs in this contest
below. Find a possible set of data that
would satisfy all of his statements.

- The measures of the jumps of the seven frogs were all integers and had a
  median of 14 meters.

- The minimum of the jump data was 11 meters and the maximum was
  15 meters.

- The mode of the jump data was 11 meters.

4-29.   LEARNING LOG

The mean, median, and mode are each different ways of
describing the "center" value of a set of data. You have
been finding mean, median, and mode for different data sets
since Chapter 1. Describe how to find the mean, median, and mode for a set of
data. If a data set includes an outlier, which measure best describes the middle?
Title this entry "Measures of Central Tendency" and include today's date.

4-30.   Mrs. Sakata is correcting math tests. Here are the scores for the first fourteen
tests she has corrected: 62, 65, 93, 51, 55, 12, 79, 85, 55, 72, 78, 83, 91, and 76.
Which score does not seem to fit in this set of data? How will the outlier score
affect the mean of the data? Explain.

4-31.   On graph paper, plot the points $A(2, 4)$, $B(0, 0)$, and $C(6, 2)$ to form
triangle ABC.

a.   Multiply the coordinates of each point by 2 and plot the new points. What
happened to the triangle?

b.   Predict what happens when you multiply each *original point* by $\frac{1}{2}$. Then
multiply the coordinates and plot the new points. Was your prediction
correct?

4-32. Sketch the algebra tile shape shown at right on your paper. Write expressions for the area and perimeter of the shape. Then, calculate the area and perimeter of the shape for each x-value.

a. $x = 9$ cm

b. $x = 0.5$ cm

c. $x = 15$ cm

4-33. Sophie claims that whenever she increases the perimeter of a rectangle, its area increases.

a. She showed the rectangle at right and said, "*If I make the base twice as long, then the area increases.*" Is her statement correct? Draw a diagram of the rectangle she described and explain whether the area is greater or less than the rectangle above.

3 cm

6 cm

b. Is her claim about the relationship of area and perimeter correct for all figures? For example, is there any way that she could have a rectangle with a greater perimeter but with the same area? Give examples and explain your **reasoning**.

4-34. Evaluate the expression $2x^2 + x + 6$ for the given values of x below.

a. $x = 3$ b. $x = -2$ c. $x = 0$ d. $x = 5$

4.2.2 How can I represent it?

Multiple Representations of Data

Mark Twain, a famous American writer and humorist (1835–1910), once said, "Get your facts first, and then you can distort them as much as you please. (Facts are stubborn, but statistics are more pliable.)" What do you think he meant? Much of what we learn and interpret about different sets of data is based on how it is presented.

In this lesson you will use several mathematical tools to look at data in different ways. As you work, use these questions to help focus your discussions with your team:

What can we conclude based on this representation?

What cannot be concluded based on this representation?

How are the representations related?

4-35.   GLOBAL WARMING?

Is the planet getting hotter? Experts look at the temperature of the air and the oceans, the kinds of molecules in the atmosphere, and many other kinds of data to try to determine how the earth is changing. However, sometimes the same data can lead to different conclusions because of how the data is represented.

Your teacher will provide you with some temperature data from November 1, 1975, and November 1, 2000. In all, there is data from 35 cities selected from different parts of the United States. To make sense of this data, you will first need to organize it in a useful way to help some relationship stand out.

a.   Your teacher will assign you a city and give you two sticky notes. Label the appropriately colored sticky note with the name of the city on the front and its temperature in 1975 on the back, and label the other sticky note with its city name on the front and temperature in 2000 on the back.

b.   Follow the directions of your teacher to place your sticky note on the class histograms. Use the axis at the bottom of the graph to decide into which **bin**, or interval, to place your sticky note.

4-36.   Look at the graphs of temperatures the class created. According to these histograms, what can you say about the temperatures on November 1 in 1975 and 2000? Do the graphs show that one date was warmer than the other? Or are the temperatures basically the same? Be prepared to share your **reasoning**.

4-37.   The histograms your class made in problem 4-35 group data together in different **bins**, that is, intervals along the horizontal axis where data is grouped.

   a. What are the benefits of a histogram? What are the limitations?

   b. Another way to restructure the data is to form a **box-and-whisker plot**, which divides the data into four equal parts, or **quartiles**. To create one, follow the steps below with the class or in your team:

      1. With a sticky dot provided by your teacher, plot the 1975 temperature for your city on a number line in front of the class.

         0 10 20 30 40 50 60 70 80 90

      2. What is the median temperature for 1975? Place a vertical line segment — about one-half inch long — marking this position above the number line on your resource page.

      3. How far does the data extend from the median? That is, what are the minimum and maximum temperatures in 1975? Place vertical line segments marking these positions above the number line on your resource page.

      4. The median splits the data into two sets: those that come before it and those that come after it when the data is ordered from least to greatest, like it is on the number line. Find the median of the lower set (called the **lower quartile**). Mark the lower quartile with a vertical line segment above the number line.

      5. Look at the temperatures that come after the median in your ordered number line. The median of this portion of data is called the **upper quartile**. Mark the upper quartile with a vertical line segment above the number line.

      6. Draw a box that contains all the data points between the lower and upper quartiles. Your graph should be similar to a "box" with "whiskers" like the one shown at right.

0 10 20 30 40 50 60 70 80 90 100

Problem continues on next page. →

4-37.   *Problem continued from previous page.*

    c.   What does the box-and-whisker plot tell you about the temperatures of the cities in 1975 that the histogram did not?

    d.   With your team, create a new box-and-whisker plot of the temperature data for the same cities on November 1, 2000 on your resource page. Be sure to identify each of the values below.

        •   The minimum and maximum data values (endpoints of the whiskers)

        •   The median temperature

        •   The upper and lower quartiles

4-38.   Compare the box-and-whisker plots for 1975 and 2000.

    a.   According to the box-and-whisker plots, how do the temperatures on November 1, 2000 compare to temperatures in 1975?

    b.   Did your observations about the differences or similarities of the temperatures from 1975 and 2000 change based on the box-and-whisker plots? If so, how and why did they change?

4-39.   The box-and-whisker plot at right shows the different grades (in percents) that students in Ms. Drew's class earned on a recent quiz.

    a.   What was the median score on the quiz? What were the highest and lowest scores?

    b.   Did most students earn a particular score? How do you know?

    c.   If Ms. Drew has 32 students in her class, about how many students earned a grade of 80% or higher? About how many earned more than 90%? Explain how you know.

    d.   Can you tell if the scores between 80% and 90% were closer to 80% or closer to 90%? Explain.

METHODS AND MEANINGS

Histograms and Bar Graphs

Data can be displayed visually in different formats depending on the kind of information collected and the purpose for displaying it. Two of those formats are histograms and bar graphs, which look similar but are used in different ways.

A **bar graph** is used to represent discrete quantities—such as the number of eighth graders in your school or the number of people who are wearing blue jeans today. The height of the bar graph shows the frequency (the number of times something occurs) of the data in each category. The quantities are "discrete" because the categories are separate. For example, in the graph at right, a student is either a seventh or an eighth grader; no one is a 7.64[th] grader. Traditionally, the bars in bar graphs are separated, and each bar has a different label.

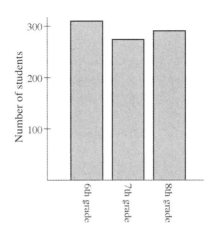

A **histogram**, on the other hand, is a way of representing a collection of data from a continuous set— such people's weight or their distance from home. Each bar represents data in an interval of numbers, called a **bin**. The vertical axis shows the number of pieces of data that fall into a bin (frequency). In the example, the bar on the left shows that there are

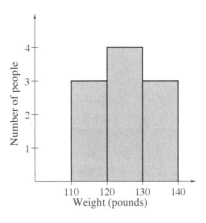

3 people in the data set whose weight is from 110 to just below 120 pounds. (Someone who weighs 120 pounds would be counted in the next bin.) For histograms, we label the horizontal axis by the numbers that mark the lower endpoints of each bin.

4-40.   Look at the two histograms below. They give you information about the heights of players on two basketball teams, the Tigers and the Panthers. Use the histograms to answer the following questions.

TIGERS   PANTHERS

a.   Which team has taller players? Shorter players? Explain your thinking.

b.   Which team has heights that vary more? Explain your thinking.

c.   Which team has more players that are about the same height?

4-41.   Erika is tracking the depth of the water in her local creek. Her first nine measurements are below, in inches:

16 15 13 12 17 14 11 9 11

a.   What is the median of her data?

b.   Erika's next three measurements are 9 inches, 10 inches, and 9 inches. What is the new median?

4-42.   Latisha wants to get at least a B+ in her history class. To do so she needs to have an overall average of at least 86%. So far she has taken three tests and her scores were 90%, 82%, and 81%.

   a.   Use the 5-D Process to help Latisha determine what percent score she needs on the fourth and last test of the grading period to get the overall grade that she wants.

   b.   The teacher decided to make the last test worth twice as much a regular test. How does this change the score that Latisha needs on the last test to get an overall average of 86%? Support your answer with mathematical work. You may choose to use the 5-D Process again.

4-43.   A lemonade recipe calls for using a ratio of 2 cups of lemon juice for every 4 cups of water.

   a.   Draw and label a diagram like the one below to show the percent of lemonade that is water and the percent that is lemon juice.

Old-Fashioned Lemonade

   b.   What is the ratio of lemon juice to total liquid?

   c.   Angel made 10 cups of lemonade. He used 3 cups of lemon juice in his mixture. Did he follow the same recipe? In other words, did he use the same ratio of lemon juice to total liquid?

4-44.   Use your **reasoning** about numbers to answer the following questions.

   a.   If multiplying by $\frac{1}{4}$ makes a positive number smaller, then what does dividing by $\frac{1}{4}$ do to the value of the number? Explain your **reasoning**.

   b.   If multiplying by 1 does not change the value of a number, then what effect does multiplying by $\frac{2}{2}$ have? Explain your **reasoning**.

   c.   If you find 80% of a number, do you expect the answer to be greater or less than the number? What if you find 120%? Explain your **reasoning**.

4-45. Darnell designed the spinner at right for a game. It still has one incomplete section.

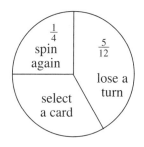

a. Help him figure out the probability of selecting a card on any turn. Show how you got your answer.

b. What is the probability that on any turn you will not get to spin again?

c. Which is more likely: to lose a turn or to select a card? Show how you know.

4-46. Elin has made 29 note cards for her friends. She plans to send out a total of 40 cards. What percentage of the cards has she finished? Represent your work clearly on your paper.

4-47. A triangle has a base that is three times longer than its height. It has an area of 486 sq cm.

Use the 5-D Process to find the base and height of the triangle. Write a variable expression for each column of your chart.

4-48. Copy and complete each of the Diamond Problems below. The pattern used in the Diamond Problems is shown at right.

a.   b.   c.   d.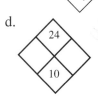

4.2.3 What happens when the data changes?

Analyzing Box-and-Whisker Plots

So far in this course, you have considered static (unchanging) sets of data, such as temperatures on a specific date in time or the lengths of leaps of the top performing frog jumpers. However, most of the time, data sets are growing and changing. For example, as you take quizzes or tests in your class, your overall average changes. Similarly, if you decided to track the average temperature on November 1 for each year, then the average you calculate each year would change as you add new pieces of data.

Today, you will explore how each representation changes when the data it describes changes. You will investigate questions like, "What happens if a new piece of data is added?" and "Is there a way to add data without changing the representation?" You can help your study team succeed today by sharing your ideas and your **reasoning** out loud in your team and by working hard to understand other people's ideas.

4-49.   ALDEN'S SODA

Alden created a box-and-whisker plot for the calories in 11 different brands of sodas as shown below.

a.   According to this graph, what can you say about the calories of the 11 brands of soda?

b.   This is a list of the calories in the sodas represented in the plot:

0, 90, 100, 100, 110, 120, 125, 140, 140, 145, 160

What can you now say about the data (besides the individual values) that you could not say before? Be prepared to **justify** your conclusions.

4-50.   Alden found information about three new sodas. The new sodas have 75, 85, and 105 calories in them.

a.   Predict how adding the three new pieces of data will change the box-and-whisker plot from problem 4-49.

b.   Add the new calories to the data in problem 4-49. What are the new median, minimum, maximum, upper quartile, and lower quartile values? Show how you get your answer.

c.   On graph paper, make a new box-and-whisker plot that includes the additional sodas. Label each of the important points (listed in part (b)).

d.   Compare this box-and-whisker plot to the plot from problem 4-49. How did the first box-and-whisker plot change when you added these three pieces of data?

e.   How could you change the data to make the whiskers longer? Shorter? **Justify** your response.

4-51.   How do box-and-whisker plots help compare data? Think about this question as you compare the data below that shows the ages of the students at three schools.

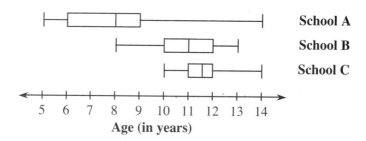

a.   Which school is a K-8 school and how do you know? Does that school have more students in K-2, grades 3-5, or 6-8? Why?

b.   What does the box-and-whisker plot for School C tell you about 11 year-olds at that school?

c.   What statements can you make about School B based on its box-and-whisker plot?

Making Connections: Course 2

4-52. Levi used the box-and-whisker plot below to say, *"Half of the class walked more than 30 laps at the walk-a-thon."* Levi also knows that his class has more than 20 students.

Number of Laps per Person

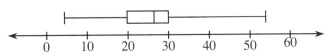

a. Do you agree with him? Explain your **reasoning**. If you do not agree with him, what statement could he say about those who walked more than 30 laps?

b. Levi wants to describe the portion of students who walked between 20 and 30 laps (the box). What statement could he say?

c. How could you alter a single data point and not change the graph? How could you change one data value and only move the median to the right?

4-53. What set of data can you add to any box-and-whisker plot to make one whisker longer, but not change anything else?

4-54. **LEARNING LOG**

What information can you get from a box-and-whisker plot? Sketch one of the box-and-whisker plots you looked at in this lesson in your Learning Log. Clearly label each number on the plot with the word that describes it. Write one question about the data that you could answer using this plot, and one question about the data that would be impossible to answer. Title this entry, "Box-and-Whisker Plot," and include today's date

4-55. **Additional Challenge:** Find a set of data that has all of these properties:

Mean = 17

Median = 16

Mode = 22

Range = 50

METHODS AND MEANINGS

Quartiles

Quartiles are points that divide a data set into four equal parts (and thus, the use of the prefix "quar" as in "quarter"). One of these points is the median, which you learned about in Chapter 1, since it marks the middle of the data set. In addition, there are two other quartiles in the middle of the lower and upper halves: the **lower quartile** and the **upper quartile**.

Suppose you have the data set: 22, 43, 14, 7, 2, 32, 9, 36, and 12.

To find **quartiles**, the data set must be placed in order from smallest to largest. Then divide the data set into two halves by finding the median of the entire data set. Next find the median of the lower and upper halves of the data set. (Note that if there are an odd number of data values, the median is not included in either half of the data set.) See the example below.

Making Connections: Course 2

4-56. Lucy and Marissa each designed a box-and-whisker plot to represent this data set:

16 18 19 19 25 26 27 32 35

Their plots are shown below. Which plot is scaled correctly and why? Explain the mistakes in the incorrect plot.

a.

b.

4-57. Simplify the expressions below.

a. $7 \cdot 2 + 4 - 2(7 + 3)$

b. $6 \cdot 2 + 3 \cdot 4 - 8$

c. $3^2 + 5(1 - 3) + 4 \cdot 5 + 1$

d. $(8 - 12) + 10 \cdot 3$

4-58. Due to differences in gravity, a 100-pound person on Earth would weigh about 38 pounds on Mars and 17 pounds on the moon.

a. What would a 150-pound person on Earth weigh on Mars? Explain your **reasoning** with words or a diagram.

b. What would a 50-pound person on Earth weigh on the moon? Explain your **reasoning** with words or a diagram.

c. **Additional Challenge:** If an astronaut on the moon weighed about 34 pounds, what would that astronaut weigh on Mars? Show how you know.

4-59. Use the 5-D Process to solve the following problem. Write an expression to represent each column of your table.

Yosemite Falls, the highest waterfall in the United States, is actually made up of three smaller falls. The Lower Yosemite Falls is 355 feet shorter than the Middle Cascades Falls. The Upper Yosemite Falls is 80 feet more than twice the Middle Cascades Falls. If the entire set of waterfalls is 2425 feet long, how tall is each of the smaller waterfalls?

4-60.   Find the perimeter and area of each algebra tile shape below. Be sure to combine like terms.

a.

b.

4.2.4   Which representation should I use?

Comparing and Choosing Representations

There are many different representations for displaying data. In this chapter, you have looked at three different representations: histograms, stem-and-leaf plots, and box-and-whisker plots. Today you will compare these representations to decide when one might be a better way to communicate information from a set of data.

4-61.   DATA SET DECISIONS

Ms. Anderson's math class has taken a test and she wants to find a good way to display the data from their test scores so that the students understand them.

- Michaela thinks the best representation is a stem-and-leaf plot because it organizes information quickly.

- Gabe thinks Ms. Anderson should use a histogram because it gives a picture that is easier to look at.

- Geri does not agree. She thinks a box-and-whisker plot shows information that the other two representations do not show.

a.   Discuss with your team which representation Ms. Anderson should use to display the data. On your paper, **justify** your choice.

b.   The test scores for the class are: 78, 62, 91, 51, 55, 93, 76, 82, 65, 85, 79, 83, 55, and 72. On the Lesson 4.2.4 Resource Page, make a stem-and-leaf plot, histogram, and a box-and-whisker plot for this data. Be sure to include a title and labels on all the representations.

Making Connections: Course 2

4-62.   The principal, Mr. Siebers, wants to get information about Ms. Anderson's latest test scores (those listed in problem 4-61). He is interested in the class median, but also wants to know what percentage of students scored lower than a C+ (less than 77 points) on the test.

   a.   What is the median of the class test scores? Which graph makes this the quickest to see?

   b.   What percentage of the students scored lower than a C+? Which graph makes this the easiest to see?

4-63.   Mrs. Smith, another math teacher, also wants to look at Ms. Anderson's test scores. She wants to see information about how many students earned more than 60 points on the test.

   a.   Which representation(s) would show her this information? **Justify** your answer.

   b.   Is your answer to this problem the same as or different from your answer to part (a) of problem 4-62? Why or why not?

4-64.   Ms. Anderson still does not know what kind of representation she should use. She knows that each representation shows different kinds of information. Using the representations that you made in problem 4-61:

   •   List and explain what measures of central tendency or other information will be easily read from each kind of graph listed below.

   •   List the information that will not be easy to obtain. **Justify** your answers.

   a.   Histogram

   b.   Stem-and-leaf plot

   c.   Box-and-whisker plot

METHODS AND MEANINGS

Box-and-Whisker Plots

A **box-and-whisker plot** displays a summary of data using the median, quartiles, and extremes of the data. The box contains "the middle half" of the data. The right whisker represents the top 25% of the data and the left whisker represents the bottom 25% of the data. A box-and-whisker plot makes it easy to see where the data are spread out and where they are concentrated. The larger the box, the more the data are spread out.

To construct a box-and-whisker plot using a number line that shows the range of the data, draw vertical line segments above the median, lower quartile and upper quartile. Then connect the lines from the lower and upper quartiles to form a rectangle. Place a vertical line segment above the number line at the highest and lowest data values. Connect the minimum value to the lower quartile and the maximum value to the upper quartile using horizontal segments. For the data set used in the Quartile Math Note, namely, 2, 7, 9, 12, 14, 22, 32, 36, and 43, the box-and-whisker plot is shown below.

4-65. Jerome is keeping track of how many books he and his friends have read during the first 100 days of school. Make a stem-and-leaf plot of how many books each person has read to help Jerome present the data to his teacher. The numbers of books are: 12, 17, 10, 24, 18, 31, 17, 21, 20, 14, 30, 9, 25.

    a. Make a stem-and-leaf plot of the data.

    b. Jerome wants to present the data with a plot that makes it possible to calculate the mean, median, and mode. Can he do this with a stem-and-leaf plot? He is not asking you to calculate them, but he wants you to tell him if it is possible and why.

    c. Use the stem-and-leaf plot to describe how the data is spread. That is, is it spread out? Or is it concentrated mostly in a narrow range?

4-66. Copy and simplify the following expressions by combining like terms. Using algebra tiles may be helpful.

    a. $3 + 4x + 2 + 2x + 2x$ b. $8x + 4 - 3 - x$

    c. $7x^2 + 3x + 4 + 7x^2 + 3x + 4$ d. $5x + 4 + x + x^2 + 1$

4-67. Twenty-five percent of the students at Marcus Garvey Middle School bring their lunches from home. 225 students do not bring their lunch. How many students attend the school? Draw and label a diagram to show the number and percent of each group of students.

4-68. Find three fractions that are equivalent to three-eighths. Explain your method.

4.3.1 How do shapes change?

Dilations and Similar Figures

Have you ever wondered how different mirrors work? Most mirrors show you a reflection that looks just like you. But other mirrors, like those commonly found at carnivals and amusement parks, reflect back a face that is stretched or squished. You may look taller, shorter, fatter or skinnier. These effects can be created on the computer if you put a picture into a photo program. If you do not follow the mathematical principles of proportionality when you enlarge or shrink a photo, you may find that the picture is stretched thin or spread out, and not at all like the original. Today you will look at enlarging and reducing shapes using dilations to explore why a shape changes in certain ways.

4-69.   UNDOING DILATION

In Chapter 2, you looked at dilations and multiplied each of the coordinates of a shape to change its size. How can you undo dilation?

Charlie multiplied each coordinate of the vertices of a shape by 4 to create the dilated shape at right.

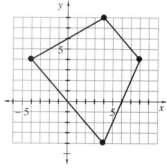

a.   If Charlie multiplied to find this shape, what operation would undo his dilation? Why?

b.   On a Lesson 4.3.1A Resource Page, undo the dilation on the graph above. Label the vertices of Charlie's original shape. How does the shape compare to the dilated shape?

Making Connections: Course 2

4-70. Alana was also working with dilations. She wondered, *"What would happen if I multiplied each coordinate of a shape by $\frac{1}{3}$?"* On the Lesson 4.3.1A Resource Page, graph and connect the points below in order to form her dilated shape.

$$(-1, -1) \quad (-1, 1) \quad (1, 2) \quad (2, -1)$$

a. Alana graphed this shape by multiplying each of her original coordinates by $\frac{1}{3}$. What do you think Alana's shape looked like before the dilation? Make a prediction.

b. On the same graph, undo the dilation to show Alana's original shape. List the coordinates of the vertices of Alana's original shape.

c. What did you do to each coordinate to undo the dilation? How did the shape change?

d. Why do you think the shape changed in this way?

4-71. With your team, look carefully at Alana's dilated and original shapes and describe how the two shapes are related. Use the questions below to help you.

- How are the sides of the small and large shape related?

- How many of the small sides does it take to measure the **corresponding** (matching) side of the large shape? Is this true for all of the sides?

- Compare the four angles of the smaller shape to those of the larger shape. What can you say for sure about one matching pair of these angles? What appears to be true about the other three pairs?

4-72. CHANGING SHAPE

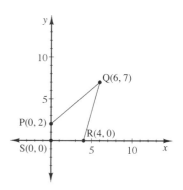

When you multiplied each coordinate of a shape by the same constant, you saw that sometimes the shape became smaller and sometimes it became larger. In Chapter 2, you moved shapes on a graph without changing their size or shape by rotating, reflecting and translating them. What other ways can you change a shape?

Your task: Work with your team to predict what you could do to the coordinates of the shape above to make it look stretched or squished, and what actions will keep the shape the same. Use the questions below to guide your discussion.

Discussion Points

What do you think will change if both the *x*- and *y*-coordinates of the points *P*, *Q*, *R*, and *S* are multiplied by the same number, such as 4?

What do you think will happen if only the *x*-coordinates are multiplied by 3?

What do you think will happen if just the *y*-coordinates are multiplied by 2?

What do you think will happen if the *x*- and *y*-coordinates are multiplied by different numbers, like 2 for *x* and 3 for *y*?

4-73. Test the predictions your team made in problem 4-72. On the Lesson 4.3.1B Resource Page, graph each of the shapes described below.

a. Dilate each coordinate of shape *PQRS* by multiplying each *x*-coordinate and each *y*-coordinate by 4. Graph the dilated shape on the same graph using a color other than black.

b. Go back to the original shape and this time multiply only the *x*-coordinates by 3. Leave the *y*-coordinates the same. Find, graph, and connect the new coordinates.

c. What happened to the shape? Why did this happen?

d. Look at the predictions your team made in problem 4-72. Do you still agree with your predictions? Revise your predictions if necessary, based on your work so far. What do you think will happen if you multiply only the *y*-coordinates of the vertices by a number? Be ready to explain your **reasoning**.

Making Connections: Course 2

4-74.   **Similar figures** are figures that have the same shape, but not necessarily the
same size. One characteristic of similar shapes is that the sides of one shape are
each the same number of times bigger than the corresponding sides of the
smaller shape.

Which pairs of shapes that you have worked with in this lesson are similar and
which are not? **Justify** your answer using specific examples.

METHODS AND MEANINGS

MATH NOTES

Corresponding Parts of Similar Shapes

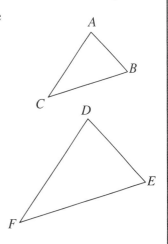

Two figures are **similar** if they have the
same shape but not necessarily the same size.
For example, all semi-circles are similar as are
all squares, no matter how they are oriented.

In order to check whether figures are similar,
you need to decide which parts of one figure
correspond (match up) to which parts of the
other. For example, in the triangles at right,
triangle *DEF* is a dilation of triangle *ABC*
where side *AB* is dilated to get side *DE*, side
AC is dilated to get side *DF* and side *BC* is
dilated to get side *EF*. We say that side *AB*
corresponds to side *DE* or that they are
corresponding sides. Notice that vertex *A*
corresponds to vertex *D*, *C* to *F*, and *B* to *E*.

Not all correspondences are so easily seen.
Sometimes you have to rotate or reflect the
shapes in your mind so that you can tell which
parts are the corresponding sides, angles, or
vertices. For example, the two triangles at right
are similar with *R* corresponding to *X*, *S* to *Y*,
and *T* to *Z*. We can get triangle *XYZ* from
triangle *RST* by a dilation of $\frac{1}{2}$ followed by a
90° counter-clockwise (↺) turn.

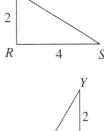

Shapes that are similar and have the same size
are called **congruent**. Congruent shapes have
corresponding sides of equal length and
corresponding angles that have equal measure.

Chapter 4: Proportional Reasoning and Statistics

235

4-75. Create a large coordinate grid on graph paper and graph the triangle at right. Multiply the y-coordinate of each point by 4. Then graph the new shape. Make sure you connect your points. List the points for the new shape. Are the two figures similar? Why or why not?

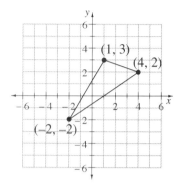

4-76. Kris said, "The Rawlings Rockets basketball team does not have any really tall players." These are the player's heights in inches: 70, 77, 75, 68, 88, 70, and 72.

a. Which number does not seem to fit this set of data?

b. Do you agree or disagree with Kris? Explain.

4-77. Dante is ordering wood flooring for his bedroom, which is shaped like a trapezoid (shown at right). If the flooring materials will cost $5 per square foot, how much should he expect to pay for the materials?

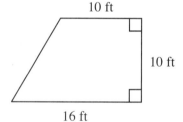

10 ft

10 ft

16 ft

4-78. Copy and complete each of the Diamond Problems below. The pattern used in the Diamond Problems is shown at right.

a.

b.

c.

d.

4-79.   Darnell is designing a new game. He will
         have 110 different colored blocks in a bag.
         While a person is blindfolded, they will reach
         in and pull out a block. The color of the
         block determines the prize according to
         Darnell's sign at right.

> blue → small toy
> purple → hat
> green → large stuffed animal

   a.   If he wants players to have a 60% probability of winning a small toy, how
        many blue blocks should he have?

   b.   If he wants players to have a 10% probability of winning a large stuffed
        animal, how many green blocks should he have?

4.3.2 Are they similar?

Identifying Similar Shapes

Have you ever noticed how many different kinds of cell phones there are? Sometimes you
might have a cell phone that is similar to one of your friends' cell phones because it is the
same brand, but it might be a different model or color. Occasionally, two people will have
the exact same cell phone, including brand, model and color. Sorting objects into groups
based on their sameness is also done in math. As you work with your team to sort shapes,
ask the following questions:

> How do the shapes grow or shrink?
>
> What parts can we compare?
>
> How can we write the comparison?

4-80.   WHICH SHAPES ARE SIMILAR?

If two shapes appear to have the same **general** relationship between sides, how can you decide for sure if those shapes are similar? Work with your team to:

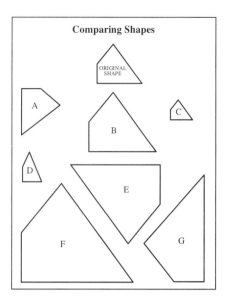

- Carefully cut out the original shape and shapes A-G from one Lesson 4.3.2 Resource Page.

- Decide how each shape is related to the original shape. (Each person should use an uncut copy of the resource page and the team's cut out shapes to help.)

- Compare the angles and the sides of shapes A-G to the original shape.

a.   Which shapes are similar to the original shape? Give specific reasons to **justify** your conclusions.

b.   Look only at the shapes that are similar to the original shape. What do these shapes have in common? What is different about them? Be specific.

c.   When two shapes are similar, the **scale factor** is the number you multiply the length of the side of one shape by to get the length of the corresponding side of the new shape. What is the scale factor between the original shape and shape E? Is each side of the shape enlarged the same number of times? Use a ruler to help you decide.

d.   What is the scale factor between the original shape and shape C? Why is it less than 1?

4-81.   Which shape from problem 4-80 is exactly equal to the original shape in every way? Shapes like this that are similar but do not grow or shrink are called **congruent** shapes.

   a.   Record the pairs of shapes below that appear to be congruent to each other.

   b.   Get a piece of tracing paper from your teacher and use it to check that the shapes you identified as congruent have exactly the same size and shape. Were you correct? If not, why not? Write your answers in complete sentences.

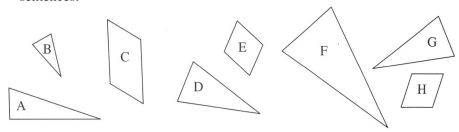

4-82.   Quan enlarged shape Q to make shape P, below. Are his shapes similar? If they are similar, identify the scale factor (multiplier). If they are not, demonstrate that at least one pair of sides does not share the scale factor.

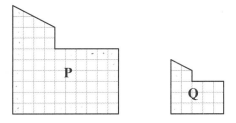

4-83.   Draw each of the shapes in problem 4-82 on graph paper. Color code the corresponding sides on each shape using the colors suggested by your teacher.

   a.   Compare the green sides of each shape. What do you notice about those sides?

   b.   Compare each of the other five sides of shape P with their corresponding sides on shape Q. What do you notice about those pairs of sides?

   c.   Imagine enlarging shape P to make a new shape R that has a base that is 25 units long. If shape R is similar to P, predict the length of the blue side of shape R *without drawing the shape.*

4-84. Using the triangle shown at right as the original figure, *predict* which of the scale factors below would enlarge (make bigger) or reduce (make smaller) the shape. (Do not actually make a new shape.)

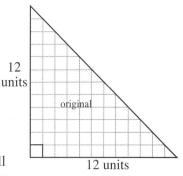

12 units

original

12 units

$$\frac{5}{3} \quad \frac{3}{4} \quad \frac{7}{6} \quad \frac{2}{3}$$

After you write down your prediction, decide which scale factor each member of your team will use. Then copy the original figure on graph paper and draw a similar triangle using your scale factor.

a. Show your new triangle to your teammates and check your predictions. Which scale factors made the triangle larger? Which made the triangle smaller? Is there a pattern?

b. Which parts of the new triangles remained the same as the original triangle? Which parts changed? How do you know?

c. Each of the new triangles is similar to the original triangle used to create it. Compare the corresponding (matching) sides and angles to each other. Describe the relationship or explain why you think there is no relationship.

d. What scale factor could you use to create a triangle that is congruent (identical) to the original? Explain.

e. **Additional Challenge:** Find a scale factor that is less than 2 that will make a similar shape that is larger than the original.

4-85. LEARNING LOG

In your Learning Log, explain how to determine when shapes are similar. In order to decide if two shapes are similar, what do you need to know about the side length? The angles? Title your entry "Finding Similar Shapes" and include today's date.

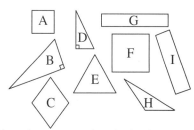

4-86.   Which of the shapes at right appear to be similar? Explain how you know.

4-87.   Mt. Rose Middle School collected canned food to donate to a local charity. Each classroom kept track of how many cans it collected. The number of cans in each room were: 107, 55, 39, 79, 86, 62, 65, 70, 80, and 77. The principal displayed the data in the box-and-whisker plot below.

a.   What is the range of the data? Are there any outliers?

b.   The main office staff collected 55 cans, the counseling staff collected 74 cans, and the custodial staff collected 67 cans.

On grid paper, make a new box-and-whisker plot that includes this data. Clearly label the median and the upper and lower quartiles.

4-88.   For the end of year party, Mt. Rose Middle School ordered 134 pizzas. There were eight fewer combo pizzas than there were pepperoni pizzas. There were three times as many combo pizzas as cheese pizzas. Use the 5-D Process to determine how many of each kind of pizza were ordered.

4-89.   Copy each part below on your paper, then use the number line to help you fill in < (less than) or > (greater than) on the blank line.

$$-15 \ -10 \ -5 \ \ 0 \ \ 5 \ \ 10 \ \ 15$$

a. $-5 \_ -2$ b. $8 \_ -1$ c. $-5 \_ 0$ d. $-15 \_ -14$

4-90.   Simplify the following expressions using the order of operations.

a. $7 \cdot 8 - 4(6-2) + 18$

b. $6^2 - (8 \cdot 3) + 2^2(7 \cdot 3)$

c. $\frac{14}{2} - 3(8-6) + 7^2$

d. $-9 - 3(7-2) + \frac{24}{3}$

4.3.3 What do similar shapes tell us?

Working With Corresponding Sides

Sometimes graphic artists have a shape that they need to make larger to use for a sign or make smaller to use for a bumper sticker. They have to be sure that the shapes look the same no matter what size they are. How do artists know what the side length of a similar shape should be, if it needs to be larger or smaller than the original?

4-91.   With your team, find the scale factor between each pair of similar shapes. That is, what are the sides of each original shape multiplied by to get the new shape? Assume shapes are drawn to scale.

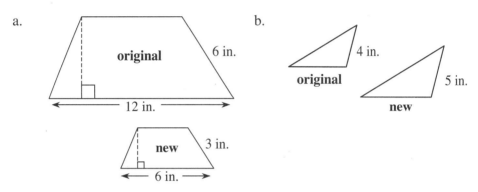

4-92.   It may have been easier to recognize the scale factor between the two shapes in part (a) of problem 4-91 than it was to determine the scale factor between the two shapes in part (b). When sides are not even multiples of each other (like the sides labeled 4 in. and 5 in. in part (b)), it is useful to have another **strategy** for finding the scale factor.

Your task: Work with your team to describe a **strategy** for finding the scale factor between any two shapes. Refer to the questions below to begin your discussion.

Discussion Points

How can we use pairs of corresponding sides to write the scale factor?

Will the scale factor between the shapes be more or less than one?

Does it matter which pair of corresponding sides we use?

4-93. A study team was working together to find the scale factor for the two similar triangles at right.

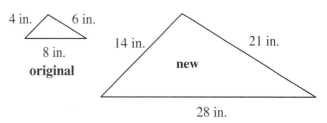

4 in. 6 in.
8 in.
original

14 in. 21 in.
new
28 in.

- Claudia set up the ratio $\frac{14}{4}$ to find the scale factor.

- Issac set up the ratio $\frac{28}{8}$ to find the scale factor.

- Paula set up the ratio $\frac{21}{6}$ to find the scale factor.

a. What did the students do differently when they found their scale factors?

b. Do the triangles have more than one scale factor? If not, show how they are the same.

c. Why does it make sense that the ratios are equal?

d. The different scale factors for this triangle form a **family of fractions**. In a fraction family, each of the fractions is equivalent to the others and can be related to the others using a Giant One. The fraction with the smallest numerator and denominator (that are still integers) in this family is the **root fraction**. For example, in the fraction family that includes $\frac{3}{6}$ and $\frac{5}{10}$, the root fraction is $\frac{1}{2}$. You have probably worked with root fractions before when you were reducing fractions to their lowest terms.

Are any of the scale factors the team wrote a root fraction for this family? If so, give **reasons** to explain how you know. If not, find the root fraction.

4-94.   Alex was working with the two triangles from problem 4-91, but he now has a few more pieces of information about the sides. He has represented the new information and his scale factor in the diagram reprinted at right. Sketch his diagram on your own paper.

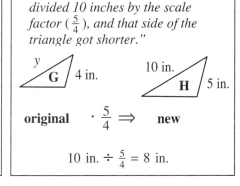

a.   Use the scale factor to find the length of the side labeled x. Show your work.

b.   Since Alex multiplied the side lengths of triangle G to get triangle H, he needs to undo the enlargement to find the side labeled y. What math operation would he use to undo the enlargement? Write an expression and be prepared to explain your **reasoning**. If you are able, simplify the expression to find y.

c.   If triangle H had been the original triangle and triangle G had been the new triangle, how would the scale factor change? What would the new scale factor be? Explain.

4-95.   Alex and Maria were trying to find the side labeled y in problem 4-94. Their work is below.

Maria: *"I made H the original triangle, then multiplied H by $\frac{4}{5}$. The side marked 10 inches became only 8 inches."*

10 in.   H   5 in.   original $\cdot \frac{4}{5} \Rightarrow$ new y G   4 in.

10 in. $\cdot \frac{4}{5}$ = 8 in.

Alex: *"To undo the change, I divided 10 inches by the scale factor ($\frac{5}{4}$), and that side of the triangle got shorter."*

y G   4 in.   original $\cdot \frac{5}{4} \Rightarrow$ new   10 in.   H   5 in.

10 in. $\div \frac{5}{4}$ = 8 in.

a.   Compare the way Alex and Maria solved for y. Why did Alex divide and Maria multiply?

b.   Compare their scale factors. Why did Maria multiply by $\frac{4}{5}$?

Problem continues on next page. →

Making Connections: Course 2

4-95.   *Problem continued from previous page.*

c.   Consider the pair of similar
parallelograms below. For these
shapes, Alex found the scale factor
$\frac{\text{new}}{\text{original}} = \frac{6}{9}$ and used it to write the
expression $15 \div \frac{6}{9}$ to find x.

Use Maria's strategy to rewrite
the problem to find x.

- Which shape would she label "new" and
which would she label "original"?

- What scale factor would she use?

- What does x equal?

4-96.   For the pairs of similar shapes below, find the lengths of the missing sides. Be
sure to show your calculation. You can choose which shape is "new" and
which is "original" in each pair. Assume the shapes are all drawn to scale. The
shapes in part (b) are parallelograms.

a.

b.

c.

d.

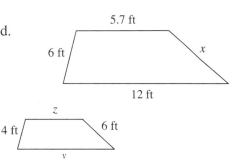

4-97.   **Additional Challenge:** Copy the figure shown
         at right on graph paper.

         a.   Find the area of the shape.

         b.   Enlarge the shape by a scale factor of 2,
              and draw the new shape. Find the area.

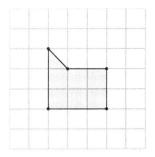

=========== Review & Preview ===========

4-98.   Sketch the two similar
         triangles at right on your
         own paper. Find the
         scale factor and the
         missing side lengths.

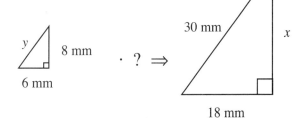

4-99.   Alex and Maria were trying to find the side labeled *x* in problem 4-98. Their
         work is shown below.

Alex: *"I noticed that when I*
multiplied by 3, the sides of the
triangle got longer."

Maria: *"I remember that when we*
were dilating shapes in Lesson 4.3.1,
my shape got bigger when I divided
by $\frac{1}{3}$."

$8 \cdot 3 = 24$

$8 \div \frac{1}{3} = 24$

         a.   Look at each student's work. Why do both multiplying by 3 and dividing
              by $\frac{1}{3}$ make the triangles larger?

         b.   Use Alex and Maria's **strategy** to write two expressions to find the value of
              y in problem 4-98.

Making Connections: Course 2

4-100.　Find the missing lengths or values on the diagram below. Assume that the line is evenly divided.

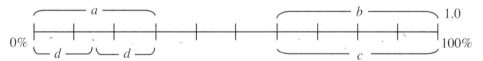

4-101.　Use graph paper to solve the following problem.

a.　Draw an *xy*-coordinate graph and label each axis. Plot the following ordered pairs: $(2, 3), (-2, 3), (-2, -3), (2, -3)$. Connect the points in the order given as you plot them, then connect the fourth point to the first one.

b.　Describe the shape on your graph. What is its area? What is its perimeter?

c.　Change only two points so that the shape has an area of 32 square units. List your points. Is there more than one answer?

4-102.　Sketch the algebra tile shape at right on your paper. Write an expression for the perimeter, then find the perimeter for each of the given values of *x*.

a.　$x = 7$ cm

b.　$x = 5.5$ cm

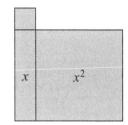

$4.3.4$ How do I find a missing side?

Solving Problems Involving Similar Shapes

Architects create scaled plans for building houses, artists use sketches to plan murals for the sides of buildings, and companies create smaller sizes of their products for display in stores. Each of these models is created to show all of the information about the "real" object, without being the actual size of the object. Today you will work with your team to find **strategies** that you can use when you are missing some of the information about a set of similar shapes. As you work, look for more than one way to solve the problem.

4-103.   MODEL TRAINS

Kenen loves trains, especially those that
run on narrow gauge tracks (the gauge of
a track measures how far apart the rails
are). He has decided to build a model
train of the Rio Grande, a popular narrow
gauge train.

Use the following information to help
him know how big his model should be:

- The real track has a gauge of 3 feet (36 inches).

- His model railroad track has a gauge of $\frac{3}{4}$ inches.

- The Rio Grande train he wants to model has driving wheels that
  measure 44 inches high.

Your task: With your team, discuss what you know about the model train
Kenen will build. What scale factor should he use? What will be the height
of the driving wheels of his model? Be prepared to share your **strategies** with
the class.

4-104.   Heather and Cindy are playing "Guess My Shape." Heather has to describe a
shape to Cindy accurately enough so that Cindy can draw it without ever seeing
the shape. Heather gives Cindy these clues:

Clue #1:   The shape is similar to a rectangle with a base of 7 cm and a
height of 4 cm.

Clue #2:   The shape is five times larger than the shape it is similar to.

a.   Has Heather given Cindy enough information to draw the shape? If so,
sketch the shape on your paper. If not, write a question to ask Heather to
get the additional information you need.

b.   Use what you know about similar shapes to write a set of "Guess My
Shape" clues to describe each of the mystery shapes below. Your clues
should be complete enough that someone in another class could read them
and draw the shape. Be sure to include at least one clue about the
relationship between the mystery shape and a similar shape.

i.   SHAPE A: Triangle

12 cm   16 cm

22 cm

ii.   SHAPE B: Parallelogram

24 in.

32 in.

4-105. Nick enlarged figure A at right so that it became the similar figure B. His diagrams are shown at right.

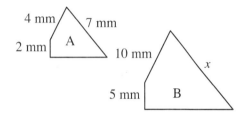

a. Write all the ratios that compare the corresponding sides of figure B to figure A.

b. What is the relationship between these ratios? How do you know?

c. Find two different ways to find the value of x in this quadrilateral. Does your solution seem reasonable? Be ready to share your **strategies** with the class.

4-106. Fatima solved for p in the diagram of similar triangles below and got $p = 30$. Looking at her answer, she knows she made a mistake. What would make Fatima think that her answer is wrong?

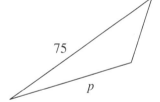

4-107. LEARNING LOG

In your Learning Log, write a description about how to find the missing side of a similar shape. Be specific about your **strategy** and include a picture with labels. Put today's date on your entry and title it "Finding Missing Sides of Similar Shapes."

METHODS AND MEANINGS

MATH NOTES

Scale Factor

A **scale factor** is a ratio that describes how two quantities or lengths are related. A scale factor that describes how two similar shapes are related can be found by writing a ratio between any pair of corresponding sides as $\frac{\text{new}}{\text{original}}$.

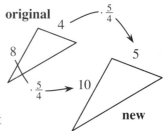

original

new

For example, the two similar triangles at right are related by a scale factor of $\frac{5}{4}$ because the side lengths of the new triangle can be found by multiplying the corresponding side lengths of the original triangle by $\frac{5}{4}$.

A scale factor greater than one **enlarges** a shape (makes it larger). A scale factor between zero and one **reduces** a shape (makes it smaller). If a scale factor is equal to one, the two similar shapes are identical and are called **congruent**.

Review & Preview

4-108. The electronics department is having a No Sales Tax Sale! In addition, all of the items in the department are on sale for 25% off. Wyatt is looking at a music player that normally costs $120. He has $95 to spend, and he is wondering if he has enough money to buy it.

a. Wyatt sketched the diagram at right. Use the work he started to find 25% of $120. Is this the price he will pay?

b. Does Wyatt have enough money?

c. Would he have enough money if he had to pay the 5.5% sales tax on the sale price?

4-109.   For each expression below:

- Sketch and label a pair of similar shapes (like those at right, or in problem 4-94) that would result in this calculation.

- Rewrite the expression so that the operation is multiplication.

- Calculate the value of the expression.

a. $6 \div \frac{1}{2}$

b. $4 \div \frac{2}{3}$

4-110.   A biologist was sitting near a pond and noticed a large number of dragonflies. He also saw both frogs and fish trying to eat the dragonflies. He counted a total of 89 fish, frogs, and dragonflies. He noticed that there were four times as many dragonflies as fish and that the frogs were five more than twice the number of fish.

Use the 5-D Process to determine how many fish, frogs, and dragonflies the biologist counted.

4-111.   Sketch the triangle, then redraw it with sides that are $\frac{1}{3}$ as long as the original.

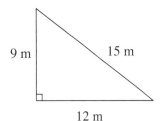

a.   Calculate the perimeters of both triangles.

b.   Calculate the areas of both triangles.

c.   What is the relationship between the perimeters of the triangles?

4-112.   Copy the following problems, then use the number line to help you fill in < (less than) or > (greater than) on the blank line.

a.   −4 __ −8

b.   7 __ −7

c.   −6 __ −5

d.   −1 __ 0

Chapter 4 Closure   What have I learned?

Reflection and Synthesis

The activities below offer you a chance to reflect about what you have learned during this chapter. As you work, look for concepts that you feel very comfortable with, ideas that you would like to learn more about, and topics you need more help with. Look for connections between ideas as well as connections with material you learned previously.

① SUMMARIZING MY UNDERSTANDING

Data is used every day in the world around us to help people make decisions. Oftentimes when people are trying to make a convincing argument or market a product, graphical displays and measures of center are chosen based on how they can help to make a strong, convincing argument.

Today you will use the skills you learned in this chapter to analyze the talents of two frogs. Look at the data provided about Frog A and Frog B and analyze the information.

- Work with your team to display the data in a box-and-whisker plot, a histogram, and a stem-and-leaf plot. Calculate any measures of central tendency that might help you decide which frog is a better jumper.

- After you learn as much as you can about these two frogs, decide which frog you think is the best jumper. Obtain a Summarizing My Understanding Graphic Organizer, choose a data display, and present the statistics that you believe will support your claim.

- Write a convincing argument for why the frog you chose is the best jumper. Make sure to refer to your graphs and measures of central tendency in your argument.

| Seven best jumps (inches) | |
Frog A	Frog B
177	177
221	201
224	203
230	230
239	236
240	236
239	257

②   WHAT HAVE I LEARNED?

Working the problems in this section will help you to evaluate which types of problems you feel comfortable with and which ones you need more help with.

Solve each problem as completely as you can. The table at the end of this closure section provides answers to these problems. It also tells you where you can find additional help and practice on problems like them.

CL 4-113. Evan is trying to save $60 to buy new parts for his bike. He has saved 45% of what he needs so far.

     a.   Draw a diagram to represent this situation.

     b.   How much has Evan saved so far?

     c.   How much does Evan still need to save? Write your answer as a dollar amount and as a percent.

CL 4-114. Mrs. Chen has two brothers. Mark is 7 years older than Mrs. Chen and Eric is 11 years younger than Mrs. Chen. The sum of all three of their ages is 149. Use the 5-D Process to determine the age of Mrs. Chen.

CL 4-115. Sketch the algebra tile shape at right on your paper.

     a.   Write and simplify an expression for the perimeter of the shape.

     b.   Evaluate your expression if $x = 5.5$.

     c.   What is x if the perimeter is 34?

CL 4-116. Find the area of the trapezoid and the triangle at right. Which figure has the larger area? Explain how you know.

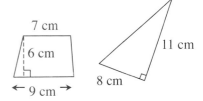

CL 4-117. Copy and complete each of the Diamond Problems below. The pattern used in the Diamond Problems is shown at right.

     a.   b.   c.   d.

CL 4-118. Copy the following expressions on your paper and simplify them by combining like terms. Using algebra tiles may be helpful.

a. $4x + 2 + 2x + x^2 + x$

b. $10x + 4 - 3 + 8x + 2$

c. $4 + x^2 + 3x + 2x^2 + 4$

d. $x + 4 + (x - 1) + 3 + 2x$

CL 4-119. The shapes at right are similar.

a. What is the scale factor?

b. Find the sides labeled x and y.

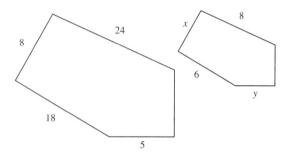

CL 4-120. Over the summer, Gabriel read books that had 192, 202, 175, 219, and 197 pages. What was the average number of pages in the books he read? Show your work.

CL 4-121. For each of the problems above, do the following:

- Draw a bar or number line that represents 0 to 10.

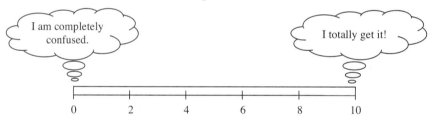

- Color or shade in a portion of the bar that represents your level of understanding and comfort with completing that problem on your own.

If any of your bars are less than a 5, choose *one* of those problems and do one of the following tasks:

- Write two questions that you would like to ask about that problem.
- Brainstorm two things that you DO know about that type of problem.

If all of your bars are a 5 or above, choose one of those problems and do one of these tasks:

- Write two questions you might ask or hints you might give to a student who was stuck on the problem.
- Make a new problem that is similar and more challenging than that problem and solve it.

Making Connections: Course 2

③   WHAT TOOLS CAN I USE?

You have several tools and references available to help support your learning – your teacher, your study team, your math book, and your Toolkit, to name only a few. At the end of each chapter you will have an opportunity to review your Toolkit for completeness as well as to revise or update it to better reflect your current understanding of big ideas.

The main elements of your Toolkit should be your Learning Log, Math Notes, and the vocabulary used in this chapter. Math words that are new to this chapter appear in bold in the text. Refer to the lists provided below and follow your teacher's instructions to revise your Toolkit, which will help make it a useful reference for you as you complete this chapter and prepare to begin the next one.

Learning Log Entries

- Lesson 4.2.1 – Measures of Central Tendency
- Lesson 4.2.3 – Box-and-Whisker Plot
- Lesson 4.3.2 – Finding Similar Shapes
- Lesson 4.3.4 – Finding Missing Sides of Similar Shapes

Math Notes

- Lesson 4.1.1 – Equivalent Ratios
- Lesson 4.1.2 – Part to Whole Relationships
- Lesson 4.2.2 – Histograms and Bar Graphs
- Lesson 4.2.3 – Quartiles
- Lesson 4.2.4 – Box-and-Whisker Plots
- Lesson 4.3.1 – Corresponding Parts of Similar Shapes
- Lesson 4.3.4 – Scale Factor

Mathematical Vocabulary

The following is a list of vocabulary found in this chapter. Some of the words have been seen in the previous chapter. The words in bold are the words new to this chapter. Make sure that you are familiar with the terms below and know what they mean. For the words you do not know, refer to the glossary or index. You might also want to add these words to your Toolkit for a way to reference them in the future.

bin	**box-and-whisker plot**	**congruent**
corresponding	histogram	**lower quartile**
median	mode	**partition**
range	**ratio**	**scale factor**
similar figure	**stem-and-leaf plot**	**upper quartile**

Process Words

The list of words below are problem solving strategies and processes that you have been involved in throughout the course of this chapter. Make sure you know what it means to do each of the following. If you are not sure, look through your book for problems when you were asked to think in the following ways.

brainstorm	choose a strategy	describe
explain your reasoning	justify	predict
rearrange	reverse your thinking	test your prediction
visualize		

Answers and Support for Closure Activity #2
What Have I Learned?

Problem	Solution	Need Help?	More Practice
CL 4-113.	a. b. $27 c. $33 dollars, or 55% of $60	Lessons 4.1.1 and 4.1.2 Math Notes box in Lesson 4.1.2	Problems 4-2 through 4-10, 4-20, 4-43, 4-67, 4-79, and 4-108
CL 4-114.	Mrs. Chen is 51 years old.	Lessons 3.2.2, through 3.2.5 Math Notes box in Lesson 3.2.3 Learning Log (problem 3-98)	Problems CL 3-113, 4-88, and 4-110
CL 4-115.	a. $P = 4x + 6$ b. 28 units c. $x = 7$	Lessons 3.1.1, 3.1.2, 3.1.3, and 3.1.5 Math Notes boxes in Lessons 3.1.1, 3.1.2, and 3.1.3 Learning Logs (problems 3-28 and 3-37)	Problems CL 3-112, 4-32, 4-60, and 4-102
CL 4-116.	Area of the trapezoid = 48 sq. un. Area of the triangle = 44 sq. un. The trapezoid has the greater area.	Lessons 2.3.4 and 2.3.5 Math Notes box in Lesson 2.3.5 Learning Logs (problems 2-126 and 2-150)	Problems CL 2-163 and CL 3-111
CL 4-117.	a. $\frac{2}{15}$, $\frac{13}{15}$ b. $\frac{2}{12}$ or $\frac{1}{6}$, $\frac{11}{12}$ c. $\frac{4}{20}$ or $\frac{1}{5}$, $\frac{1}{4}$ d. $\frac{9}{32}$, $\frac{3}{8}$	Lessons 1.2.4 and 1.2.5 Math Notes box in Lesson 1.2.4 Learning Log (problem 1-107)	Problems 2-46, 2-57, 2-87, 2-118, 3-63, 4-48, and 4-78

Problem	Solution	Need Help?	More Practice
CL 4-118.	a. $x^2 + 7x + 2$ b. $18x + 3$ c. $3x^2 + 3x + 8$ d. $4x + 6$	Lesson 3.1.3 Math Notes box in Lesson 3.1.3 Learning Log (problem 3-28)	Problems 3-32, 3-101, and 4-66
CL 4-119.	a. Divide by 3 or multiply by $\frac{1}{3}$ b. $x = \frac{8}{3}$ or $2\frac{2}{3}$ $y = \frac{5}{3}$ or $1\frac{2}{3}$	Lessons 4.3.1, through 4.3.4 Math Notes boxes in Lessons 4.3.1 and 4.3.4 Learning Logs (problems 4-85 and 4-107)	Problems 4-82, 4-83, 4-84, 4-91 through 4-99, 4-105, and 4-106
CL 4-120.	197 pages	Lessons 1.1.3, 1.1.4, and 4.2.1 Math Notes box in Lesson 1.1.3 Learning Log (problem 4-29)	Problems CL 1-144 and CL 2-157

Puzzle Investigator Problems

PI-7.   MAKING TRACKS!

Vu got a new bicycle for her birthday and
cannot wait to ride it all around her favorite
park. To find out which paths are best, she
wants to ride each of them exactly once,
without repeating any path and without missing
any. When she can do this, it is called an
"Euler" (pronounced "oy-ler") path after a
mathematician who investigated similar paths.

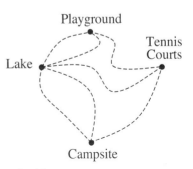

The map of the park is shown at right. Vu needs to decide
where her mother should drop her off to begin her ride.

a.   Is it possible for Vu to ride each trail exactly once without repeating any
path and without missing any?

   • If it is possible, show all the possible ways for her to do this.

   • If none exist, find a new path you could add to the park to create an Euler
     path.

b.   The park manager is planning to add a parking lot as a new point on the
map. It will need to be connected to at least one of the other locations in
the park with a path. Propose a location of a parking lot and at least one
other path so that the park will have an Euler path. Remember that to be an
Euler path, it must use all the paths exactly once.

c.   Vu is thinking about going to one of the parks shown below. Which of
them have Euler paths? Which do not? If an Euler path exists, show where
Vu could start and stop her ride, and use arrows to show the direction she
should travel. Look for reasons why some parks have Euler paths and
others do not.

   i.   *ii.*   *iii.*   *iv.*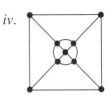

d.   Draw two new parks that have Euler paths and two that do not.

e.   Why do some parks have Euler paths and others do not?

PI-8.   TILING THE LAUNDRY ROOM

Travis is planning to tile his
laundry room with large L-shaped
tiles made with 3 squares. (See an
example at right.) According to
his floor plan, the room is a
4 ft. × 4 ft. square. There is a drain
in the floor that cannot be covered
and is shaded in the diagram.

Tile

**Laundry
Room Floor**

a.   Show one way that Travis could tile his floor using his L-shaped tiles
      without breaking tiles and so that no tiles overlap or cover the drain. Use
      colors to help distinguish the tiles in your diagram. Is there more than one
      way to tile his floor?

b.   While at the store, Travis suddenly worried that his diagram is wrong and
      he cannot remember where the drain is located. Does it matter? Can the
      floor be tiled no matter where the drain is located? Test the different
      possible locations of the drain (listed below) and write a short note to
      Travis about what you discovered.

      i.   Drain is located in the middle   *ii.*   Drain is located in the corner

c.   Uh oh! Travis came home with his tiles and found out that his floor is
      actually a 5 ft. × 5 ft. square and the drain is in the corner. (This is why
      measurements should always be checked twice!) Luckily, he bought extra
      tiles. However, can this floor be tiled? Using graph paper, draw a diagram
      of Travis' laundry room floor and find a way he can tile his floor with the
      same L-shaped tiles.

d.   Given that his laundry room is a 5 ft. × 5 ft. square, does it matter where the
      drain is located? Find at least one more location (not in the corner) for the
      drain that would allow Travis to tile the floor. Also find at least one
      location for the drain that would not allow the floor to be tiled without
      breaking a tile.

Making Connections: Course 2

Inequalities and Descriptive Geometry

CHAPTER 5 Inequalities and Descriptive Geometry

In Chapter 1 your teacher asked you to think of a number and then do several mathematical operations with it to find a specific answer. In Section 5.1, you will be using mathematical operations to do mathematical "magic" tricks. You will also learn how the tricks work and be able to create your own tricks using variables and algebra tiles.

In Section 5.2, you will compare two expressions using algebra tiles on Expression Comparison Mats, discovering the legal moves that allow you to simplify expressions. Then you will determine which expression is greater (or if they are equal) and learn how to record solutions to inequalities using number lines with boundary points. Then your class will study the amazing number zero.

Guiding Questions

Think about these questions throughout this chapter:

How can I build it?

What's the relationship?

Are they equivalent?

Is there more than one way?

How can I measure it?

Section 5.3 has you explore different geometric shapes using a compass, a straightedge, and a protractor. You will do a circle walk and learn how to find the area of a circle.

In this chapter, you will learn how to:

➢ Rewrite expressions by combining like terms and using the Distributive Property.

➢ Simplify and compare two algebraic expressions.

➢ Write and solve algebraic inequalities.

➢ Construct geometric shapes.

➢ Find the circumference and area of a circle.

Chapter Outline

Section 5.1 As you play math tricks, you will learn symbolic manipulation skills such as simplifying, combining like terms, distributing multiplication across addition, and making zeros.

Section 5.2 In order to compare expressions, you will build additional strategies to maintain equivalence and relationships between expressions. You will solve inequalities and represent their solutions on a number line.

Section 5.3 You will use a straightedge and a compass as tools to create geometric shapes. You will also investigate how to find the area and circumference of a circle.

Section 5.4 This section offers several problems to use what you have learned in the first five chapters of this course.

Making Connections: Course 2

5.1.1 Why does it work?

Inverse Operations

Variables are useful tools to represent an unknown number. In some situations they represent a specific number, and in other situations they represent a collection of possible values. In previous chapters you have used variables to describe patterns in rules, to write lengths in perimeter expressions, and to define unknown quantities in word problems. In this chapter you will continue your work with variables and explore new ways to use them to identify specific values.

As you work in this chapter, you will often be called upon to **reverse** a process or operation in order to rewrite an expression or relationship. Applying this Way of Thinking by considering how to work in a different direction will help you understand several of the tools you will learn about in this chapter.

5-1. THE MATHEMATICAL MAGIC TRICK

Have you ever seen a magician perform a seemingly impossible feat and wondered how the trick works? Follow the steps below to participate in a math magic trick.

Think of a number and write it down.
Add five to it.
Double the result.
Subtract four.
Divide by two.
Take away your original number.

What did you get?

a. Check with others in your study team and compare answers. What was the result?

b. Does this trick work no matter what number you pick? Have each member of your team test it with a different number. Consider numbers that you think might lead to different answers, including zero, fractions, decimals and integers.

c. Which steps made the number you chose increase? When did the number decrease? What connections do you see between the steps in which the number got larger and the steps in which it got smaller?

d. How could this trick be represented with math symbols? To get started, think about different ways to represent just the first step, "Think of a Number."

5-2. Why does the magic trick from problem 5-1 work? Will the result always be the same?

To answer this question, Shakar decided to represent the steps with algebra tiles. Since he could start the trick with any number, he let an *x*-tile represent the "pick a number" step. With your team, analyze his work with the tiles. Then answer the questions below.

Steps	Trial 1	Trial 2	Trial 3	Algebra Tile Picture
1. Pick a number				x
2. Add 5				x ▭
3. Double it				x ▭ x ▭
4. Subtract 4				x ▭ x ▭
5. Divide by 2				x ▭
6. Subtract the original number				▭

a. For the step "Add 5," what did Shakar do with the tiles?

b. What did Shakar do with his tiles to "double it?" Explain why that works.

c. How can you tell from his table that this trick will always end with 3? Explain why the original number does not matter.

5-3.   The table below has the steps for a new "magic trick." Use the Lesson 5.1.1
        Resource Page to complete parts (a) through (d) below.

Steps	Trial 1	Trial 2	Trial 3	Algebra Tile Picture
1. Pick a number				
2. Add 2				
3. Multiply by 3				
4. Take away 3				
5. Divide by 3				
6. Subtract the original number				

a. Pick a number and place it in the top row of the "Trial 1" column. Then
    follow each of the steps for that number. What was the end result?

b. Now repeat this process for two new numbers in the "Trial 2" and "Trial 3"
    columns. What do you notice about the end result?

c. Now use algebra tiles to see why your observation from part (b) works. Let
    an *x*-tile represent the number chosen in Step 1 (just like Shakar did in
    problem 5-2). Then follow the instructions with the tiles. Be sure to draw
    diagrams on your resource page to show how you built each step.

d. Explain how the algebra tiles help show that your conclusion in part (b) will
    always be true no matter what number you originally selected.

5-4.   Now **reverse your thinking** to figure out a new "magic trick." Locate the
        table below on the Lesson 5.1.1 Resource Page and complete parts (a)
        through (c) below.

Steps	Trial 1	Trial 2	Trial 3	Algebra Tile Picture
Pick a number				
1.				
2.				
3.				
4.				
5.				

a.   Use words to fill in the steps of the trick like those in the previous tables.

b.   Use your own numbers in the trials, again considering fractions, decimals,
      and integers. What do you notice about the result?

c.   Why did this result happen? Use the algebra tiles to help explain this result.

5-5.   In the previous math "magic tricks," did you notice how *multiplication* by a
        number was later followed by *division* by the same number? These are known
        as **inverse operations** (operations which "undo" each other).

a.   What is the inverse operation for addition?

b.   What is the inverse operation for multiplication?

c.   What is the inverse operation for "divide by 2?"

d.   What is the inverse operation for "subtract –9?"

5-6.   How does a trick (like the one from problem 5-1) work? You will answer this
         question by examining one more trick. In this last trick:

         • Complete three trials using different numbers. Use at least one fraction
           or decimal.

         • Use algebra tiles to help you analyze the trick, as you did in problem 5-3.
           Draw the tiles in the table on the resource page.

         • Find at least two pairs of inverse operations in the process that are
           "undoing" each other.

Steps	Trial 1	Trial 2	Trial 3	Algebra Tile Picture
1. Pick a number				
2. Double it				
3. Add 4				
4. Multiply by 2				
5. Divide by 4				
6. Subtract the original number				

5-7.   Write the inverse operations, that is, operations that "undo" one another for each
         situation below.

         a.   What is the inverse operation for "add $\frac{3}{4}$?"

         b.   What is the inverse operation for "subtract $1\frac{2}{3}$?"

         c.   What is the inverse operation for "divide by 8?"

         d.   What is the inverse operation for "multiply by 12?"

5-8.   Simplify the following expressions.

         a. $1\frac{1}{2} + 2\frac{1}{8}$ b. $\frac{4}{5} - \frac{2}{3} + \frac{1}{6}$ c. $5\frac{3}{5} - 1\frac{4}{5}$

5-9. Draw the table below on your paper and look carefully at the algebra tiles in order to fill in each of the "Steps." Use your own numbers in the trials, again considering fractions, decimals, and integers.

Steps	Trial 1	Trial 2	Trial 3	Algebra Tile Picture
1. Pick a number				
2. Add ____				
3. Multiply by ____				
4. Subtract ____				
5. Divide by ____				
6. Subtract the original number				

5-10. The trapezoids at right are similar shapes.

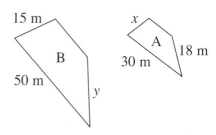

a. What is the scale factor between shapes A and shape B?

b. Find the lengths of the missing sides.

5-11. The Aloha Stadium in Honolulu, Hawaii, has seats for 50,000 people. At an upcoming football game, a company is planning to give away free hats to people based on where they are sitting.

a. The seats are divided into 40 different sections. If hats are given in only 5 sections, what is the probability of a guest sitting in a section that gets a hat?

b. The company is going to choose three rows in each section to win the hats. There are 46 rows in a section. If you are sitting in a winning section, what is the probability that you are not sitting in a winning row?

c. The company plans to give away 750 hats. If you buy a ticket to the game, what is the probability you will receive a hat?

5-12. **Additional Challenge:** Robert found an old game in a closet and wanted to play it. However, a portion of the spinner shown at right could not be read. Find the missing portion of the spinner for Robert.

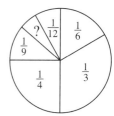

Making Connections: Course 2

5.1.2 How can I represent it?

Translating Situations into Algebraic Expressions

In Lesson 5.1.1, you looked at how mathematical "magic tricks" work by using inverse operations. In this lesson, we will connect the algebra tile picture to another representation of the situation: the variable expression. Consider the following questions today:

How can I **visualize** it?

How can I write it?

How can I express this situation efficiently?

5-13. Today you will consider a more complex math magic trick. Today the table you use to record your steps will have only two trials, but it will add a new column to represent the algebra tiles with a variable expression. Get a Lesson 5.1.2 Resource Page from your teacher.

- Work with your team to choose different numbers for the trials.

- Decide how to write variable expressions that represent what is happening in each step.

Steps	Trial 1	Trial 2	Algebra Tile Picture	Variable Expression
1. Pick a number				
2. Add 7				
3. Triple the result				
4. Add nine				
5. Divide by 3				
6. Subtract the original number				

5-14.   For this number trick, the steps and trials are left for you to complete by using the variable expressions. To start, copy the table below on your paper and build each step with algebra tiles. Describe Steps 1, 2, and 3 in words.

Steps	Trial 1	Trial 2	Variable Expression
1.			x
2.			$x + 4$
3.			$2(x + 4)$
4.			$2x + 20$
5.			$x + 10$
6.			10

a.   Look at the algebra tiles you used to build Step 3. Write a different expression to represent those tiles.

b.   What tiles do you have to add to build Step 4? Complete steps 4, 5, and 6 in the chart.

c.   Complete two trials and record them in the chart.

5-15.   In Step 3 of the last magic trick (problem 5-14) you rewrote the expression $2(x + 4)$ as $2x + 8$. Can all expressions like $2(x + 4)$ be rewritten without parentheses? For example, can $3(x + 5)$ be rewritten without parentheses? Build it with tiles and write another expression to represent it. Does this work for all expressions?

5-16.   Diana, Sam, and Elliot were working on two different mathematical magic tricks shown below. Compare the steps in their magic tricks. You may want to build the steps with algebra tiles.

Magic Trick A	**Magic Trick B**
1. Think of a number.	1. Think of a number.
2. Add three.	2. Multiply by two.
3. Multiply by two.	3. Add three.

a.   Each student had completed one of the tricks. After the third step, Diana had written $2x + 6$, Sam had written $2(x + 3)$ and Elliot had written $2x + 3$. Which expression(s) are valid for Magic Trick A? Which one(s) are valid for Magic Trick B? How do you know? Use tiles, sketches, numbers, and **reasons** to explain your thinking.

b.   How are the two magic tricks different? How does this difference show in the expression used to represent each trick?

5-17.   Parentheses allow us to consider the number of groups of tiles that are present. For example, when the group of tiles $x + 3$ in problem 5-16 is doubled in Magic Trick A, the result can be written $2(x + 3)$. However, sometimes it is more efficient to write the result as $2x + 6$ instead of $2(x + 3)$.

a.   Show at least two ways to write the result of these steps:

1. Think of a number.
2. Add five.
3. Multiply by three.

b.   Write three steps that will result in $5(x - 2)$.

c.   How can the result from part (b) be written so that there are no parentheses?

5-18.   At right is an algebra tile drawing showing the result of the first three steps of a number trick.

    a.   What could have been the three steps that led to this drawing?

    b.   Use a variable to write at least two expressions to represent the tiles in this problem, one of which contains parentheses.

    c.   If the next step in the trick is "Divide by 2," what should the simplified drawing and variable expression look like?

5-19.   You have been writing expressions in different ways to mean the same thing. These expressions depend on whether you see tiles grouped by rows (like four sets of $x + 3$ in problem 5-18) or whether you see separate groups (like $4x$ and 12). The **Distributive Property** is the formal name for linking these two equivalent expressions.

Write the following descriptions in two ways, one with parentheses and one without. For example, $4(x + 3)$ can also be written $4x + 12$.

    a.   1. Think of a number.   b.   1. Think of a number.

           2. Add 5.   2. Add 7.

           3. Double it.   3. Multiply by 3.

5-20.   **Additional Challenge:** Mrs. Baker demonstrated an interesting math magic trick to her class. She said,

"Think of a two digit number and write it down without showing me."

"Add the 'magic number' of 90 to your number."

"Take whatever digit is now in the hundreds place, cross it out and add it to the ones place. Now tell me the result."

As each student told Mrs. Baker their result, she quickly told them their original number. Why does this trick work? Consider the following questions as you unravel this trick:

    a.   Could you represent the original number with a variable? What is the algebraic expression after they add 90?

    b.   What is the largest number the students could have now? The smallest?

Problem continues on next page. $\rightarrow$

5-20.   *Problem continued from previous page.*

    c.   When the students cross off the 1 in the hundreds place (was any other number possible?), what have they subtracted from the expression? What is the new expression?

    d.   When the students add the 1 to the ones place, what is the simplified version of the expression they have created? What does Mrs. Baker mentally add to their result to reveal their original number?

(M)ETHODS AND MEANINGS

MATH NOTES

Algebraic Expressions

An **algebraic expression** consists of one or more variables, or a combination of numbers and variables possibly connected by mathematical operations. Each part of the expression separated by an addition or multiplication sign is called a **term**. A numerical term in an algebraic expression (like the 7 and 9 below) is called a **constant**. Expressions do not contain an equal sign (=). Four examples of algebraic expressions are:

$$4x, \ 4x - 3y + 7, \ \frac{3x^2}{2x+5} - 9, \ 3x - 5(x^2 + 2) + 1$$

In the examples above, the expressions have one term, three terms, two terms, and three terms, respectively. Algebraic expressions may be simplified or, if the values of the variables are known, expressions may be evaluated. See the examples below.

Simplify this expression:

$$4x + 5 - 2x + 1$$
becomes
$$2x + 6$$

Evaluate the expression $3y + y^2$ for $y = -2$.

$$3(-2) + (-2)^2$$
$$-6 + 4$$
$$-2$$

5-21.   Copy the chart on your paper, then complete two trials by reading the variable expressions. Write in the steps as well.

	Steps	Trial 1	Trial 2	Variable Expression
1.				x
2.				$6x$
3.				$6x + 24$
4.				$6x + 18$
5.				$x + 3$
6.				3

5-22.   Translate each of these situations into a variable expression such as those found in a magic number chart.

a.   Think of a number and multiply it by seven.

b.   Think of a number and divide it by eight.

c.   Think of a number and reduce it by ten.

d.   Think of a number, add two, then multiply by five.

5-23.   Ms. Poppy has finished grading her students' tests. The scores were: 62, 65, 93, 51, 55, 76, 79, 85, 55, 72, 78, 83, 91, and 82.

a.   Find the median.   b.   Find the range.

c.   Find the mode.   d.   Find the quartiles.

e.   Find the mean.

5-24. The scale drawing at right shows the first floor of a house. The actual dimensions of the garage are 20 feet by 25 feet. All angles are right angles.

2 inches | 1 inch

| Living Room | Garage | $1\frac{1}{4}$ inch |
| Dining Room | Kitchen | Office |

a. How many feet does each inch represent?

b. What is the length and width of the living room in inches?

c. What is the length and width of the living room in feet?

d. What is the area of the living room (in square feet)?

e. What is the perimeter of the garage (in feet)?

5-25. Graph the following points on a coordinate grid: $A(1,1)$, $B(2,3)$, $C(5,3)$, $D(5,1)$. Connect the points, including the last one to the first point.

a. What shape have you created?

b. What point can you move to create a rectangle? What would be the new coordinate?

c. Reflect trapezoid *ABCD* across the *y*-axis. What are the new coordinate points of the trapezoids vertices?

5.1.3 How can I simplify it?

Simplifying Algebraic Expressions

In the previous lesson, you represented more complex mathematical tricks with variable expressions instead of algebra tiles because the expressions were more efficient. In this lesson, you will explore various ways to make expressions simpler by making parts of them zero.

Zero is a relative newcomer to the number system. Its first appearance was as a placeholder around 400 B.C. in Babylon. The Ancient Greeks philosophized about whether zero was even a number: "How can nothing be something?" East Indian mathematicians are generally recognized as the first culture to represent the quantity zero as a numeral and number in its own right about 600 A.D.

Zero now holds an important place in mathematics both as a numeral representing the absence of quantity as well as a placeholder. Did you know there is no year 0 in the Gregorian calendar system (our current calendar system of 365 days in a year)? Until the creation of zero, number systems began at one. Consider the following questions as you work today:

How can I create a zero?

How can I rewrite this expression in the most efficient way?

5-26. CONCEPTS OF ZERO

Zero is a special and unusual number. As you read above, it has an interesting history. What do you know about zero mathematically? The questions below will test your knowledge of zero.

a. If two quantities are added and the sum is zero, what do we know about the quantities?

b. If we add zero to a number, how does the number change?

c. If we multiply a number by zero, what do we know about the product?

d. What is the opposite of zero?

e. If three numbers have a product of zero, what do we know about at least one of the numbers?

f. Is zero even or odd?

5-27. As you know, +1 is represented with algebra tiles as a shaded small square and is always a positive unit. The opposite of 1, written −1, is an open small square and is always negative. Is this true with the variable x-tiles too?

a. The variable x-tile is shaded, but is the number represented by a variable such as x always positive? Why or why not?

b. The opposite of the variable x, written −x, looks like it might be negative, but since the value of a variable can be any number (the opposite of −2 is 2), what can you say about the opposite of the variable x?

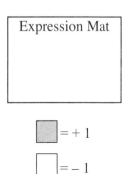

c. Is it possible to determine which is greater: x or −x? Explain.

d. What is true about $6 + (-6)$? What is true about $x + (-x)$ (the sum of a variable and its opposite)?

5-28. Get a Lesson 5.1.3 Resource Page, from your teacher, which is called "Expression Mat." This will help you so you can tell the difference between the expression you are working on and everything else on your desk.

From your work in problem 5-27, we can say that situations like $6 + (-6)$ and $x + (-x)$ create "zeros," that is, when we add an equal number of tiles and their opposites, the result is zero. The pairs of unit tiles and x tiles shown in that problem are examples of "zero pairs" of tiles.

Build each collection of tiles represented below on the mat. Name the collection using a simpler algebraic expression (one that has fewer terms) by finding and removing zero pairs and combining like terms.

a. $2 + 2x + x + (-3) + (-3x)$

b. $-2 + 2x + 1 - x + (-5) + 2x$

5-29. An **equivalent expression** refers to the same amount with a different name.

Build the expression mats shown in the pictures below. Write the expression shown on the expression mat, then write its simplified equivalent expression by making zeros (zero pairs) and combining like terms.

a.

b.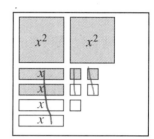

5-30. Build what is described in words below on your expression mat. Then write two different equivalent expressions to describe what is represented. One of the two representations should include parentheses.

a. The area of a rectangle with a width of 3 units and a length of $x + 5$.

b. Two equal groups of $3x - 2$.

c. Four rows of $2x + 1$.

d. A number increased by one, then tripled.

5-31. Copy and rewrite the following expressions by combining like terms and making zeros. Using algebra tiles may be helpful.

a. $(-1) + (-4x) + 2 + 2x + x$

b. $2x + 4 + (-3) + 3x$

c. $3x^2 + (-2x^2) + 5x + (-4x)$

d. $x - 6 + 4x + 5$

5-32. **Additional Challenge:** Division by zero is an interesting concept. Some students believe that when you divide by zero, the result is zero. Consider how the numerical equation $30 \div 6 = 5$ can be **reversed** to make the multiplication equation $5 \cdot 6 = 30$.

a. **Reverse** the division equation $24 \div 4 = 6$ into a multiplication equation.

b. Now take the equation $24 \div 0 = x$ and **reverse** it into a multiplication equation. What value of x can make this equation true? Explain.

c. Why do you think the solution to a number divided by zero is called "undefined?"

d. Is $0 \div 24$ also "undefined?" Why or why not?

Making Connections: Course 2

5-33.   LEARNING LOG

In your Learning Log, explain how to simplify expressions in your own words. Include an example of different ways to write the expression $3(x+4)$ by drawing pictures and writing equivalent expressions. Title this entry "Simplifying Expressions" and include today's date.

5-34.   Sketch each collection of tiles below. Name the collection using a simpler algebraic expression, if possible. If it is not possible to simplify the expression, explain why not.

a. $(-x) + 7 + 4x + x + (-3) + (-3x)$

b.   Seven plus three times a number, plus three minus three times the number.

c.   Two groups of a number plus three.

d. $7 + 4x^2 + 5x$

e. $x^2 + x^2 + (-5) + 2$

5-35.   What number do you get with this number magic trick? Support your answer
        with at least three trials.

        1. Think of a number
        2. Add the next higher number
        3. Add nine
        4. Divide by two
        5. Subtract your original number

5-36.   Alden found a partially completed 5-D chart:

Define			Do	Decide
				Target 74
Trial 1: 15	$2(15) = 30$	$15 + 2 = 17$	$15 + 30 + 17 =$	62 too small
Trial 2: 18	$2(18) = 36$	$18 + 2 = 20$	$18 + 36 + 20 =$	74 just right

    a.   Create a word problem that could have been solved using this chart.

    b.   What words would you put above the numbers in the three empty sections
         in the "Trial" and "Define" parts of the chart?

    c.   What word(s) would you put above the "Do" column?

5-37.   Rachel is collecting donations for the local animal shelter. So far she has
        collected $245, which is 70% of what she hopes to collect. How much money
        does Rachel plan to collect for the shelter? Show your work.

5-38.   Simplify each expression.

    a. $1.2 - 0.8$ b. $-4 - (-2)$ c. $-\frac{6}{11} - (-\frac{1}{4})$

    d. $\frac{2}{3} \cdot \frac{2}{5}$ e. $0.6 \cdot 8$ f. $-\frac{5}{4} \cdot \frac{8}{13}$

Making Connections: Course 2

5-39.   Alex is trying to simplify the expression $-1\frac{1}{4}+(2\frac{1}{2})+(3\frac{1}{4})$. He started by rewriting it like this:

$$-1+(-\tfrac{1}{4})+2+\tfrac{1}{2}+3+\tfrac{1}{4}$$
$$(-1+2+3)+(-\tfrac{1}{4}+\tfrac{1}{4}+\tfrac{1}{2})$$

a.   Why might he have regrouped the expression in this way?

b.   Simplify the expression. What is the result?

c.   What property was Alex using when he rewrote the problem?

d.   Use this strategy to regroup the expression $\frac{3}{10}+2\frac{1}{10}+(-1\frac{2}{5})$ and find the result.

5.2.1 How do these compare?

Comparing Expressions

You have been working with writing and simplifying expressions that represent the steps of a number trick. As you wrote these expressions you learned that it was helpful to simplify them by combining like terms and removing zeros. In this lesson you and your teammates will use a tool for comparing expressions to determine if one expression is greater than the other or if they are equal, that is, equivalent ways of writing the same thing.

Remember that to represent expressions with algebra tiles, you will need to be very careful about how positive and negative are distinguished. To help understand the diagrams in the text, the legend showing the shading for +1 and –1 at right will be placed on every page. This model also represents a zero pair.

5-40.   COMPARING EXPRESSIONS

Ignacio and Olivia were playing a game. Each of them grabbed a handful of algebra tiles. They wanted to see whose expression had the greater value.

Two expressions can be compared by dividing the expression mat in half to change it into an **Expression Comparison Mat**. Then the two expressions can be built side by side and compared to see which one is greater.

- Olivia put her tiles on Mat A in the picture above and described it as $5 + (-3)$.

- Ignacio put his tiles on Mat B and said it was $(-5) + 2$.

With your team, find two different methods to simplify the two expressions in order to compare them. Which side of the mat is larger?

Mat A   Mat B

$5 + (-3)$ $(-5) + 2$

5-41. Using your Expression Comparison Mat, build the two expressions at right. Find a way to determine which side is greater, if possible. Show your work by sketching it on the Lesson 5.2.1B Resource Page. Be ready to share your conclusion and your **justification**.

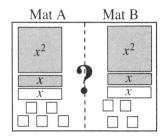

5-42. MORE COMPARING EXPRESSIONS – Is one expression greater?

Consider how you were able to compare the expressions in the previous problems. When is it possible to remove tiles to compare the expressions on the mats? In this problem you will work with your team to identify two different "legal moves" for simplifying expressions.

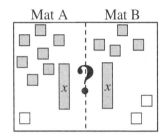

Build the mat at right using tiles and simplify the expressions. Record your work by drawing circles around the zeros or the balanced sets of tiles that you remove in each step on the Lesson 5.2.1B Resource Page. Which expression is greater?

5-43. There are two kinds of moves you could use in problem 5-42 to simplify expressions with algebra tiles. They are removing zeros and removing matching (or balanced) sets of tiles from both sides of the mat as shown in the figures below. **Justify** why each of these moves can be used to simplify expressions.

Removing Balanced Sets

Removing Zeros

5-44.   WHICH SIDE IS GREATER?

For each of the problems below, use the Lesson 5.2.1 Resource Page and:

- Build the two expressions on your mat.

- Write an expression for each side below the mats for parts (a) through (d).

- Draw the tiles in the space given on the resource page for parts (e) and (f).

- Use legal moves to determine which mat is greater, if possible. Record your work by drawing circles around the zeros or the balanced (matching) sets of tiles that you remove in each problem.

a.

b.

c.

d.
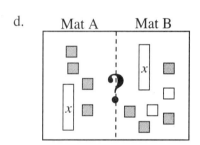

e.   Mat A: $3x - 4 - 2$

Mat B: $3(x - 1)$

f.   Mat A: $5 + (-3x) + 5x$

Mat B: $x^2 + 2x + 1 - x^2$

METHODS AND MEANINGS

Inequality Symbols

MATH NOTES

Just as the symbol "=" is used to represent that two quantities are equal in mathematics, the **inequality symbols** at right are used when describing the relationships between quantities that are not necessarily equal. Examples: $3 < 7$, $14 \leq 14$, $7 > 3$, $19 \geq 14$.

< less than
≤ less than or equal to
> greater than
≥ greater than or equal

Review & Preview

5-45. Write the expression shown on each of the Expression Mats below, then simplify them by making zeros and combining like terms.

a.

b.

5-46. Copy and rewrite the following expressions by combining like terms, making zeros, and using the Distributive Property. **Visualizing** the expressions by using algebra tiles may be helpful.

a. $(-3) + 4x + 2 + 2x + 2x$

b. $-8x + 4 + (-3)$

c. $7x^2 + 3x + 4 + 7x^2 + 3x + 4$

d. $5(x - 4)$

5-47. Simplify the following expressions.

a. $-\frac{3}{4}-\frac{2}{5}$

b. $\frac{7}{8}-\frac{2}{3}$

c. $\frac{1}{3}-\frac{5}{6}$

d. $1\frac{2}{3}+(-\frac{2}{5})$

e. $\frac{4}{7}-(-\frac{3}{8})$

f. $-4\frac{1}{2}+3\frac{1}{9}$

5-48. Figures A and B at right are similar. Assuming that figure A is the original figure, find the scale factor and find the lengths of the missing sides of figure B.

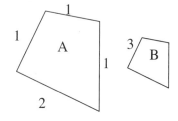

5-49. Desmond is rolling a standard six-sided number cube. He plans to roll it 72 times.

a. About how many times would you expect Desmond to roll a 4? Why?

b. About how many times would you expect him to roll an even number? Why?

c. Desmond kept track of his results for all 72 rolls. The chart at right shows some of his results.

Based on his partial results, how many times did he roll a 5 or a 6?

Result	Number of outcomes
1	9
2	14
3	11
4	8

5.2.2 What if I can't tell?

Comparing Quantities with Variables

Have you ever tried to make a decision when the information you have is uncertain? Perhaps you have tried to make plans on a summer day only to learn that it *might* rain. In that case, your decision might have been based on the weather, such as, "I will go swimming if it doesn't rain, or stay home and play video games if it does rain." Sometimes in mathematics solutions might depend on something you do not know, like the value of the variable. Today you will study this kind of situation.

5-50.   For each of the problems below, build the given expressions on your Expression Comparison Mat. Then use the simplification **strategies** of removing zeros and simplifying by removing matching pairs of tiles to determine which side is greater, if possible. Record your steps on the Lesson 5.2.2 Resource Page.

a.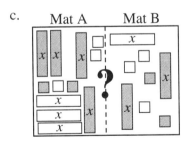

b.   Mat A: $2(x+3)-4$

   Mat B: $3x+(-1)-x+4$

c.

d.

5-51.   WHAT HAPPENED?

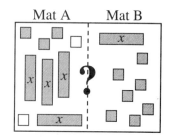

When Ignacio and Olivia compared the expressions in part (d) of
problem 5-50, they could not figure out which side was greater.

    a.   Is it always possible to determine which
         side of the Expression Comparison Mat is
         greater (has the larger value)? Why or why
         not? Be prepared to share your **reasoning**.

    b.   How is it possible for Mat A to have the
         greater value?

    c.   How is it possible for Mat B to have the
         greater value?

    d.   What other way can Mat A and B be related? Explain.

5-52.   Ignacio and Olivia are playing another game
        with the algebra tiles. After they simplify
        two new expressions, they are left with the
        expressions on their mats shown at right.
        Can you tell by looking which part of the mat
        is greater?

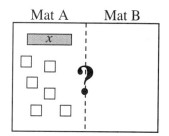

    a.   One way to compare is to separate the
         x-tiles and the unit tiles on different sides
         of the mat. Work with your team to find
         a way to have only *x*-tiles on Mat A.
         Make sure that you are able to **justify**
         that your moves are legal.

    b.   Using the same **reasoning** from part (a),
         what would you do to have only
         variables on Mat B in the Expression
         Comparison Mat at right?

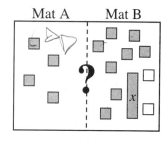

    c.   Write a short note to Ignacio and Olivia
         explaining this new **strategy**. Feel free
         to give it a name so it is easier for them
         to remember.

5-53.   Ignacio and Olivia are trying to decide if there are other ways to change expressions on the Expression Comparison Mat without affecting which side is greater. They have invented some new **strategies** and described them below.

$\boxed{\begin{array}{l}\blacksquare = +1 \\ \square = -1\end{array}}$

Your task: For each of the moves below:

- Build the Expression Comparison Mats on your paper.

- Follow each set of directions for the mat shown in each **strategy** below.

- Determine if the move in the **strategy** is valid for maintaining the relationship between the two expressions. Be prepared to **justify** your response.

Strategy #1

"If you have a mat like the one drawn below, you can add the same number of tiles to both sides. In this case, I added 3 negative tiles to both sides."

Strategy #2

"On a mat like the one below, I added +3 to Mat A and added –3 to Mat B."

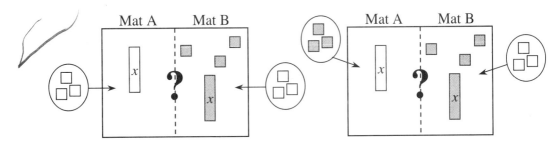

Strategy #3

"To simplify, I removed a positive x-tile from one side and a negative x-tile from the other side."

Strategy #4

"On a mat like the one below, I would add three zero pairs to Mat B."

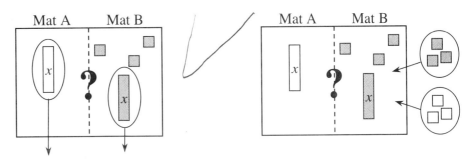

5-54.　LEARNING LOG

In your Learning Log, summarize the methods that your team and class developed to simplify expressions on the Expression Comparison Mat. Label your Learning Log entry "Simplifying Expressions (Legal Moves)" and include today's date.

METHODS AND MEANINGS

Additive Identity and Additive Inverse

Formal properties that state some of the legal moves that you have been using are listed below.

Additive Identity: The number 0 is the additive identity because zero added to any number is equal to that number. The value is unchanged. For example, $5.2 + 0 = 5.2$ and $x + 0 = x$.

Additive Inverse: The sum of a number and its opposite is equal to 0. That is, the additive inverse of a number is what needs to be added to the number to get a sum of 0.

Examples: For 2, –2 is the additive inverse and $2 + (-2) = 0$.

For –5, 5 is the additive inverse and $-5 + 5 = 0$.

For x, $x + (-x) = 0$.

5-55.　Simplify the expressions below.

a.　$5^2 \cdot (-3) - 4 \cdot 6 + 7$

b.　$-3 \cdot (6 + 4 \cdot 2)$

c.　$9 + 8 \div (-4) - 12$

d.　$2^3 - 3 \cdot 4 + 6(-1 + 2)$

e.　$4 + (3 + 4)^2$

f.　$\frac{8 - 13}{10}$

5-56.   Write the following expressions in two ways, one with parentheses and one without. For example, $4(x-3)$ can be written $4x-12$.

a.   A number reduced by 3, then multiplied by 2.

b.   A number increased by 7, then multiplied by 5.

c.   Ten times a number, then add twenty.

5-57.   Graph these points on a coordinate grid: $A(-2,0)$, $B(0,4)$, $C(4,1)$, $D(2,-3)$. Connect the points in order, with point D connected to point A. What shape have you created?

5-58.   Alan was paying a dinner check, but he was not sure how much he should tip for his bill of $27.38. If a 15% tip is standard, about how much should Alan leave for the server?

5-59.   Consider what you know about circles as you answer the questions below.

a.   What do you know about the lengths of the spokes of a bicycle wheel? Draw a picture of a bicycle wheel with spokes and explain what you mean.

b.   As a bicycle travels on flat ground, how does the center of its wheels (the hub) move? Explain and draw a picture showing what you mean.

5-60.   Elvin found the box-and-whisker plot below in the school newspaper.

Number of hours spent watching TV each week

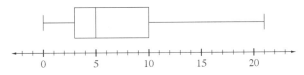

a.   Based on the plot, what percent of students watch more than 10 hours of television each week?

b.   Based on the plot, what percent of students watch less than 5 hours of television each week?

c.   Can Elvin use the box-and-whisker plot to find the mean (average) number of hours of television students watch each week? If so, what is it? Explain your **reasoning**.

d.   Can he use the plot to find the median? If so, what is it? Explain your **reasoning**.

5.2.3 Where do the solutions begin and end?

One Variable Inequalities

You have used Expression Comparison Mats to compare two expressions and found that sometimes it is possible to determine which expression is greater. You will again compare expressions, this time finding the values for the variable that make one expression greater than the other.

$\blacksquare = +1$
$\square = -1$

5-61. Maria has been recording her work to see which side of an Expression Comparison Mat is greater, but she has been called away. Garth looked at her work, but he cannot figure out what Maria did to get from one step to another.

Mat A	Mat B
$5x + 2 + (-6)$	$2x + 2 + (-8)$
$5x + (-4)$	$2x + (-6)$
$3x + (-4)$	-6
$3x$	-2

Look at Maria's work above and help Garth by building the expressions on your mat and simplifying them. Write him a note explaining what Maria did to get from one step to another.

5-62. Use Maria's method of recording to show your steps while you compare the expressions $2 + 2x + (-3)$ and $2x + (-4) + 1$ using algebra tiles. Make sure you record each step so that your teacher can see what you did on your Expression Comparison Mat.

   a. Which mat is greater?

   b. Use symbols (such as <, =, or >) to show the relationship of the final expressions on Mat A and Mat B.

5-63.   Maria and Garth were playing a game with the
algebra tiles. They each grabbed a handful of
tiles and put them on the Expression
Comparison Mat at right to see whose side
had greater value.

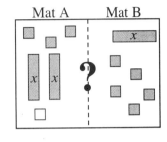

Maria said, *"I have Mat A and my side has
more value."* Garth, who had Mat B,
disagreed with her.

a.   Write expressions for Mat A and Mat B.

b.   Work with your team to simplify the expressions on the Expression
Comparison Mat while carefully recording your work for each step on your
paper. Can you tell whose side is greater? Why or why not?

c.   With your team, find at least four values for x that would make the
expression on Maria's side (Mat A) greater than the expression on Garth's
side (Mat B). Be prepared to share your values with the class.

d.   Any value for x that makes Mat A greater than Mat B is a solution to the
inequality $2x + 3 + (-1) > x + 5$. This is read, *"Two x plus three plus
negative one is greater than x plus five."*

Share your solutions with another team and see if you have the same
solutions that they do.

5-64.   Karla had a hard time keeping track of all of the
solutions to the inequality in problem 5-63 in her
head. She decided to try to organize her answers.
First she needed to know more about the problem.

a.   Is there a greatest number that is a solution?
Discuss this question with your team and be
prepared to share your ideas with the class.

b.   Is there a smallest number that is a solution?
Again, be prepared to share your team's
thinking with the class.

Problem continues on next page. →

5-64.   *Problem continued from previous page.*

    c.   What is special about the point where the solutions end? (This number is called the **boundary point**.) In other words, what relationship does this number have to the two expressions being compared?

    d.   Karla was tired of listing so many solutions and wanted a way to show all of the solutions to this inequality quickly. She decided to draw a number line like the one below.

On your own paper, draw a number line such as the one above then follow your teacher's directions to represent the answer to this question on your number line.

5-65.   Now consider the inequality $2x + 5 < 3$, which can be read *"Two x plus five is <u>less</u> than 3."*

Build the inequality on your Expression Comparison Mat and record each step using variables on your paper. Work with your team to describe the least and greatest solutions to the inequality and draw your solution on a number line. Be prepared to **justify** your ideas.

5-66.   Jerry and Ken were solving the inequality $6 > 2x + 2$. They set up the inequality on their Expression Comparison Mat and simplified it.

    a.   Write a sentence in words to represent the original inequality.

    b.   What did they get on each side of the mat when they simplified? Record your work on your paper.

    c.   Graph all the solutions to this inequality on a number line.

5-67.   Write an algebraic expression for each mat below. Then use the legal moves that you have developed to simplify each mat and, if possible, decide which expression is greater.

a.

b.

5-68.   Graph these inequalities on a number line.

a. $x > 3$ b. $x \le 5$ c. $x \ge -4$

5-69.   Lynn was shopping and found a purse that was marked with a discount of "$\frac{1}{3}$ off." If the original cost of the purse was $80, how much will Lynn pay?

5-70.   The girls' basketball team weighed each player. Their weights in pounds were 120, 122, 126, 130, 133, 147, 115, 106, 120, 112, and 142.

a.   Make a stem-and-leaf plot of the teams' weights.

b.   What is the median weight of girls on the team?

c.   What is the range of the data?

d.   What are the mean and mode?

5-71.   Simplify each expression.

a. $\frac{2}{3}(0.8)$ b. $\frac{4}{3} \cdot \frac{3}{7}$ c. $-\frac{5}{6} \cdot \frac{4}{7}$ d. $-\frac{4}{5} \cdot (-1\frac{1}{3})$

5.2.4 How can I find all solutions?

Solving One Variable Inequalities

In this lesson, you will work with your team to develop and describe a process for solving linear inequalities. As you work, use the following questions to focus your discussion.

What is a solution?

What do all of the solutions have in common?

What is the greatest solution? What is the smallest solution?

5-72. Jerry and Ken were working on solving the inequality $3x - 1 \leq 2x$. They found the boundary point and Ken made the number line graph shown at right.

Jerry noticed a problem. *"Doesn't the line at the bottom of the $\leq$ symbol mean the equal part? That means that $x = 1$ is also a solution. How could we show that?"*

"Hmmm," Jerry said. *"Well, the solution $x = 1$ would look like this on a number line. Is there a way that we can combine the two number lines?"*

Discuss this idea with your team and be prepared to share your ideas with the class.

5-73. The diagram at right shows three possible ways to represent inequality statements. Review the meanings of the inequality symbols >, <, $\geq$, and $\leq$ with your team. Then, generate the two missing representations from each inequality described in parts (a) through (c) below.

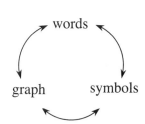

a. $x < -1\frac{1}{2}$

b. x is greater than or equal to two.

c.

5-74.   WHEN IS THE BOUNDARY POINT INCLUDED?

Represent the solution for each of the variables described below as an inequality on a number line graph and with symbols.

a.   The speed limit on certain freeways is 65 miles per hour. Let x represent any speed that could get a speeding ticket.

b.   You brought $10 to the mall. Let y represent any amount of money you can spend.

c.   In order to ride your favorite roller coaster, you must be at least five feet tall but less than seven feet tall. Let h represent any height that is allowed to ride the roller coaster.

5-75.   Jordyn, Geri, and Morgan are going to have a kite-flying contest. Jordyn and Geri each have one roll of kite string. Together they also have 90 yards of extra string. Morgan has three rolls of kite string plus 10 yards of extra string. All of the rolls of string are the same length. The girls want to see who can fly their kite the highest.

a.   Since Jordyn and Geri have fewer rolls of kite string, they decide to tie their string together so their kite can fly

higher. Write at least two expressions to show how much kite string Jordyn and Geri have. Let x represent the number of yards of string on one roll.

b.   Write an expression to show how much kite string Morgan has. x is the number of yards of string on one roll.

c.   How long does a roll of string have to be for Jordyn and Geri to be able to fly their kite higher than Morgan's kite? Show your answer as an inequality and on a number line.

d.   How long does a roll of string have to be for Morgan to be able to fly her kite higher than Jordyn and Geri's kite? Show your answer as an inequality and on a number line.

e.   What length would the roll of string have to be for the girls' kites to fly at the same height?

5-76.   **Additional Challenge:** Travis loves trains! Today he is beginning a train ride
from Madison, Wisconsin all the way to Seattle, Washington.

Shortly after the train left the station in Madison, Travis fell asleep. When he
woke up, it was dark outside and he had no idea how long he had been asleep.
A fellow passenger told him they had already passed La Crosse, which is 135
miles from Madison. If the train travels at an average speed of 50 miles per
hour, at least how long has Travis been asleep? Work with your team to
represent this problem with an inequality and to solve it. Be prepared to share
your ideas with the class.

5-77.   LEARNING LOG

Work with your team to describe each step of your
process for finding boundary points and deciding what
part of the number line to shade. Then write down each
step in your Learning Log. Be sure to illustrate your
ideas with examples. Title this entry "Finding
Boundary Points" and label it with today's date.

5-78.   Solve each of the following inequalities. Represent the solutions algebraically
(with symbols) and graphically (on a number line).

a. $3x - 4 < 3 - 2x$

b. $\frac{4}{5}x \geq 7$

5-79.   Kindra would like to have more than $1500 in her savings account.

a.   If she starts with $61 in her savings account, write an inequality to show
how much she wants to have.

b.   How much does Kindra need to save?

5-80.   Reflect quadrilateral ABCD across the line
$y = -2$. Write the new coordinate points.

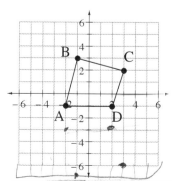

5-81. Copy and complete each of the Diamond Problems below. The pattern used in the Diamond Problems is shown at right.

a.

b.

c.

d.

5-82. Find the perimeter and area of each triangle below.

a.

b.

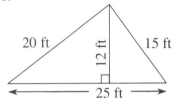

5.3.1 What can I build?

Introduction to Constructions

Architects and drafters make careful drawings before buildings are built. The drawings represent how the building should be constructed. They show the thickness of the walls and where doors, windows, and pipes will be. To make these precise diagrams, professionals often use special computer software. However, some architects prefer to draw the diagrams by hand. They use special drawing tools that look something like those in the drawing at right, including a right triangle tool and a device for measuring angles called a protractor.

Building plans are just one example of a precise geometric drawing. Mathematicians have used these basic tools to draw accurate diagrams for other reasons. The process of **constructing**, or building, shapes that meet different guidelines can help you understand many of the specific characteristics of those shapes.

In this lesson, you will be introduced to some ideas of mathematical construction and will construct your own shapes. As you work today, use the questions below to start mathematical discussions:

What is the relationship?

How can we describe it?

How do we know for sure?

5-83.   TRANSLATING THE LINE SEGMENT

One of the most basic drafting tools used is called a
T-square, a long straightedge that has a "T" at one
end. This tool slides along an edge of a table to allow
a person to draw several lines that go in exactly the
same direction, as if they were translated on the page.
An example of a T-square is shown at right.

Using tracing paper provided by your teacher, explore how a T-square works.

- Trace the line segment *AB* on the Lesson 5.3.1A Resource Page on
  tracing paper along with the "grid marker," an ∟ shape that can help
  you keep the tracing paper lined up with the grid as you move it.

- Use the tracing paper to translate the segment *AB* on the tracing paper
  vertically ($\updownarrow$) and horizontally ($\leftrightarrow$) on the graph any distance you
  choose. Be careful not to rotate the tracing paper or the resource
  page! One way to make sure that they stay lined up is to make sure
  that the ∟ shape matches up with two intersecting gridlines.

- How did the new translated segment compare to the original?

- Translate the segment to different positions on the grid. Pay attention
  to how the translated segment and the original segment compare.

Based on the translations you have made, what
is the relationship between two line segments
when one is a translation of the other? On the
resource page, sketch and describe the **general**
relationship you see.

5-84.   ROTATING THE LINE SEGMENT

You have seen how line segments are related when one is a translation of the other. How does the relationship change if the segment is rotated? Trace segment *CD* and the grid marker from the Lesson 5.3.1A Resource Page to begin investigating.

- With the traced segment matched up on top of the original line segment, rotate the line segment 90° counter-clockwise (↺) about point *C*. Your grid marker will look like ⌐ when you have rotated a complete 90°. Pay attention to how the rotated segments compare to the original line. Sketch your line segment on the graph and label the endpoint *E*.

- Use a straightedge to extend segments *CD* and *CE* by starting at point C and moving out along each segment. Place an arrow at the end of each segment. The 90° angle formed by this rotation is a special angle called a **right angle**.

- Line your traced segment up with segment *CD* again. Choose another point on the segment and rotate the segment 90° clockwise or counter-clockwise about that point. Sketch where the new segment lands.

a. What relationships do you notice between the rotated line segments and the original segment *CD*?

b. When lines meet and form 90° angles they are called **perpendicular** lines. Are the rotated line segments you drew **perpendicular** to segment *CD*? Explain why or why not.

c. How many total times would you need to rotate your line segment by 90° around the endpoint so that the rotated segment forms a straight line segment with the original segment? The new segment should be twice the original length. How many degrees of rotation is that?

d. How many times would you rotate the segment by 90° to complete a full turn and end up back where you started?

5-85.   MEASURING ANGLES

Different angles are created when lines are rotated by different amounts around a point of intersection.

a.   On the Lesson 5.3.1B Resource Page, locate the segment with endpoints at points *A* and *B*.

   • Trace segment *AB* on tracing paper and rotate it more than 90° (a $\frac{1}{4}$ turn) and less than 180° (a $\frac{1}{2}$ turn) about point *A*.

   • Copy this segment onto the resource page using a straightedge.

   • Label the new endpoint as point *C*.

Estimate how many degrees you have rotated the line segment. What kind of angle is this?

b.   Find segment *GH* on your resource page.

   • Use your tracing paper to rotate the segment around point *G* less than 90° (a $\frac{1}{4}$ turn).

   • Copy the rotated segment onto the resource page using a straightedge.

   • Label the new endpoint as point *K*.

Estimate how many degrees you have rotated the line segment. Be prepared to explain your thinking. What kind of angle is this?

5-86.   A **protractor** is a tool for measuring angles. With a protractor you can measure the number of degrees of rotation that create an angle. Cliff used the protractor pictured here to measure the acute angle he created.

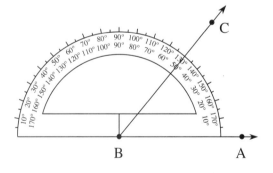

a.   What is the measure of his angle? Make sure that your answer makes sense based on the size of the angle.

b.   Obtain a protractor from your teacher and measure each of the angles you created in problem 5-85. How close were your estimates to the actual measurements?

c.   Draw a new angle on your paper using a straightedge. Determine if it is obtuse, acute, or right, and estimate its measure in degrees. Then use your protractor to measure the angle. How close was your estimate? Use the Math Notes box at the end of this lesson if you need help with the names of the angle types.

Making Connections: Course 2

5-87.   Architects and contractors often need to create angles that measure 45° or 60° as they build. Their measurements must be accurate in order for the buildings they design to fit together when they are built.

    a.   On your paper, create a 45° angle by following the steps below.

- Use a straightedge to draw a line at least 4 inches long.

- Mark a point on one end of the line and label it *X*.

- Position the center point of your protractor on the point you marked *X* and the zero degree mark on the line.

- From the line, read around the edge of the protractor to find the 45° mark. Make a point at 45°.

- Draw a line connecting point *X* to your new point to create the angle with a measure of 45°.

        Label the angle with the measure 45°. Is your drawing **reasonable**?

    b.   Draw three new angles with the measures below. Label each one with its measure.

       i.   30°   *ii.*   75°   *iii.* 135°

5-88.   **Additional Challenge:** If you make four 90° rotations in the same direction, one after the other around the same point, you will complete a full circular angle.

    a.   How many 45° rotations does it take to make a circular angle?

    b.   Suppose you want to divide a circular angle into 3 angles of equal measure. What would the degree measure of each angle be? Draw and label a figure using a protractor.

    c.   Suppose you want to divide a circular angle into 5 angles of equal measure. What would the degree measure of each angle be? Draw and label a figure using a protractor.

    d.   Suppose you want to divide a circular angle into 24 angles of equal measure. What would the degree of each angle be?

METHODS AND MEANINGS

Angles and Their Measures

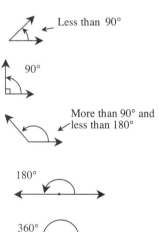

An **angle** is formed by two rays that start at a single point (called an **endpoint**), as shown in the diagram at right. A **ray** is part of a line that starts at an endpoint and extends without stopping in one direction. The **measure** of an angle is how much you rotate the starting ray to get to the ray that forms the other side of the angle. In this course, angles will be measured in degrees.

When trying to describe shapes, it is convenient to classify them by types of angles. This course will use the following terms to refer to angles:

Acute: Any angle with measure *between* (but not including) 0° and 90°.

Less than 90°

Right: Any angle that measures 90°.

90°

Obtuse: Any angle with measure *between* (but not including) 90° and 180°.

More than 90° and less than 180°

Straight: Straight angles have a measure of 180° and the two rays of the angle form a straight line.

180°

Circular: Any angle that measures 360°.

360°

5-89.   Look at the shapes below. Determine if they include a parallel set of line segments, a perpendicular set of line segments, both, or neither one.

a.   trapezoid

b.

c.

d.   rectangle

Making Connections: Course 2

5-90.   Decide if these angles are acute, obtuse, or right angles. All diagrams are drawn to scale.

a.   b.   c.   d.

5-91.   Edwin's friends guessed how many jelly beans were in a jar at his birthday party. Here are their guesses: 75, 80, 95, 92, 100, 72, 71, 60, 65, 88, 60

a.   Make a stem-and-leaf plot to display the data.

b.   Make a box-and-whisker plot to display the data.

c.   Which data display most clearly shows the median of the data? What is the median?

d.   Based on the box-and-whisker plot, estimate what percent of students guessed more than 65 jellybeans.

e.   Use the stem-and-leaf plot to determine the actual percent of students who guessed more than 65 jellybeans.

5-92.   Copy each problem, then find the sum, difference, product, or quotient. Remember to show all your steps.

a. $23.6 + 12$ b. $16.5 + 52.43$

c. $46.21 - 31.2$ d. $27.5 - 13.11$

e. $4.5(6)$ f. $55 \div 2$

5-93.   Mr. Crow, the head groundskeeper at High Tech Middle School, mows the lawn along the side of the gym. The lawn is rectangular, and the length is 5 feet more than twice the width. The perimeter of the lawn is 250 feet.

a.   Use the 5-D Process to find the dimensions of the lawn.

b.   Use the dimensions you calculated in part (a) to find the area of the lawn.

5.3.2 What is the relationship?

Compass Constructions

A compass is a simple tool that allows circles to be drawn quickly and accurately. Using this simple tool along with a ruler allows one to make precise drawings. In this lesson you will use a compass and ruler to build shapes, construct perpendicular lines, and partition segments.

5-94.   Benjamin was drawing angles with a broken protractor and the largest angle he could measure was a 47° angle. Benjamin wanted to draw a 90° angle as well as a 180° angle.

a.   Suppose Benjamin started by drawing a 47° angle. What angle would he need to measure to complete his right angle?

b.   When the sum of the measures of two angles is 90°, they are called **complementary angles**. What angle would be complementary to an 83° angle? Sketch a right angle showing this relationship.

c.   Angles that sum to make a 180° angle are called **supplementary angles**. What angle would you need to add to the angles below to create a 180° angle?

   i.   32°   *ii.*   90°   *iii.*   75°

5-95.   DESIGNS WITH CIRCLES

Celeste was playing with her compass and created the figure at right. When a compass and/or a straightedge is used to create a figure, the process is called **constructing**. Use a straightedge to draw a horizontal segment on your paper that is two inches long, label the endpoints *A* and *B*, then follow the directions below to recreate her **construction**.

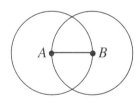

- Use your compass to construct a circle that has a center at point *A* and passes through point *B*.

- Construct a second circle that has a center at point *B* and passes through point *A*. Label the points where the circles **intersect** (cross) as points *C* and *D*.

Problem continues on next page. →

Making Connections: Course 2

5-95.   *Problem continued from previous page.*

- Use a straightedge to draw segments from the center of each circle to point *C* and point *D*. Each of these line segments is a **radius** of the circle. A **radius** measures the distance from the center of the circle to any point on the circle itself.

a.   How are the four segments related? Is there another pair of points in the figure that create a segment that is the same as the ones you drew?

b.   What shapes do you see in the construction? Describe them and **justify** your descriptions.

5-96.   In part (a) of problem 5-95 you found that the segment that connects point *A* to point *B* is also a radius. Now connect point *C* to point *D*.

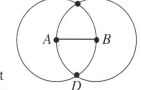

a.   How are segments *AB* and *CD* related? Use your protractor to measure the angles where line segment *CD* crosses segment *AB* to confirm the relationships.

b.   The word **bisect** means to cut into two equal pieces. Use a ruler to check that the segment connecting *C* and *D* goes through the **midpoint** (exact middle) of segment *AB*. Segment *CD* is called a **perpendicular bisector** of the segment connecting point *A* and point *B*.

c.   On a new piece of paper, use a straight edge to draw a line segment. Label the endpoints *E* and *F*. Use the construction process you used to construct segment *CD* (problems 5-95 and 5-96) to construct a perpendicular bisector for segment *EF*.

5-97.   SPECIAL TRIANGLES

Two of the triangles you created on the intersecting circles in problem 5-95 have special properties.

a.   Based on your work in the previous problems, how are the lengths of the sides of triangle *ABC* related?

b.   Examine triangle *ABD*. How is it related to triangle *ABC*?

c.   Use your protractor to measure each of the angles in triangle *ABC*. What do you notice about the angles?

Triangles like triangle *ABC* and *ABD* are called **equilateral** (all sides equal) and **equiangular** (all angles equal) because of the special relationships between their sides and angles.

5-98.   **Additional Challenge:** FLOWER PETALS

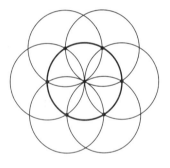

Using the idea of overlapping circles, Samantha constructed the picture at right. Follow the directions below to construct her pattern on your paper. Then answer the questions that follow.

- In the middle of a large blank piece of paper, construct a circle. Be sure to mark the center of the circle. This point will be the center of the pattern.

- Pick and label a point (*A*) on the circle. Then use your compass to construct a circle with the same radius as the original circle, but with its center at point *A*. This new circle should intersect your original circle twice. Call these points *B* and *C*.

- Now draw new circles with centers at points *B* and *C* so that each circle has the same radius as the original circle. Each circle should intersect the original circle in two new points. Label these points *D* and *E*.

- Finally, draw two new circles with centers *D* and *E* so that they have the same radius as the original circle. They should intersect the original circle at the same point. Label this point *F*.

a.   Find a "flower petal" pattern in your diagram (you may see more than one). You may want to color the petals so that they are easy to find.

b.   If you connect the intersection points (*A*, *B*, *C*, …) in order around the original circle, what shape appears? Describe it.

METHODS AND **M**EANINGS

Circle Vocabulary

The **radius** of a circle is a line segment from its center to any point on the circle. The term is also used for the length of these segments. More than one radius are called **radii**.

A **chord** of a circle is a line segment joining any two points on a circle.

A **diameter** of a circle is a chord that goes through its center. The term is also used for the length of these chords. The length of a diameter is twice the length of a radius.

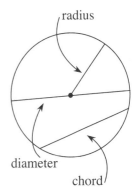

The **circumference** of a circle is its perimeter, or the "distance around" the circle.

5-99.   The angle at right measures 90°. Estimate the measure (in degrees) of each angle below. Note: The angles are drawn to scale.

a.   b.   c.   d.

e.   If the angle in part (a) measures 65°, what would be the measure of its supplementary angle? **Justify** your answer.

5-100.   What number do you get with this number "magic trick"? Use at least two different original numbers for step #1 to confirm your solution.

> 1. Think of a number.
>
> 2. Add the next higher number.
>
> 3. Add nine.
>
> 4. Divide by two.
>
> 5. Subtract your original number.

5-101.   Write the expression as shown on the expression mats, then simplify by making zeros and combining like terms.

a.

b.

5-102.   Draw an isosceles trapezoid. Label the top base 6 cm and the height 4 cm. If the area of this trapezoid is 36 square cm, what is the length of the other base? You may find it helpful to use the 5-D Process.

5-103.   Look at the algebra tile shape at right.

a.   Write an algebraic expression for the perimeter of the shape in two ways, first by finding the length of each of the sides and adding them all together and then by writing an equivalent, simplified expression.

b.   Write an algebraic expression for the area of the shape.

5-104.   The average annual rainfall in Tucson, Arizona is 12 inches. Between January and April, 2.4 inches of rain fell. What percentage of the annual rainfall fell after April (May through December)? You may want to draw a diagram to organize information.

Making Connections: Course 2

5.3.3 What is the relationship?

Circumference and Diameter Ratios

The ability to measure objects without standard measuring tools is often very convenient. Have you ever seen anyone estimate the time until the sun sets by extending their arms and seeing how many fists there are from the horizon to the sun? Others use the distance from the tip of their thumb to their knuckle as an approximate inch. Today you will use your own foot as a unit of measure to look at another mathematical relationship.

5-105.   WALKING CIRCLES

Manny was walking around the edge of the circle painted on one of the basketball courts on the playground. He was carefully placing his feet heel-to-toe and counting as he walked. After he went all the way around the circle, he started to walk along the line across the middle of the circle.

His friend Jose was watching Manny walk this way and thought it was unusual. Jose asked, *"Why are you walking like that?"*

"I found a pattern in the number of steps I have to take around the circle and the number of steps across the circle. I'm testing to see if the relationship is true on different circles," Manny answered.

What relationship did Manny find? Today you and your team will walk around and across circles to see if you can find a pattern. You will need a Lesson 5.3.3A Resource Page to record your measurements (available at www.cpm.org/students).

a.   Your teacher will direct your team to a circle to measure. Measure the distance around the circle, called the **circumference**, using Manny's walking method. How many heel-to-toe steps does it take to trace the full circle? Record your result on the resource page.

b.   Measure the **diameter**, or distance across the circle through the center, once again using heel-to-toe units. Make sure you carefully count your steps and record your measurement.

c.   When each person in your team has made measurements using their own heel-to-toe units, look at your results. As a team, discuss the patterns you see. What relationship did Manny find? Write your observations and be prepared to explain your ideas.

5-106.   You may have noticed that the circumference measurement, C, was always larger than the diameter measurement, d, for the circles you measured. Could you determine how much larger?

   a.   Divide each circumference measurement by the diameter measurement. Record your results in the last column of your team chart, and label the column "$\frac{C}{d}$."

   b.   What relationship do you see in the results? Discuss with your team and then write a sentence summarizing the relationship between circumference and diameter.

5-107.   Looking at large amounts of data can help to confirm patterns that you identify in smaller data sets. To share your team data with the class, find the mean of your team's data in each column of the chart on your resource page and add your results to the class chart. Record the class results on your own resource page.

   a.   Are the class results similar to what your team found when it measured? Explain any differences you see, and what may have caused them.

   b.   Do the class results confirm the patterns you saw in problems 5-105 and 5-106? Describe any new patterns that you see and, if you are revising the patterns you found, explain why you are doing so.

   c.   With your team, go back to the sentence you wrote in part (b) of problem 5-106, summarizing the relationship between circumference and diameter. Add to or change your summary as needed.

5-108.   Use the relationships you have found to approximate the missing circumference and diameter measurements.

   a.   circumference = ?   b.   diameter = ?   c.   circumference =?
                                                                  diameter = ?

5-109. Mathematicians have studied circles and the challenge of measuring them accurately for many years. Through their studies, mathematicians identified the ratio between the circumference and diameter of a circle as a special number. No matter how large or small a circle is, and no matter what units of measure are used, the circumference divided by the diameter is always equal to a little more than three. The Greek letter π (pi) is used to represent this number:

$$\pi = \frac{C}{d} \approx 3.14159265358979....$$

a. The relationship between circumference and diameter is often written as $\pi \cdot d = C$. Is this the same as writing $\frac{C}{d} = \pi$? Discuss this question with your team, and be prepared to share your **reasoning** with the class.

b. If the diameter of a circle is 100 inches, what is the circumference?

c. If the circumference of a circle measures 96 feet, what is the diameter?

METHODS AND MEANINGS

Angle Relationships

MATH NOTES

If two angles have measures whose sum is 90°, they are called **complementary angles**. For example, in the diagram at right, the 40° and 50° angles are complementary because together they form a right angle.

If two angles have measures whose sum is 180°, they are called **supplementary angles**. For example, in the diagram at right, the 60° and the 120° angles are supplementary because together they form a straight angle.

Two angles do not have to share a vertex to be complementary or supplementary. The first pair of angles at right are supplementary; the second pair of angles are complementary.

120° 60°
Supplementary

50°
40°
Complementary

5-110. Remember that the circumference of a circle is equal to π times the diameter. Find the circumference of a circle with:

    a. diameter = 10   b. radius = 10   c. diameter = 15

5-111. Alexa is looking at the shape at right. She needs to make several different figures that are similar to it.

    a. If she uses the scale factor $\frac{8}{5}$, will the new shape that she creates be larger or smaller than the original? **Justify** your answer.

    b. List two different scale factors Alexa could use to make a smaller shape.

    c. List two different scale factors Alexa could use to make a larger shape.

5-112. Simplify each numerical expression.

    a. $\frac{1}{2}(5+13)-4\cdot5$ b. $(5+11)-(24-15)\cdot(3)$ c. $6^2+3\cdot7-9\div3$

5-113. Simplify the following variable expressions.

    a. $2x+5+x-6+3x$ b. $x-8+x-5+x+1$

5-114. Rewrite each fraction below as an equivalent fraction, a decimal, and a percent.

    a. $\frac{6}{18}$ b. $\frac{7}{20}$ c. $\frac{9}{10}$ d. $\frac{4}{25}$

5-115. A radio station is giving away free t-shirts to students in local schools. It plans to give away 40 shirts at Big Sky Middle School and 75 shirts at High Peaks High School. Three hundred and fifty students attend Big Sky Middle School and 800 students attend High Peaks High School.

    a. What is the probability of getting a t-shirt if you are a student at the middle school?

    b. What is the probability of getting a t-shirt if you are a student at the high school?

    c. Are you more likely to get a t-shirt if you are a student at the high school, or at the middle school?

5.3.4 How can I measure the area?

Circle Area

The ratio known as π (read, "pi") was first discovered by the Babylonians nearly 4000 years ago. Over the years, Egyptian, Chinese, and Greek mathematicians also found the constant ratio between the circumference and diameter of a circle by using measurement. The Greek letter π has been used to represent this ratio since the 1700s when it was made popular by the Swiss mathematician Euler (pronounced "oy-ler"). Even though this ratio has been known for many years, the value commonly used for π is still only an approximation.

5-116.   ESTIMATING CIRCLE AREA

A circle is different from any shape we have studied so far because it has no sides or corners. This makes it difficult to apply the **strategy** of decomposing it into rectangles and triangles. In this situation, estimating its area can be a useful technique. Obtain a Lesson 5.3.4A Resource Page from your teacher.

a.   Using the first circle with a radius of 5 units on the resource page, estimate the area of the circle by counting whole and part squares. When each person in your team has finished their own estimate, share your results.

b.   Are all of the estimates in your team identical? How can you combine your data as a team to get a new estimate that may be more accurate?

5-117.   THE INSIDE OUTSIDE AVERAGE METHOD

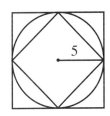

While it is convenient to estimate area when shapes are drawn on grid paper, often shapes are not presented in that way. How can other shapes be used to help estimate area? Look carefully at the shape at right.

a.   What is the area of the larger square (also shown on the resource page)?

b.   What is the area of the smaller square (also shown on the resource page)?

c.   How does the area of each square compare to the area of the circle? Is either a good estimate of the circle's area? Why?

d.   Discuss with your team how to use the areas of both the squares to estimate the area of the circle. You might consider using what you have learned about analyzing data. Explain your thinking.

5-118.   Julia needs to estimate the area of a circle with a radius of 6. She is planning to use the Inside Outside Average method to make her estimate.

   a.   On the Lesson 5.3.4A Resource Page, estimate the area of the circle with a radius of 6 by counting whole squares and parts of squares. Share your results with your team.

   b.   When Julia was calculating the area of the outside square, she started by dividing the large square into four smaller ones. Her picture is at right.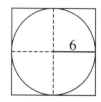

        To find the area of each small square, Julia multiplied the length times the width:

$$Area = 6^2 = 36$$

        How are the length, width, and area of each small square related to the radius of the circle? How is the area of the outside square related to the radius?

   c.   Julia divided the inside square into triangles. How is each triangle related to the radius? How is the area of the inside square related to the radius?

   d.   If the area of the two squares is related to the radius of the circle, Julia wonders if she can relate her circle estimate back to the radius as well. With your team, look at the estimate for area you have from part (a). How is that area estimate related to the radius of the circle?

5-119.   Julia is looking at a new square with a radius of 10. So far on her paper, she has written the work at right. What expression should she write to estimate the area of the circle?

Outside area = $4(10)^2$
Inside area = $2(10)^2$

5-120.   A FORMULA FOR CIRCLE AREA

By using the Inside Outside Average method for estimating, you discovered that the area of a circle is approximately three times the radius squared. There is another way to decompose and rearrange a circle in order to find a formula for its area. As you go through this process, think about these questions:

- *If a circle is cut up and rearranged into a new shape, is the area of the new shape the same as the area of the circle?*

- *How are the dimensions (base and height) of the new shape related to the circle?*

- *Would this process work for any circle? Does it matter how large the circle is?*

Take a circle and cut it into 8 equal parts and arrange them like this:

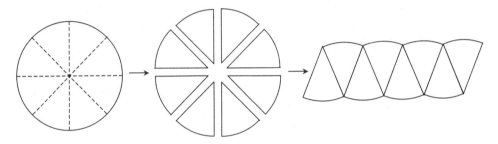

This rearrangement of the circle would look even more like a parallelogram or rectangle if we cut the circle into more pieces:

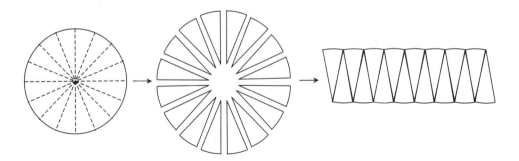

Problem continues on next page. →

5-120.   *Problem continued from previous page.*

The measurements of this parallelogram are actually related to the original measurements of the circle. The height of the parallelogram is the same as the radius of the circle:

The length of the parallelogram is approximately half of the circumference of the circle. Since the circumference is equal to πd, half of the circumference is equal to:

$$\frac{\pi d}{2} = \frac{\pi(2r)}{2} = \pi r.$$

Substituting these values into the formula for the area of a parallelogram, you get:

$$A = hb = r(\pi r) = r^2\pi.$$

5-121.   Calculate the area for the circles with a radius of 5 and 6 using this new method (the formula $A = r^2\pi$) and compare your answers to your team's estimates in problems 5-117 and 5-118. How are the areas using this new method different from the estimates in the Inside Outside Average Method?

5-122.   How does the area that you found in problem 5-116 (counting estimate) compare to the calculating the area of a circle with a radius of 5 using the formula $A = r^2\pi$?

5-123.   **Additional Challenge:** A circle with radius 6 inches is cut into four quarters. Those pieces are rearranged into the shape at right. Find the area and the perimeter of the shape.

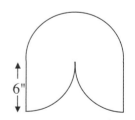

5-124.   LEARNING LOG

Write a Learning Log entry that explains how to use the formula for the area of a circle. Include a solved example problem. Title this entry "Area of Circles" and include today's date.

MᴇᴛHODS AND MᴇANINGS

Circumference and Area of Circles

The **circumference** (*C*) of a circle is its perimeter, that is, the "distance around" the circle.

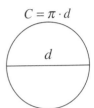

$$C = \pi \cdot d$$

The number π (read "pi") is the ratio of the circumference of a circle to its diameter. That is, $\pi = \frac{\text{circumference}}{\text{diameter}}$. This definition is also used as a way of computing the circumference of a circle if you know the diameter as in the formula $C = \pi d$ where C is the circumference and d is the diameter. Since the diameter is twice the radius (that is, $d = 2r$) the formula for the circumference of a circle using its radius is $C = \pi(2r)$ or $C = 2\pi \cdot r$.

The first few digits of π are 3.141592.

To find the **area** (*A*) of a circle when given its radius (*r*), square the radius and multiply by π. This formula can be written as $A = r^2 \cdot \pi$. Another way the area formula is often written is $A = \pi \cdot r^2$.

5-125.   The circle shown at right has a diameter of 20 cm.

a.   What measurement do you need to find in order to calculate the area inside the circle?

b.   Find the area inside the circle using the formula $A = r^2\pi$. Write your answer as a product of r^2 and π, and as an approximation using $\pi \approx 3.14$.

5-126.   Quintrell was writing a "Guess My Number" game. He decided to write the clues in a different way. He wrote, *"When 35 is added to my number, the answer is 4 times my original number plus 8. What is my number?"* Use the 5-D Process to find Quintrell's number.

5-127.   Find the area and circumference of the following circles. You may want to refer to the Math Notes box in this lesson.

a.

b.

c.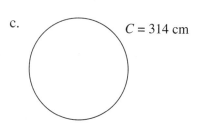

5-128.   One student rewrote the expression $17 \cdot 102$ as $17(100 + 2)$, and then simplified to get the expression 1700+34.

a.   Are the three expressions equal? **Justify** your answer.

b.   What property of numbers does this demonstrate?

5-129.   Find the area of each of these trapezoids. Show all of your steps.

a.

b.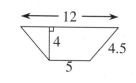

5.4 How are they related?

Mid-Course Reflection Activities

The activities in this section review several major ideas you have studied so far. As you work, think about the topics you have studied and the activities that you have done during the first half of this course and how they connect to each other. Also think about which concepts you are comfortable using and those with which you need more practice.

As you work on this activity, keep in mind the following questions:

What mathematical concepts have you studied in this course so far?

What do you still want to know more about?

What connections did you find?

5-130. MEMORY LANE

Have you ever heard someone talk about "taking a trip down memory lane"? People use this phrase to mean taking time to remember things that have happened in the past, especially things that a group of people have in common.

As you follow your teacher's directions to visit your mathematical "memory lane," think about all the activities you have done and what you have learned in this class so far this year. Your Toolkit should be a useful resource to help you with this activity.

Focus your memories in six areas:

- Probability
- Geometry
- Data and Statistics
- Representing and Working with Numbers
- Algebraic Thinking
- Graphing

5-131.   SCAVENGER HUNT

Today your teacher will give you several clues
about different mathematical situations.
(These clues can be found on a resource page
at www.cpm.org/students.) For each clue,
work with your team to find all of the
situations (posted around the classroom or
provided on a resource page) that match each
clue. Remember that more than one situation
— up to five — may match each clue. Once
you have decided which situation(s) match a
clue, defend your decision to your teacher and
receive the next clue. Be sure to record your
matches on paper.

Your goal is to
find the match (or
more than one
match) for each
different clue.

5-132.   WAYS OF THINKING

This course focuses on five different **Ways of Thinking**: generalizing,
reasoning and justifying, reversing thinking, choosing a strategy, and
visualizing. These are some of the ways in which you think while trying to
make sense of a concept or while solving a problem (even outside of math
class). During this course, you have probably used each Way of Thinking
multiple times without even realizing it!

The following problems will focus on the Ways of Thinking. As you work
them, refer to the description of the Ways of Thinking found at the end of this
lesson, and think about which Ways of Thinking you are using for each
problem.

1. DESIGN YOUR OWN TRICK

   In this question, you will be designing your own number trick. Use these questions to guide your thinking.

   a. If your trick includes a subtraction step, what step will likely follow later? Why?

   b. If you "multiply by five" in your trick, what inverse operation will likely follow later?

   c. It is helpful to **visualize** how the expressions are being built up and reduced back down so that the original number does not matter. Do you prefer to use variable expressions or algebra tiles when you **visualize** how a variable can represent any number? Why?

   d. Individually or with your team design a new number trick that always results in the same integer answer no matter what number you start with. Organize your trick in a table that lists the steps, include three trials to show it works with specific numbers, and include the algebra tile drawings or expressions to show it works with any number.

2. Use the 5-D Process and table below to find a solution. Write a possible word problem that would fit the table.

   Describe/Draw:

	Define and Predict		Do	Decide
	Length	Width	Perimeter	Target Perimeter = 88 ft
Trial 1:	10	$2 \cdot 10 + 5 = 25$	$10 + 25 + 10 + 25 = 70$	70 Too small

3. Each of the following shapes is missing either the height and/or the perimeter. Find the missing value for each problem. Explain your **strategy** for solving each problem.

a. Area = 24 sq. inches
   Perimeter ≈ 26.4 inches
   Height = ?

12 inches

b. Area = 42 sq. inches
   Height = ?
   Perimeter = ?

h

12 inches

c. Area = $4x + 12$
   Perimeter = ?
   Height = ?

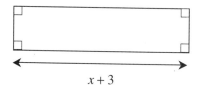

$x + 3$

d. Area = 198 sq. inches
   Perimeter = ?
   Top Base = ?

12 inches

13 in.

19 inches

4. Design a data set that satisfies the requirement listed each time.

a. Write six ages that would have modes of 12 and 13.

b. Write five heights that would have a median of 63 inches.

c. Write four different quiz scores that would have a mean of 75%.

d. Write 11 test scores that would be represented with the following box-and-whisker plot.

0   72 83 91 100

0 10 20 30 40 50 60 70 80 90

5. Use the triangle at right to answer the questions below.

21 cm

12 cm

a. Enlarge the triangle to create a similar triangle with side lengths that are twice as long as in the diagram. Label the new triangle B and be sure to label the lengths that you can determine.

b. Reduce the original triangle to create a similar triangle with side lengths that are one-third as long as in the diagram. Label it triangle C and be sure to label the lengths that you know.

c. Find the area of each triangle.

d. How do the areas of the enlarged and reduced triangles compare to the original? Be as specific as you can.

e. If triangle B were dilated to become triangle C, what would the scale factor be? How do you know?

Ways of Thinking

Reasoning and Justifying:

To use logical reasoning means to organize information in order to draw a conclusion. When you explain why you think an idea is true, you are justifying. You often think this way when you try to convince yourself or someone else that an idea or solution is correct. Often, a justification is the answer to the questions, "Why?" or, "How do you know for sure?" When you think or say, *"I think this is true because..."*, you are justifying.

Choosing a Strategy:

To choose a strategy means to think about what you know about a problem and match that information with methods and processes for solving problems. As you develop this way of thinking you learn how to choose ways of solving problems based on given information. You think this way when you ask/answer questions like, "What strategy might work for...?" or , "How can I use this information to answer...?" When you are looking for a method to answer a question or solve a problem, you are choosing a strategy/tool.

Generalizing:

To generalize means to make a statement or conclusion, like a rule stating common properties, from a collection of evidence. You think this way when you describe patterns, because you are looking for a general statement that describes each term in the pattern. Often, a generalization is the answer to the question, "What is in common?" When you think or say, *"I think this is always true..."*, you are generalizing.

Reversing Thinking:

To reverse your thinking can be described as "thinking backward." You think this way when you want to understand a concept in a new direction. Often, it requires you to try to undo a process. When you think or say, *"What if I try to go backwards?"*, you are reversing your thinking.

Visualizing:

To visualize means to make a picture in your mind that represents a situation or description. As you develop this Way of Thinking, you learn how to turn a variety of situations into mental pictures. You think this way when you ask or answer questions like, "What does it look like when...?" or "How can I draw...?" When you wonder what something might look like and work to create an image of it, you are visualizing.

Chapter 5 Closure   What have I learned?

Reflection and Synthesis

The activities below offer you a chance to reflect about what you have learned during this chapter. As you work, look for concepts that you feel very comfortable with, ideas that you would like to learn more about, and topics you need more help with. Look for connections between ideas as well as connections with material you learned previously.

①   WHAT HAVE I LEARNED?

Working the problems in this section will help you to evaluate which types of problems you feel comfortable with and which ones you need more help with.

Solve each problem as completely as you can. The table at the end of this closure section has answers to these problems. It also tells you where you can find additional help and practice on problems like them.

CL 5-133. Copy the chart on your paper. Complete two trials by reading the variable expressions. Write in the steps as well.

Steps	Trial 1	Trial 2	Variable Expression
			x
			$3x$
			$3x + 27$
			$3x + 21$
			$x + 7$
			7

CL 5-134. When algebra tiles are grouped in sets, as shown below, they can be written in two different ways. Write two equivalent expressions that represent these collections of algebra tiles.

a.

b.

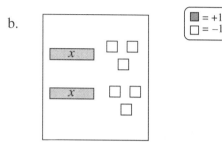

CL 5-135. Use the 5-D Process to help you solve the following problem.

Lillian and Isabella went shopping for school supplies. Lillian found her favorite notebook on sale so she bought three of the exact same notebook. Isabella also wanted a notebook. She bought one of the same notebooks that Lillian bought. Both girls started shopping with the same amount of money. If Lillian spent all of her money and Isabella had $5 left, then how much money did each girl have when she arrived at the store?

CL 5-136. Adriel and Gustavo were playing a game with algebra tiles. As they compared them, they were left with the following expressions on their mats. Use legal moves to simplify what is on the mats. Be sure to record your work in a way that others can understand.

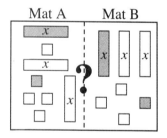

Can you determine which side has the greater value? If so, show why. If not, for what values of x is Mat A larger?

CL 5-137. Use graph paper to solve the following problem.

a. Draw an xy-coordinate graph and label each axis. Plot the following ordered pairs: $(3, 4)$, $(3, -5)$, $(-1, -2)$, and $(-1, 3)$. Connect the points in the order given as you plot them, then connect the fourth point to the first one.

b. Describe your shape. Where do you see the base(s) and height of your shape?

c. What is the area of your shape?

CL 5-138. Alejandra has been practicing her free-throw shots as she gets ready for basketball season. At her last practice, she made 70% of her shots from the free-throw line. If she shot the ball 130 times,

    a.   How many times did she make a free-throw?

    b.   How many times did she miss? What percentage of her shots did she miss?

CL 5-139. Copy and complete each of the Diamond Problems below. The pattern used in the Diamond Problems is shown at right.

    a.   b.   c.   d.

CL 5-140. Build each collection of tiles represented below on a mat. Name the collection using a simpler algebraic expression, if possible. If it is not possible to simplify the expression, explain why not.

    a. $(-x) + 5 - 4x + x - (-3) + (-3x)$

    b.   Nine plus four times a number, plus three minus seven times the number

    c. $3 - 7x^2 + 9x$

    d. $2x + 3x^2 - 7 + (-x^2)$

CL 5-141. For each of the problems in this section of closure, do the following:

a.   Draw a bar or number line like the one below that represents 0 to 10.

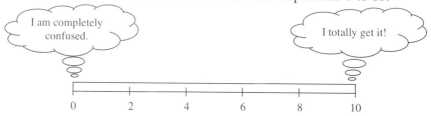

b.   Color or shade in a portion of the bar that represents your current level of understanding and comfort with completing that problem on your own.

c.   If any of your bars are less than a 5, choose *one* of those problems and do one of the following tasks:

   •   Write two questions that you would like to ask about that problem.

   •   Brainstorm two things that you DO know about that type of problem.

d.   If all of your bars are a 5 or above, choose one of those problems and do one of these tasks:

   •   Write two questions you might ask or hints you might give to a student who was stuck on the problem.

   •   Make a new problem that is similar and more challenging than that problem and solve it.

②   WHAT TOOLS CAN I USE?

You have several tools and references available to help support your learning – your teacher, your study team, your math book, and your Toolkit to name only a few. At the end of each chapter you will have an opportunity to review your Toolkit for completeness as well as to revise or update it to better reflect your current understanding of big ideas.

The main elements of your Toolkit should be your Learning Log, Math Notes, and the vocabulary used in this chapter. Math words that are new to this chapter appear in bold in the text. Refer to the lists provided below and follow your teacher's instructions to revise your Toolkit, which will help make it useful for you as you complete this chapter and as you work in future chapters.

Learning Log Entries

- Lesson 5.1.3 – Simplifying Expressions
- Lesson 5.2.2 – Simplifying Expressions (Legal Moves)
- Lesson 5.2.4 – Finding Boundary Points
- Lesson 5.3.4 – Area of Circles

Math Notes

- Lesson 5.1.2 – Algebraic Expressions
- Lesson 5.1.3 – Distributive Property
- Lesson 5.2.1 – Inequality Symbols
- Lesson 5.2.2 – Additive Identity and Additive Inverse
- Lesson 5.3.1 – Angles and Their Measures
- Lesson 5.3.2 – Circle Vocabulary
- Lesson 5.3.3 – Angle Relationships
- Lesson 5.3.4 – Circumference and Area of Circles

Mathematical Vocabulary

The following is a list of vocabulary found in this chapter. The words in bold are the words new to this chapter. It is a good idea to make sure that you are familiar with these words and know what they mean. For the words you do not know, refer to the glossary or index. You might also want to add these words to your Toolkit for a way to reference them in the future.

acute angle	**boundary point**	**circumference**
complementary angle	**diameter**	**Distributive Property**
equilateral triangles	equivalent expressions	**inequality**
line segment	**midpoint**	obtuse angle
parallel	perpendicular	**perpendicular bisector**
pi (π)	**radius**	right angle
supplementary angle		

Process Words

These words describe problem solving strategies and processes that you have been involved in as you worked in this chapter. Make sure you know what each of these words means. If you are not sure, you can talk with your teacher or other students or look through your book for problems in which you were asked to do these things.

analyze	construct	estimate
explain	express	generate
justify	organize	record
represent	reverse	simplify expressions

Answers and Support for Closure Activity #1
What Have I Learned?

Problem	Solution	Need Help?	More Practice
CL 5-133.	Pick a number Multiply by 3 Add 27 Subtract 6 Divide by 3 Subtract the original number.	Lessons 5.1.1 and 5.1.2 Math Notes box in Lesson 5.1.2	Problems 5-2 through 5-4, 5-6, 5-9, 5-14, and 5-20
CL 5-134.	a. $3(x+4)$ and $3x+12$ b. $2(x-3)$ and $2x-6$	Lessons 5.1.2 and 5.1.3 Math Notes box in Lesson 5.1.3 Learning Log (problem 5-33)	Problems 5-15, 5-19, 5-29, and 5-45
CL 5-135.	Each girl started with $7.50.	Lessons 3.2.2 through 3.2.5 Math Notes box in Lesson 3.2.3 Learning Log (problem 3-98)	Problems CL 3-113, CL 4-113, 5-93, 5-102, and 5-126
CL 5-136.	Mat A has -3 and Mat B has -2, so Mat B is greater.	Lessons 5.2.1 and 5.2.2 Math Notes box in Lesson 5.2.1 Learning Log (problem 5-54)	Problems 5-40 through 5-44, 5-50 through 5-53, 5-61, 5-62, 5-63, and 5-67

Problem	Solution	Need Help?	More Practice
CL 5-137.	a.	Lesson 2.3.5 Math Notes box in Lesson 2.2.2 Learning Log (problem 2-150)	Problems 2-135, 2-137, 2-151, 4-21, 5-24, 5-57, and 5-129
	b. There is a trapezoid with two vertical bases: $(3, 4)$ to $(3, -5)$ and $(-1, -2)$ to $(-1, 3)$. The height can be seen on any horizontal line segment between $x = 3$ and $x = -1$.		
	c. 28 square units		
CL 5-138.	a. 91	Lessons 4.1.1 and 4.1.2 Math Notes box in Lesson 4.1.2	Problems CL 4-112, 5-37, 5-58, and 5-104
	b. 39 shots, 30%		
CL 5-139.	a. $\frac{15}{8}$ and $\frac{37}{12}$	Lessons 1.2.4, 1.2.5, and 2.3.1 Math Notes box in Lesson 1.2.4 Learning Log (problem 1-107)	Problems CL 4-116, and 5-81
	b. 3 and $\frac{13}{2}$		
	c. -12 and 2		
	d. 16 and -3		
CL 5-140.	a. $-7x + 8$	Lessons 3.1.3 and 5.1.2 Math Notes boxes in Lessons 3.1.3 and 5.1.2 Learning Log (problem 3-28)	Problems CL 4-117, 5-31, 5-3, 5-46, and 5-113
	b. $-3x + 12$		
	c. Fully simplified.		
	d. $2x^2 + 2x - 7$		

Puzzle Investigator Problems

PI-9.   WHAT'S MY NUMBER?

Francesca has a game for you. She decided to show the rules of the game using a flowchart, at right.

a.   Show that if you start with the number 60, you will lose.

b.   How many starting numbers less than 100 will win? List the possible winning numbers and show how you know they will win.

c.   What if Francesca changed the rules so that you win if you end up with the number 1? What numbers would win?

PI-10.   WAY TO GO!

The map at right shows the
streets in Old Town. Assume
Jacqueline is standing at the
corner of A and 1ˢᵗ Streets.
Assume Jacqueline will only
walk South or East. The
shaded rectangles represent
large buildings. Assume
Jacqueline will not pass
through any buildings.

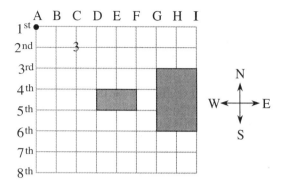

a.   The number "3" at the intersection of C and 2ⁿᵈ Streets means that there are
      three different ways she can get there from her starting position. What are
      those three ways? Describe them in words.

b.   How many different ways can she walk to the corner of F and 4ᵗʰ Streets?

c.   How many different ways can she walk to the corner of D and 5ᵗʰ Streets?

d.   Explain how you can use your answers to parts (b) and (c) to find the
      number of ways she can walk to the corner of F and 5ᵗʰ Streets. Why does
      this make sense?

e.   Find the number of different ways she can walk to the corner of I and
      8ᵗʰ Streets.

f.   How could you change the map so that Jacqueline has only 7 ways to get to
      the corner of D and 3ʳᵈ streets? You can remove blocks or add them.

Glossary

5-D Process An organized method to solve problems. The 5 D's stand for Describe/Draw, Define, Do, Decide, and Declare. This is a problem-solving strategy for which solving begins by making a prediction about the answer or one element of it (a trial), and then confirming whether the result of the trial is correct. If not, information is gained about how close the trial is to the correct value, so that adjustments to the trial value may be made. Being organized is extremely important to the success of this method, as well as writing a usable table. The 5-D process leads to writing equations to represent word problems. (p. 179)

absolute value The absolute value of a number is the distance of the number from zero. Since the absolute value represents a distance, without regard to direction, absolute value is always non-negative. Thus, the absolute value of a negative number is its opposite, while the absolute value of a non-negative number is just the number itself. The absolute value of x is usually written "$|x|$." For example, $|-5| = 5$ and $|22| = 22$. (p. 637)

acute angle An angle with a measure greater than 0° and less than 90°. An example is shown at right. (p. 304)

acute triangle A triangle with all three angle measures less than 90°.

addition (+) An operation that tells how many objects there are when two sets are combined. The result is the number of objects in the two sets together which is called a sum. In arithmetic, the word "object" usually means "number." (p. 90)

Additive Inverse Property The Additive Inverse Property states that for every number a there is a number $-a$ such that $a + (-a) = 0$. For example, the number 5 has an additive inverse of –5; $5 + (-5) = 0$. The additive inverse of a number is often called its opposite. For example, 5 and –5 are opposites. (p. 290)

adjacent angles For two angles to be adjacent, the angles must satisfy these three conditions: (1) the two angles must have a common side; (2) the two angles must have a common vertex; and (3) the two angles may have no interior points in common. Meeting these three conditions means that the common side must be between the two angles. No overlap between the angles is permitted. In the example at right, $\angle ABC$ and $\angle CBD$ are adjacent angles.

algebra A branch of mathematics that uses variables to generalize the rules of numbers and numerical operations.

algebra tiles   An algebra tile is a manipulative whose
area represents a constant or variable quantity. The
algebra tiles used in this course consist of large squares
with dimensions x-by-x and y-by-y; rectangles with
dimensions x-by-1, y-by-1, and x-by-y; and small squares
with dimensions 1-by-1. These tiles are named by their
areas: x^2, y^2, x, y, xy, and 1, respectively. The smallest
squares are called "unit tiles." In this text, shaded tiles
will represent positive quantities while unshaded tiles will
represent negative quantities. (p. 156)

algebraic expression   See *expression*.

algorithm   A fixed rule for carrying out a mathematical procedure. For example, to find
the average of a set of values, find the sum of the values and divide by the number of
values.

altitude of a triangle   The length of a segment that connects a vertex of the
triangle to a line containing the opposite base (side) and is perpendicular to
that line. (See *height*.)

angle   Generally, an angle is formed by two rays that
are joined at a common endpoint. Angles in geometric
figures are usually formed by two segments that have a
common endpoint (such as the angle shaded in the
figure at right). (Also see *acute angle*, *obtuse angle*,
and *right angle*.) (p. 304)

arc

angle bisector   A ray that divides an angle into two congruent parts.

arc   A part of a circle or curve between two points on the circle.

area   For this course, area is the number of square units needed to
fill up a region on a flat surface. In later courses, the idea will be
extended to cones, spheres, and more complex surfaces. (Also see
surface area.) (p. 10, 603)

Area = 15 square units

area of a circle $A = \pi r^2$, where r is the length of the radius of the circle. (See "circle.")
(p. 319)

area of a triangle   To find the area of a triangle, multiply the length of the base b by the
height h and divide by two: $A = \frac{1}{2}bh$. (Also see *altitude of a triangle*.) (p. 127)

Associative Property of Addition   The Associative Property of Addition states that if a sum contains terms that are grouped, then the sum may be grouped differently with no effect on the total, that is, $a + (b + c) = (a + b) + c$. For example, $3 + (4 + 5) = (3 + 4) + 5$. (p. 78)

Associative Property of Multiplication   The Associative Property of Multiplication states that if a product contains terms that are grouped, then the product may be grouped differently with no effect on the result, that is, $a(bc) = (ab)c$. For example, $2 \cdot (3 \cdot 4) = (2 \cdot 3) \cdot 4$. (p. 581)

average   The sum of given values divided by the number of values used in computing the sum. For example, the average of 1, 4, and 10 is $(1 + 4 + 10)/3$. (See *mean*.) (p. 13)

axis (plural: axes)   In a coordinate plane, two number lines that meet at right angles at the origin (0, 0). The x-axis runs horizontally and the y-axis runs vertically. (p. 85, 94)

bar graph   A bar graph is a set of rectangular bars that have height proportional to the number of data elements in each category. Each bar stands for all of the elements in a single distinguishable category (such as "red"). Usually all of the bars are the same width and separated from each other. (Also see *histogram*.) (p. 219)

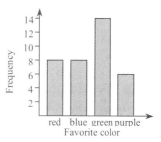

base of a geometric figure   (a) The base of a triangle: any side of a triangle to which a height is drawn. There are three possible bases in each triangle. (b) The base of a trapezoid: either of the two parallel sides. (c) The base of a parallelogram (including rectangle, rhombus, and square): any side to which a height is drawn. There are four possible bases. (d) The base of a solid: also see *cone*, *cylinder*, *prism*, and *pyramid*. (p. 115, 595)

base of an exponent   When working with an exponential expression in the form a^b, a is called the base. For example, 2 is the base in 2^5. (5 is the exponent, and 32 is the value.) (Also see *exponent*.) (p. 572)

bimodal   A set of numbers that has two modes.

boundary point   The endpoint or endpoints of a ray or segment on a number line where an inequality is true, marked with a solid dot. For strict inequalities (that is,

inequalities involving < or >), the point is not part of the solution, and is marked with an open dot. Boundary points may be found by solving the equality associated with the given inequality. For example, the solution to the equation $2x + 5 = 11$ is $x = 3$, so the inequality $2x + 5 \geq 11$ has a boundary point at 3. A boundary point is also sometimes called a "dividing point." (p. 294)

box-and-whisker plot   A graphic way of showing a summary of data using the median, quartiles, and extremes of the data. (p. 230)

center (center point)   Within a flat surface, the point that is the same distance from all points of a circle. (Also see *circle*.)

central angle   An angle with its vertex at the center of a circle. (Also see *circle*.) (p. 339)

certainty   When an event will definitely happen. The probability of a certain event is 1. (p. 33)

chord   A line segment with its endpoints on a circle. A chord that passes through the center of a circle is called a "diameter." (Also see *circle*.) (p. 309)

circle   The set of all points on a flat surface that are the same distance from a fixed point. If the fixed point (center) is O, then the symbol $\odot O$ represents a circle with center O. If r is the length of the radius of a circle and d is the length of its diameter, then the circumference of the circle is $C = 2\pi r$ or $C = \pi d$. (p. 309)

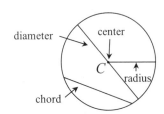

circumference   The perimeter of (distance around) a circle. (Also see *circle*.) (p. 309, 319)

coefficient (numerical)   A number multiplying a variable or product of variables. For example, -7 is the coefficient of $-7xy^2$. (p. 159)

combining like terms   Combining two or more like terms simplifies an expression by summing constants and summing those variable terms in which the same variables are raised to the same power. For example, combining like terms in the expression $3x + 7 + 5x - 3 + 2x^2 + 3y^2$ gives $8x + 4 + 2x^2 + 3y^2$. When working with algebra tiles, combining like terms involves putting together tiles with the same dimensions. (p. 161)

common   Shared.

common factor   A common factor is a factor that is the same for two or more terms. For example, x^2 is a common factor for $3x^2$ and $-5x^2y$.

common multiple   A number that is a multiple of the two or more numbers. For example, 24 and 48 are common multiples of 3 and 8.

Commutative Property of Addition   The Commutative Property of Addition states that if two terms are added, then the order may be reversed with no effect on the total. That is, $a + b = b + a$. For example, $7 + 12 = 12 + 7$. (p. 78)

Commutative Property of Multiplication The Commutative Property of Multiplication states that if two expressions are multiplied, then the order may be reversed with no effect on the result. That is, $ab = ba$. For example, $5 \cdot 8 = 8 \cdot 5$. (p. 581)

complementary angles Two angles whose measures add up to 90°. Angles T and V are complementary because $m\angle T + m\angle V = 90°$. Complementary angles may also be adjacent, like $\angle ABC$ and $\angle CBD$ in the diagram at far right. (p. 313)

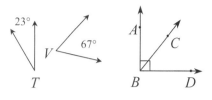

complementary probabilities Two probabilities are complementary if the sum of the probabilities is one.

complex fraction A fraction with a fraction in the numerator and/or denominator.

composite figure A shape made of several simpler figures.

composite number A number with more than two factors.

compound event A compound event in probability is an outcome that depends on two or more other events. For example, finding the probability that both a red ball and also a blue block are drawn from a bag in two draws. (p. 650, 655)

compound interest Interest that is paid on both the principal and the previous interest earned which grows over time. Compound interest may be calculated using the formula $B = p(1+r)^t$, in which B is the balance, p is the principal, r is the annual rate, and t is the time in years that the account earns interest. (p. 576)

cone A three-dimensional figure that consists of a circular face, called the "base," a point called the "apex," that is not in the flat surface (plane) of the base, and the slant surface that connects the apex to each point on the circular edge of the base. (p. 614)

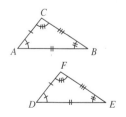

congruent Two shapes are congruent if they have exactly the same shape and size. Congruent shapes are similar and have a scale factor of 1. The symbol for congruence is $\cong$. (p. 235, 250)

conjecture An educated guess that often results from noticing a pattern. Conjectures are also often written in conditional ("If…, then…") form. Once a conjecture is proven, then the conjecture becomes a theorem. (p. 103)

consecutive numbers Integers that are in order without skipping any integers. For example, 8, 9, and 10 are consecutive numbers. (p. 185)

constant   A symbol representing a value that does not change. For example, in the equation $y = 2x + 5$, the number 5 is a constant. (p. 161, 273)

construction with a compass and straightedge   The process of using a straightedge and compass to solve a problem and/or create a geometric diagram. (p. 299)

coordinate   The number corresponding to a point on the number line or an ordered pair (x, y) that corresponds to a point in a two-dimensional coordinate system. In an ordered pair, the x-coordinate appears first and the y-coordinate appears second. For example, the point $(3, 5)$ has an x-coordinate of 3. (See *ordered pair*.) (p. 79)

coordinate grid (system)   A system of graphing ordered pairs of numbers on a coordinate plane. An ordered pair represents a point, with the first number giving the horizontal position relative to the x-axis and the second number giving the vertical position relative to the y-axis. (Also see *ordered pair*.) (p. 92)

correlation   A measure of the relationship between two sets of data. (p. 355)

corresponding parts   Points, sides, edges, or angles in two or more figures that are images of each other with respect to a transformation. If two figures are congruent, then the corresponding parts of the figures are congruent to each other. (See *ratio of similarity* and *congruent*.) (p. 242)

cube   A polyhedron of six faces, each of which is a square.

cubic unit   A cube, each of whose edges measure 1 unit in length. Volume is measured in cubic units. (p. 603)

cylinder   A three-dimensional figure that consists of two parallel congruent circular regions (called *bases*) and a vertical surface containing segments connecting each point on the circular boundary of one base to the corresponding point on the circular boundary of the other. (p. 617)

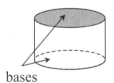
bases

decimal point   The dot separating the whole number from the decimal portion, that is, the ones and tenths places in a decimal number. (p. 46)

decompose   If a geometric figure is broken up into separate parts, then the figure is decomposed. Similarly, if a number is written as a sum or difference (such as $28 = 30 - 2$), then the number is decomposed. (Also see *recompose*.) (p. 123)

denominator   The lower part of a fraction, which expresses into how many equal parts the whole is divided. (p. 37)

dependent events   Two events are dependent if the outcome of one event affects the probability of the other event. For example, if one card is drawn out of a deck of cards, then the probability that the first card is red is $\frac{26}{52} = \frac{1}{2}$ because 26 of the 52 cards are red. However, the probability of the second card now depends on the result of the first selection. If the first card was red, then there are now 25 red cards remaining in a deck of 51 cards, and the probability that the second card is red is $\frac{25}{51}$. The second event (selecting the second card) is dependent on the first event (selecting the first card).

diagonal   In a polygon, a diagonal is a line segment that connects two vertices of the polygon but is not a side of the polygon.

diameter   A line segment drawn through the center of a circle with both endpoints on the circle. The length of a diameter is usually denoted *d*. Note that the length of the diameter of a circle is twice the length of its radius. (Also see *circle*.) (p. 309)

difference   The result of subtraction. (p. 90)

digit   One of the ten numerals: 0, 1, 2, 3, 4, 5, 6, 7, 8, or 9.

dilation   A transformation which produces a figure similar to the original by proportionally shrinking or stretching the figure. In a dilation, a shape is stretched (or compressed) proportionally from a point, called the point of dilation. (p. 102)

dimensions   The dimensions of a figure that is a flat region or space tell how far that the figure extends in each direction. For example, the dimensions of a rectangle might be 16 cm wide by 7 cm high. (p. 603)

Distributive Property   For any *a*, *b*, and *c*, $a(b + c) = ab + ac$. For example, $10(7 + 2) = 10 \cdot 7 + 10 \cdot 2$. (p. 279)

dividend   A quantity to be divided. (See *divisor*.)

divisible   A number is divisible by another if the remainder of the division is zero.

division (÷)   The inverse operation to multiplication, or the operation that creates equal groups.

divisor   The quantity by which another quantity is to be divided. dividend/divisor = quotient + remainder (if there is any).

edge   In three dimensions, a line segment formed by the intersection of two faces of a polyhedron. (p. 595)

endpoint   Either of the two points that mark the ends of a line segment. (Also see *line segment*.) (p. 304)

enlargement ratio   The ratio of similarity comparing a figure to a similar larger figure is often called the enlargement ratio. This ratio shows by what factor the first figure is enlarged to get the second figure. (p. 250, 477)

equal (=)   Two quantities are equal when they have the same value. For example, when $x = 4$, the expression $x + 8$ is equal to the expression $3x$ because the values of the expressions are the same. (p. 285)

equal ratios   Two equivalent fractions, also called a proportion. For example, $\frac{40 \text{ miles}}{2 \text{ gallons}} = \frac{100 \text{ miles}}{50 \text{ gallons}}$. (p. 205)

equation   A mathematical sentence in which two expressions appear on either side of an "equals" sign (=), stating that the two expressions are equivalent. For example, the equation $7x + 4.2 = -8$ states that the expression $7x + 4.2$ has the value –8. In this course, an equation is often used to represent a rule relating two quantities. For example, a rule for finding the area y of a tile pattern with figure number x might be written $y = 4x - 3$. (p. 371)

equilateral   A polygon is equilateral if all of its sides have equal length. The word "equilateral" comes from "equi" (meaning "equal") and "lateral" (meaning "side"). Equilateral triangles not only have sides of equal length, but also angles of equal measure. However, a polygon with more than three sides may be equilateral without having congruent angles. For example, see the rhombus at right. (p. 308)

equivalent   Two expressions are equivalent if they have the same value. For example, $2 + 3$ is equivalent to $1 + 4$. Two equations are equivalent if they have all the same solutions. For example, $y = 3x$ is equivalent to $2y = 6x$. Equivalent equations also have the same graph. (p. 278)

equivalent fractions   Two fractions are equivalent if they have the same numerical value. For example, 3/6 and 5/10 are equivalent fractions. (p. 38, 46, 243)

evaluate (an expression)   To find the numerical value of. To evaluate an expression, substitute the value(s) given for the variable(s) and perform the operations according to the order of operations. For example, evaluating $2x + y - 10$ when $x = 4$ and $y = 3$ gives the value 1. (Also see *expression*.) (p. 273)

even number   A whole number that is divisible by two with no remainder. (p. 185)

event   One or more results of an experiment. (p. 33)

experimental probability   The probability based on data collected in experiments. The experimental probability of an event is defined to be $\frac{\text{number of successful outcomes in the experiment}}{\text{total number of outcomes in the experiment}}$. (p. 33)

exponent In an expression of the form a^b, b is called the exponent. For example, in the expression 2^5, 5 is called the exponent (2 is the base, and 32 is the value). The exponent indicates how many times to use the base as a multiplier. For example, in 2^5, 2 is used 5 times: $2^5 = 2 \cdot 2 \cdot 2 \cdot 2 \cdot 2 = 32$. For exponents of zero, the rule is: for any number $x \neq 0$, $x^0 = 1$. (p. 572, 591)

expression An expression is a combination of individual terms separated by plus or minus signs. Numerical expressions combine numbers and operation symbols; algebraic (variable) expressions include variables. For example, $4 + (5 - 3)$ is a numerical expression. In an algebraic expression, if each of the following terms, $6xy^2$, 24, and $\frac{y-3}{4+x}$, are combined, the result may be $6xy^2 + 24 - \frac{y-3}{4+x}$. An expression does not have an "equals" sign. (p. 273)

expression mat An organizing tool used to visually represent an expression with algebra tiles. An expression mat has two regions, a positive region at the top and a negative region at the bottom. The tiles on the expression mat at right represent a value of –3. (p. 277)

Value: –3

face One of the flat surfaces of a polyhedron, including the base(s). (p. 595)

factor (1) In arithmetic: when two or more integers are multiplied, each of the integers is a factor of the product. For example, 4 is a factor of 24, because $4 \cdot 6 = 24$.
(2) In algebra: when two or more algebraic expressions are multiplied together, each of the expressions is a factor of the product. For example, x^2 is a factor of $-17x^2y^3$, because $(x^2)(-17y^3) = -17x^2y^3$. (3) To factor an expression is to write the expression as a product. For example, the factored form of $x^2 - 3x - 18$ is $(x - 6)(x + 3)$. (p. 44)

family of fractions All fractions that are equivalent to each other form a family of fractions. (See *equivalent fractions*.) (p. 38, 243)

formula An equation that shows a mathematical relationship. (p. 129)

fraction A number expressed in the form $\frac{a}{b}$ for which a and b are integers and b is not equal to 0. A fraction is also called a rational number. (p. 22, 103)

frequency The number of times that something occurs within an interval or data set. (p. 219)

generic rectangle A type of diagram used to visualize multiplying expressions without algebra tiles. Each expression to be multiplied forms a side length of the rectangle, and the product is the sum of the areas of the sections of the rectangle. For example, the generic rectangle at right may be used to multiply $(2x + 5)$ by $(x + 3)$.

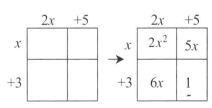

$(2x + 5)(x + 3) = 2x^2 + 11x + 15$

area as a product   area as a sum

graph   A graph represents numerical information in a visual form. The numbers may come from a table, situation (pattern), or rule (equation or inequality). Most of the graphs in this course show points, lines, and/or curves on a two-dimensional coordinate system like the one at right or on a single axis called a number line (see diagram below right). (p. 94, 359)

greatest common factor (GCF)   (1) For integers, the greatest positive integer that is a common factor of two or more integers. For example, the greatest common factor of 28 and 42 is 14. (2) For two or more algebraic monomials, the product of the greatest common integer factor of the coefficients of the monomials and the variable(s) in each algebraic term with the smallest degree of that variable in every term. For example, the greatest common factor of $12x^3y^2$ and $8xy^4$ is $4xy^2$. (3) For a polynomial, the greatest common monomial factor of its terms. For example, the greatest common factor of $16x^4 + 8x^3 + 12x$ is $4x$.

height   (a) Triangle: the length of a segment that connects a vertex of the triangle to a line containing the opposite base (side) and is perpendicular to that line. (b) Trapezoid: the length of any segment that connects a point on one base of the trapezoid to the line containing the opposite base and is perpendicular to that line. (c) Parallelogram (includes rectangle, rhombus, and square): the length of any segment that connects a point on one base of the parallelogram to the line containing the opposite base and is perpendicular to that line. (d) Pyramid and cone: the length of the segment that connects the apex to a point in the plane containing the base of a figure and is perpendicular to that plane. (e) Prism or cylinder: the length of a segment that connects one base of the figure to the plane containing the other base and is perpendicular to that plane. (See *altitude*.) (p. 115)

hexagon   A polygon with six sides. (p. 595)

histogram   A way of displaying data that is much like a bar graph in that the height of the bars is proportional to the number of elements. The difference is that each bar of a histogram represents the number of data elements in a range of values, such as the number of people who weigh from 100 pounds up to, but not including, 120 pounds. Each range of values should have the same width. (See *bar graph*.) (p. 219)

horizontal   Parallel to the horizon. The *x*-axis of a coordinate grid is the horizontal axis. (p. 93, 94)

hypotenuse   The longest side of a right triangle (the side that is opposite of the right angle). (See *Pythagorean Theorem* for a diagram.) (p. 541)

Identity Property of Addition   The Identity Property of Addition states that adding zero to any expression leaves the expression unchanged. That is, $a + 0 = a$. For example, $7 + 0 = 7$, and $-2y + 0 = -2y$. (p. 290)

Identity Property of Multiplication   The Identity Property of Multiplication states that multiplying any expression by 1 leaves the expression unchanged. That is, $a(1) = a$. For example, $437x \cdot 1 = 437x$. (p. 39)

impossibility   An event with a probability of zero. (p. 33)

independent events   If the outcome of a probabilistic event does not affect the probability of another event, then the events are independent. For example, assume that a normal six-sided die is being rolled twice to determine the probability of rolling a 1 twice. The result of the first roll does not affect the probability of rolling a 1 on the second roll. Since the probability of rolling a 1 on the first roll is $\frac{1}{6}$ and the probability of rolling a 1 on the second roll is also $\frac{1}{6}$, then the probability of rolling two 1s in a row is $\frac{1}{6} \cdot \frac{1}{6} = \frac{1}{36}$. (p. 655)

inequality   An inequality consists of two expressions on either side of an inequality symbol. For example, the inequality $7x + 4.2 < -8$ states that the expression $7x + 4.2$ has a value less than –8. (p. 285, 294)

inequality symbols   The symbol $\leq$ read from left to right means "less than or equal to," the symbol $\geq$ read from left to right means "greater than or equal to," and the symbols $<$ and $>$ mean "less than" and "greater than," respectively. For example, "$7 < 13$" means that 7 is less than 13. (p. 285)

integers   The set of numbers $\{\ldots, -3, -2, -1, 0, 1, 2, 3, \ldots\}$. (p. 86, 90)

intersect   To meet or cross. The x-axis intersects the y-axis at the origin. (See *axis*.) (p. 441)

interval   A set of numbers between two given numbers. (p. 51)

inverse operation   An operation that undoes another operation. For example, multiplication is the inverse operation for division. (p. 266)

irrational numbers   The set of numbers that cannot be expressed in the form $\frac{a}{b}$, where a and b are integers and $b \neq 0$. For example, π and $\sqrt{2}$ are irrational numbers. (p. 545)

isosceles triangle   A triangle with two sides of equal length.

iterate   The process of repeating a measurement many times, such as the use of a one-foot ruler to measure a long room by placing the ruler end-to-end many times.

kite   A quadrilateral with two distinct pairs of consecutive congruent sides.

least common multiple (LCM)   (1) The smallest common multiple of a set of two or more integers. For example, the least common multiple of 4, 6, and 8 is 24. (2) For two or more algebraic monomials, the product of the least common integer multiples of the coefficients of the monomials and the variable(s) in each algebraic term with the greatest degree of that variable in every term. For example, the least common multiple of $12x^3y^2$ and $8xy^4$ is $24x^3y^4$.

leg of a right triangle   Either of the two shorter sides of a right triangle that form the right angle. (See *Pythagorean Theorem* for a diagram.) (p. 539, 541)

less than   (1) One expression is less than another if its value is not as large. This relationship is indicated with the less than symbol "$<$." For example, $1+1$ is less than $4+5$, so the comparison is written as $1+1 < 4+5$. (2) Sometimes the comparison is made that one amount is a certain quantity less than another amount. For example, a student movie ticket might cost two dollars *less than* an adult ticket. (p. 285)

like terms   Two or more terms that contain the same variable(s), with corresponding variables raised to the same power. For example, $5x^2$ and $2x^2$ are like terms. (See *combining like terms*.) (p. 161)

line   A line is an undefined term in geometry. A line is one-dimensional and continues without end in two directions. A line is made up of points and has no thickness. A line may be named with a letter (such as *l*), but also may be labeled using two points on the line, such as $\overleftrightarrow{AB}$ shown the right.

line segment   The portion of a line between two points. A line segment is named using its endpoints. For example, the line segment at right may be named either $\overline{AB}$ or $\overline{BA}$.

linear equation   An equation in two variables whose graph is a line. For example, $y = 2.1x - 8$ is a *linear equation*. The standard form for a linear equation is $ax + by = c$, where a, b, and c are constants and a and b are not both zero. Most linear equations may be written in $y = mx + b$ form, which is more useful for determining the slope and y-intercept of the line. (p. 359)

linear expression   An expression in the form of $ax + b$ for which a and b are numbers.

lower quartile   The median of the lower half of an ordered set of data is the lower quartile. (p. 226)

lowest common denominator (LCD)   The smallest common multiple of the denominators of two or more fractions. For example, the LCD of $\frac{5}{12}$ and $\frac{3}{8}$ is 24. (p. 44)

mean   The mean, or average, of several numbers is one way of defining the "middle" of the numbers. To find the average of a group of numbers, add the numbers together then divide by the number of numbers in the set. For example, the average of the numbers 1, 5, and 6 is $(1+5+6) \div 3 = 4$. (See *average*.) (p. 13)

measure of central tendency   Mean, median, and mode are all measures of central tendency, reflecting special statistical information about a set of data. (p. 13, 18)

median   The middle number of an ordered set of data. If there is no distinct middle, then the average of the two middle numbers is the median. (p. 18)

midpoint   A point that divides a segment into two segments of equal length. For example, D is the midpoint of $\overline{BC}$ in $\triangle ABC$ at right. (p. 307)

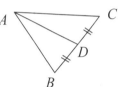

mixed number (fraction)   A number that consists of an integer and a fraction. For example, $3\frac{3}{8}$. (p. 103)

mode   The number or numbers that occur the most often within a set of data. There may be more than one mode for a set of data. (p. 18)

multiple   The product of a whole number and any other (nonzero) whole number. For example, 15 is a multiple of 5.

multiplication (·)   An operation that reflects repeated addition. For example, $3 \cdot 4 = 4 + 4 + 4$. (p. 44, 108)

Multiplicative Identity   The Multiplicative Identity Property states that multiplying any expression by 1 leaves the expression unchanged. That is, $a(1) = a$. For example, $437x \cdot 1 = 437x$. (p. 39)

natural numbers   The counting numbers beginning with 1. For example, 1, 2, 3....

negative correlation   A relationship between two sets of variables in which one generally increases while the other decreases. (p. 355)

negative number   A negative number is a number less than zero. Negative numbers are graphed on the negative side of a number line, which is to the left of the origin. (p. 83)

negative slope   Lines are said to have negative slope if they slant downward from left to right. That is, as the x-values increases, the y-value decreases. (p. 433)

non-linear   A set of points that do not lie on a straight line when connected. (p. 631)

number line   A diagram representing all real numbers as points on a line. All real numbers are assigned to points. The numbers are called the coordinates of the points and the point for which the number 0 is assigned is called the origin. (Also see *boundary point*.) (p. 11)

numeral   A symbol that names a number. For example, each item of the following list is a numeral: 22.6, –19, 0.

numerator   The number above the bar in a fraction that tells the numbers of parts in relationship to the number of parts in the whole. (p. 37)

obtuse angle   Any angle that measures between (but not including) 90° and 180°. (p. 304)

obtuse triangle   A triangle with one obtuse angle. (p. 112)

octagon   A polygon with eight sides. (p. 595)

odd number   An integer that cannot be evenly divided by two. (p. 185)

operation   A mathematical process such as addition, subtraction, multiplication, division, raising to a power, or taking a root. (p. 130)

order of operations   The specific order in which certain operations are to be carried out to evaluate or simplify expressions: parentheses (or other grouping symbols), exponents (powers or roots), multiplication and division (from left to right), and addition and subtraction (from left to right). (p. 133)

ordered pair   Two numbers written in order as follows: (x, y). The primary use of ordered pairs in this course is to represent points in an xy-coordinate system. The first coordinate (x) represents the distance from the x-axis. The second coordinate (y) represents the distance from the y-axis. For example, the ordered pair $(3, 5)$ represents the point shown in bold at right. (p. 94)

origin   The point on a coordinate plane where the x-axis and y-axis intersect is called the origin. This point has coordinates $(0, 0)$. The point assigned to zero on a number line is also called the origin. (See *axis*.) (p. 94)

outcome   Possible result in an experiment or consequence of an action. (p. 33, 650)

outlier   A number in a set of data that is much larger or much smaller than the other numbers in the set. (p. 13)

parallel Two or more straight lines on a flat surface that do not intersect (no matter how far they are extended) are parallel. If two lines have the same slope and do not coincide, then they are parallel. For example, the graphs of $y = 2x + 3$ and $y = 2x - 2$ are parallel (see diagram at right). When two equations have parallel graphs, the equations have no solutions in common. (p. 119)

parallelogram A quadrilateral with two pairs of parallel sides. (p. 119, 342)

pentagon A polygon with five sides. (p. 595)

percent (%) A ratio that compares a number to 100. Percents are often written using the "%" symbol. For example, 0.75 is equal to $\frac{75}{100}$ or 75%. (p. 22, 57)

perfect square The product of an integer multiplied by itself gives a perfect square. For example, 1, 4, and 9 are perfect squares because $1 = 1 \cdot 1$, $4 = 2 \cdot 2$, and $9 = 3 \cdot 3$. (p. 543)

perimeter The distance around a figure on a flat surface. (p. 10)

Perimeter = 5 + 8 + 4 + 6 = 23 units

perpendicular Two rays, line segments, or lines that meet (intersect) to form a right angle (90°) are called perpendicular. A line and a flat surface may also be perpendicular if the line does not lie on the flat surface but intersects the surface and forms a right angle with every line on the flat surface passing through the point of intersection. A small square at the point of intersection of two lines or segments indicates that the lines form a right angle and are therefore perpendicular. (p. 119, 301)

perpendicular bisector A line, ray, or segment that divides a segment into two congruent segments and is perpendicular to the segment. (p. 307)

pi (π) The ratio of the circumference (C) of the circle to its diameter (d). For every circle, $\pi = \frac{\text{circumference}}{\text{diameter}} = \frac{C}{d}$. Numbers such as 3.14, 3.1416, or $\frac{22}{7}$ are approximations of π. (p. 313, 319)

place value The number assigned to each place that a digit occupies. (p. 46)

plane. A plane is a two-dimensional flat surface that extends without end. It is made up of points and has no thickness. (p. 660)

point An exact location in space. In two dimensions, an ordered pair specifies a point on a coordinate plane. (See *ordered pair*.) (p. 94)

polygon   A two-dimensional closed figure of three or more line segments (sides) connected end to end. Each segment is a side and only intersects the endpoints of its two adjacent sides. Each point of intersection is a vertex. At right are two examples of polygons. (p. 595)

polyhedron   A three-dimensional figure with no holes for which all faces are polygons. (p. 595)

population   A collection of objects or group of people about whom information is gathered.

portion   A part of something; a part of a whole. (p. 22, 57)

portions web   The web diagram at right illustrates that fractions, decimals, and percents are different ways to represent a portion of a number. Portions may also be represented in words, such as "four-fifths" or "seven-fourths," or as diagrams. (p. 57)

positive correlation   A relationship between two sets of variables in which one generally increases while the other also increases. (p. 355)

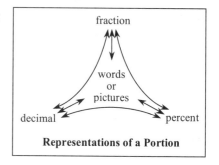

positive numbers   Numbers that are greater than zero.

positive slope   Lines are said to have positive slope if they slant upwards from left to right. That is, as the x-value increases, the y-value also increases. (p. 433)

power   A number or variable raised to an exponent in the form x^n. (See *exponent*.) (p. 572)

prime factorization   The expression of a number as the product of prime factors. (p. 45)

prime number   A positive integer with exactly two factors. The only factors of a prime number are 1 and itself. For example, the numbers 2, 3, 17, and 31 are all prime. (p. 45)

prism   A three-dimensional figure that consists of two parallel congruent polygons (called *bases*) and a vertical surface containing segments connecting each point on each side of one base to the corresponding point on the other base. The lateral surface of a prism consists of parallelograms. (p. 595)

probability   A number that represents how likely an event is to happen.   When a event has a finite number of equally-likely outcomes, the probability that one of those outcomes, called *A*, will occur is expressed as a ratio and written as: $P(A) = \frac{\text{number of successful outcomes}}{\text{total number of possible outcomes}}$. For example, when flipping a coin, the probability of getting tails, *P*(tails), is 1/2 because there is only one tail (successful outcome) out of the two possible equally likely outcomes (a head and a tail).   Probability may be written as a ratio, decimal, or percent.   A probability of 0 (or 0%) indicates that the occurrence of that outcome is impossible, while a probability of 1 (or 100%) indicates that the event must occur.   Events that "might happen" will have values somewhere between 0 and 1 (or between 0% and 100%). (p. 27, 33, 650, 655)

product   The result of multiplying.   For example, the product of 4 and 5 is 20.   The product of $3a$ and $8b^2$ is $24ab^2$.

proportion   An equation stating that two ratios (fractions) are equal.   For example, the equation at right is a proportion.   A proportion is a useful type of equation to set up when solving problems involving proportional relationships. (p. 517)

$$\frac{68 \text{ votes for Mr. Mears}}{100 \text{ people surveyed}} = \frac{34 \text{ votes for Mr. Mears}}{50 \text{ people surveyed}}$$

proportional relationship   Two values are in a proportional relationship if a proportion may be set up that relates the values. (p. 512)

protractor   A geometric tool used for physically measuring the number of degrees in an angle. (p. 302)

pyramid   A polyhedron with a polygonal base formed by connecting each point of the base to a single given point (the apex) that is above or below the flat surface containing the base.   Each triangular slant face of the pyramid is formed by the segments from the apex to the endpoints of a side of the base and the side itself.   A tetrahedron is a special pyramid because any face may act as its base. (p. 614)

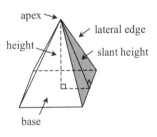

Pythagorean Theorem   The statement relating the lengths of the legs of a right triangle to the length of the hypotenuse: $(\text{leg \#1})^2 + (\text{leg \#2})^2 = \text{hypotenuse}^2$.   The Pythagorean Theorem is powerful because if the lengths of any two sides of a right triangle are known, then this relationship may be used to find the length of the third side. (p. 541)

quadrants The coordinate plane is divided by its axes into four quadrants. The quadrants are numbered as shown in the first diagram at right. When graphing data that has no negative values, sometimes a graph that shows only the first quadrant is used. (p. 93)

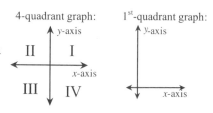

quadrilateral A polygon with four sides. The shape at right is a quadrilateral. (p. 342, 595)

quartile Along with the median, the quartiles divide a set of data into four groups of the same size. (p. 226)

quotient The result of a division problem.

radius (plural: radii) Of a circle: The line segment drawn from the center of a circle to a point on the circle. Of a regular polygon: A line segment that connects the center of a regular polygon with a vertex. The length of a radius is usually denoted *r*. (p. 309)

random sample A sample in which each item in the population or sample space has an equal chance of being selected.

range The range of a set of data is the difference between the highest and lowest values. (p. 211)

rate A ratio comparing two quantities, often a comparison of time. For example, miles per hour. (p. 420, 433, 459)

ratio A ratio compares two quantities by division. A ratio may be written using a colon, but is more often written as a fraction. For example, the comparison may be made of the ratio of female students in a particular school to the total number of students in the school. This ratio could be written as 1521:2906 or as the fraction shown at right. (p. 205, 250)

$$\frac{1521 \text{ female students}}{2906 \text{ total students}}$$

ratio of similarity The ratio of any pair of corresponding sides of two similar figures. This means that once it is determined that two figures are similar, all of the pairs of corresponding sides of the figures have the same ratio. For example, for the similar triangles $\triangle ABC$ and $\triangle DEF$ at right, the ratio of similarity is $\frac{5}{11}$. The ratio of similarity may also be called the linear scale factor. (p. 250)

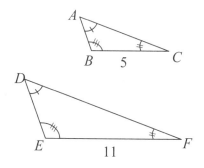

rational number   Numbers that may be expressed in the form $\frac{a}{b}$, where a and b are integers and $b \neq 0$. For example, 0.75 is a rational number because 0.75 may be expressed in the form $\frac{3}{4}$. (p. 545)

ray   A ray is part of a line that starts at one point and extends without end in one direction. In the example at right, ray $\overrightarrow{AB}$ is part of line $\overleftrightarrow{AB}$ that starts at A and contains all of the points of $\overleftrightarrow{AB}$ that are on the same side of A as point B, including A. Point A is the endpoint of $\overrightarrow{AB}$. (p. 304)

real numbers   Irrational numbers together with rational numbers form the set of the real numbers. For example, the following are all real numbers: $2.78, -13267, 0, \frac{3}{7}, \pi, \sqrt{2}$. All real numbers are represented on the number line.

reciprocals   The reciprocal of a nonzero number is its multiplicative inverse, that is, the reciprocal of x is $\frac{1}{x}$. For a number in the form $\frac{a}{b}$, where a and b are non-zero, the reciprocal is $\frac{b}{a}$. The product of a number and its reciprocal is 1. For example, the reciprocal of 12 is $\frac{1}{12}$, because $12 \cdot \frac{1}{12} = 1$.

recompose   If a geometric figure is broken up into pieces and the pieces are put back together, possibly in a new way, then the figure is recomposed. Similarly, if two or more numbers have been written as sums or differences in an expression and these numbers are put back together into sums or differences, then the expression is recomposed. (Also see *decompose*.) (p. 123)

rectangle   A quadrilateral with four right angles. (p. 10, 342)

reduce   To put a fraction into simplest form. (p. 243)

reflection   A transformation across a line that produces a mirror image of the original (pre-image) shape. The reflection is called the "image" of the original figure. The line is called a "line of reflection." Note that a reflection is also sometimes referred to as a "flip." See the example at right above. (p. 99)

original   image

Line of reflection

regular polygon   A polygon is regular if the polygon is a convex polygon with congruent angles and congruent sides. For example, the shape at right is a regular hexagon. (p. 94)

REGULAR HEXAGON

repeating decimal   A repeating decimal is a decimal that repeats the same sequence of digits forever from some point onward. For example, 4.56073073073… is a decimal for which the three digits 073 continue to repeat forever. Repeating decimals are always the decimal expansions of rational numbers. (p. 21)

representative sample   A subset (group) of a given population with the same characteristics as the whole population.

rhombus   A quadrilateral with four congruent sides. (Also see *equilateral*.) (p. 342)

right angle   An angle that measures 90°. A small square is used to note a right angle, as shown in the example at right. (p. 304)

right triangle   A triangle that has one right angle. The side of a right triangle opposite the right angle is called the "hypotenuse," and the two sides adjacent to the right angle are called "legs." (See *Pythagorean Theorem* for a diagram.) (p. 451)

rigid transformations   Movements of figures that preserve the shape and size of the figures. (p. 99)

root fraction   The member of a family of fractions with the smallest integer values, the most simplified form. For the fraction family $\frac{2}{3}, \frac{4}{6}, \frac{6}{9}$, etc., $\frac{2}{3}$ is the root fraction. (p. 243)

rotation   A transformation that rotates (or turns) all of the points in the original (pre-image) figure the same number of degrees around a fixed center point (such as the origin on a graph). The result is called the "image" of the original figure. The point that the shape is rotated about is called the "center of rotation." To define a rotation, the measure of turn (in degrees) must be stated, the direction in which the shape is turned (such as clockwise or counter-clockwise), and the center of rotation. See the example at right. Note that a rotation is also sometimes referred to as a "turn." (p. 99)

scale (scaling)   The ratio between a length of the representation (such as a map, model, or diagram) and the corresponding length of the actual object. For example, the map of a city may use one inch to represent one mile. (p. 250, 468)

scale factor   A ratio that compares the sizes of the parts of one figure or object to the sizes of the corresponding parts of a similar figure or object. (p. 250, 468)

scalene triangle   A triangle with no congruent sides. (p. 177)

scatterplot   Two related sets of data may have the corresponding values of the sets listed as ordered pairs. If these ordered pairs are graphed in the coordinate plane, then the result is a scatterplot. (Also see *negative correlation* and *positive correlation*.) (p. 346, 355)

scientific notation   A number is expressed in scientific notation when the number is in the form $a \times 10^n$, where $1 \le a < 10$ and n is an integer. For example, the number 31,000 may be expressed in scientific notation as 3.1×10^4. (p. 587)

sector   A region formed by two radii of a central angle and the arc between the endpoints of the radii on the circle. The shaded portion of the drawing at right is a sector. (p. 347, 460)

sector

semi-circle   In a circle, a semicircle is an arc with endpoints that are endpoints of any diameter of the circle. A semi-circle is a half circle and has a measure of 180°.

set   A collection of items.

similar figures   Similar figures have the same shape but are not necessarily the same size. For example the two triangles at right are similar. In similar figures, the measures of corresponding angles are equal and the lengths of corresponding sides are proportional. (p. 235)

simple interest   Interest that is paid only on the principal (the amount originally invested). Simple interest (I) is found by multiplying the principal (P), the rate (r), and the amount of time (t): $I = Prt$. (p. 491)

simplest form of a fraction   A fraction for which the numerator and the denominator have no common factor greater than one. (p. 243)

simplify   To simplify an expression is to write a less complicated expression with the same value. A simplified expression has no parentheses and no like terms. For example, the expression $3 - (2x + 7) - 4x$ may be simplified to $-4 - 6x$. When working with algebra tiles, a simplified expression uses the fewest possible tiles to represent the original expression. (p. 273)

skew lines   Lines that do not lie in the same flat surface. (p. 660)

slope   A ratio that describes how steep (or flat) a line is. Slope may be positive, negative, or even zero, but a straight line has only one slope. Slope is the ratio $\frac{\text{vertical change}}{\text{horizontal change}}$ or $\frac{\text{change in } y\text{-value}}{\text{change in } x\text{-value}}$, sometimes written $\frac{\Delta y}{\Delta x}$. When the equation of a line is written in $y = mx + b$ form, m is the slope of the line. A line has positive slope if the line slopes upward from left to right on a graph, negative slope if the line slopes downward from left to right, zero slope if the line is horizontal, and undefined slope if the line is vertical. Parallel lines have equal slopes, and the slopes of perpendicular lines are opposite reciprocals of each other (e.g., $\frac{3}{5}$ and $-\frac{5}{3}$). (p. 433)

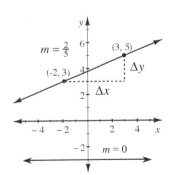

solution   The number or numbers that when substituted into an equation or inequality make the equation or inequality true. For example, $x = 4$ is a solution to the equation $3x - 2 = 10$ because $3x - 2$ equals 10 when $x = 4$. A solution to a two-variable equation is sometimes written as an ordered pair (x, y). For example, $x = 3$ and $y = -2$ is a solution to the equation $y = x - 5$. This solution may be written as $(3, -2)$. (p. 379, 391, 441)

square   A quadrilateral with four right angles and four congruent sides. (p. 342)

square

square measure   The units used to describe the measure of an area in the form of 1×1 unit squares. (p. 10)

square number   The numbers in the pattern 1, 4, 9, 16, 25, …. That is, the squares of the counting numbers 1, 2, 3, 4, 5, … are known as square numbers. (p. 543)

square root ($\sqrt{\ }$)   A number a is the square root of b if $a^2 = b$ and $a \geq 0$. The square root of 9 ($\sqrt{9}$) is 3. A negative number has no real square root, a non-negative number has just one square root. (p. 543)

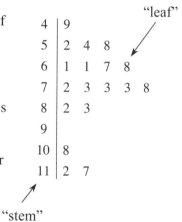

stem-and-leaf plot   A frequency distribution that arranges data so that all digits except the last digit in each piece of data are in the stem, the last digit of each piece of data are the leaves, and both stems and leaves are arranged in order from least to greatest. The example at right displays the data: 49, 52, 54, 58, 61, 61, 67, 68, 72, 73, 73, 73, 78, 82, 83, 108, 112, and 117. (p. 213)

"stem"

straight angle   An angle that measures 180°. This occurs when the rays of the angle point in opposite directions, forming a line. (p. 304)

180°

subproblems   A problem solving strategy that breaks a problem into smaller parts that must be solved in order to solve the original, more complex problem.

substitution   Replacing one symbol with a number, a variable, or another algebraic expression of the same value. Substitution does not change the value of the overall expression. For example, suppose that the expression $13x - 6$ must be evaluated for $x = 4$. Since x has the value 4, 4 may be substituted into the expression wherever x appears, giving the equivalent expression $13(4) - 6$. (p. 130, 273)

subtraction (–)   An operation that gives the difference between two numbers. (p. 90)

sum   The result of adding two or more numbers. For example, the sum of 4 and 5 is 9. (p. 90)

supplementary angles Two angles A and B for which $A + B = 180°$. Each angle is called the supplement of the other. In the example at right, angles A and B are supplementary. Supplementary angles are often adjacent. For example, since $\angle LMN$ is a straight angle, then $\angle LMP$ and $\angle PMN$ are supplementary angles because $m\angle LMP + m\angle PMN = 180°$. (p. 313)

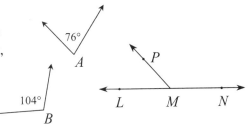

surface area The sum of all the area(s) of the surface(s) of a three-dimensional solid. For example, the surface area of a prism is the sum of the areas of its top and bottom bases, and its vertical surfaces (lateral faces). (p. 592, 599, 617)

term A term is a single number, variable, or the product of numbers and variables, such as –45, 1.2x, and $3xy^2$. (p. 133, 273)

terminating decimal A terminating decimal is a decimal that has only a finite number of non-zero digits, such as 4.067. Terminating decimals are a particular kind of repeating decimal for which the repeating portion is zeros, so the example could be written 4.0670000000… but it is not necessary to write the zeros at the end. (p. 53)

tetrahedron A polyhedron with four faces.

theoretical probability A calculated probability based on the possible outcomes when each outcome has the same chance of occurring: (number of successful outcomes)/(total number of possible outcomes). (p. 33)

tick mark A symbol that shows that a number line has been divided into intervals of equal length. (See *number line*.)

translation A transformation that preserves the size, shape, and orientation of a figure while sliding (moving) it to a new location. The result is called the "image" of the original figure (pre-image). See the example at right. Note that a translation is sometimes referred to as a "slide." (p. 99)

original   image

trapezoid A quadrilateral with at least one pair of parallel sides. (p. 125)

triangle A polygon with three sides. (p. 595)

unit of measure A standard quantity (such as a centimeter, second, square foot, or gallon) that is used to measure and describe an object. A single object may be measured using different units of measure. For example, a pencil may be 80 mm long, meaning that the pencil is 80 times as long as a unit of 1 mm. However, the same pencil is 8 cm long, so that the pencil is the same length as 8 cm laid end-to-end. This is because 1 cm is the same length as 10 mm. (p. 10, 84, 464)

unit price The cost of one item or one measure of an item. For example, cost for one pound or one gallon.

unit rate A rate with a denominator of one when simplified. (p. 420)

units digit The numeral in the ones place.

upper quartile The median of the upper half of an ordered set of data. (p. 226)

variable A symbol used to represent one or more numbers. In this course, letters of the English alphabet are used as variables. For example, in the expression $3x - (8.6xy + z)$, the variables are x, y, and z. (p. 156, 384)

Venn diagram A type of diagram used to classify objects that is usually composed of two or more overlapping circles representing different conditions. An item is placed or represented in the Venn diagram in the appropriate position based on the conditions that the item meets. In the example of the Venn diagram at right, if an object meets one of two conditions, then the object is placed in region A or C but outside region B. If an object meets both conditions, then the object is placed in the intersection (B) of both circles. If an object does not meet either condition, then the object is placed outside of both circles (region D).

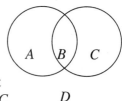

vertex (plural: vertices) (a) For polygon, a vertex is the point at which two line segments meet to form a "corner." (See *regular polygon*.) (b) For an angle, the common endpoint of the defining rays. (See *vertical angles*.) (c) For a three-dimensional polyhedron, a vertex is a point where the edges of the solid meet. (See *edge*.) (p. 93, 595)

vertical At right angles to the horizon. In a coordinate grid, the y-axis runs vertically. (p. 93, 94)

vertical angles The two opposite (that is, non-adjacent) angles formed by two intersecting lines. "Vertical" is a relationship between pairs of angles, so one angle cannot be called vertical. Angles that form a vertical pair are always congruent.

volume A measurement of the size of the three-dimensional region enclosed within an object. Volume is expressed as the number of $1 \times 1 \times 1$ unit cubes (or parts of cubes) that fit inside a solid. (p. 593, 603)

x-axis The horizontal number line on a coordinate grid. (See *axis*.) (p. 94)

x-coordinate In an ordered pair, (x, y), that represents a point in the coordinate plane, x is the value of the x-coordinate of the point. That is, the distance from the x-axis that is needed to plot the point. (p. 94)

x-intercept The point(s) where a graph intersects the x-axis. A graph may have several x-intercepts, no x-intercepts, or just one. An x-intercept may be written as an ordered pair $(x, 0)$ or as a single number. For example, in the graph below for "y-intercept," the x-intercept may be written as $(-2, 0)$ or simply -2. (See *y-intercept*.) (p. 358, 359)

y-axis The vertical number line on a coordinate grid. (See *axis*.) (p. 94)

y-coordinate In an ordered pair, (x, y), that represents a point in the coordinate plane, y is the value of the y-coordinate of the point. That is, the distance from the y-axis that is needed to plot the point. (p. 94)

y-intercept The point(s) where a graph intersects the y-axis. A function has at most one y-intercept while a relation may have several. The y-intercept of a graph is important because the y-intercept often represents the starting value of a quantity in a real-world situation. A y-intercept may be written as an ordered pair $(0, y)$ or as a single number. For example, it may be said that that the y-intercept of the graph at right is $(0, 2)$, or it may also be said that the y-intercept is 2. When a linear equation is written in $y = mx + b$ form, b is the y-intercept of the graph. For example, the equation of the graph at right is $y = x + 2$ and its y-intercept is 2. (p. 358, 359)

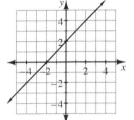

Index
Student Version

Many of the pages referenced here contain a definition or an example of the topic listed, often within the body of a Math Notes box. Others contain problems that develop or demonstrate the topic. It may be necessary to read the text on several pages to fully understand the topic. Also, some problems listed here are good examples of the topic and may not offer any explanation. The page numbers below reflect the pages in the Student Version. References to Math Notes boxes are bolded.

THIS BOOK IS THE PROPERTY OF:

Book No._____

ISSUED TO	Year Used	CONDITION	
		ISSUED	RETURNED
_____	_____		
_____	_____		
_____	_____		
_____	_____		
_____	_____		
_____	_____		
_____	_____		
_____	_____		
_____	_____		
_____	_____		

PUPILS to whom this texbook is issued must not write on any part of it in any way, unless otherwise instructed by the teacher.